Principles Of

ELECTRONIC INSTRUMENTS

Principles Of

ELECTRONIC INSTRUMENTS

By

GORDON R. PARTRIDGE, Ph.D.

*Raytheon Manufacturing Company, Wayland,
Massachusetts. Formerly Associate Professor of Electrical
Engineering, Purdue University*

Englewood Cliffs, N.J.
PRENTICE-HALL, INC.

Library of Congress Catalog Card Number: 58-9610

First printing.................April, 1958
Second printing................June, 1959

PRINTED IN THE UNITED STATES OF AMERICA
70919

*Almighty God . . . Bless all who teach
and all who learn; and grant that in
humility of heart they may ever look
unto thee, who art the fountain of
all wisdom. . . .*

American Book of Common Prayer

PREFACE

The use of electronic instruments has increased in the last few decades to the point where one finds it difficult to name any branch of science where electronics is not at work gathering data for man's information. The time is long since passed when electronic instruments were employed chiefly by electrical engineers for the study of electric circuits. In the industrial world of today, the electronic instrument finds a place in measuring almost any quantity one might mention—acceleration, velocity, displacement, stress, strain, thickness of materials, mass and weight, pressure and vacuum, temperature, light intensity and color, the frequency and intensity of sound, radioactivity, chemical quantities, medical and biological measurements, applications to safety and inspection devices, and thousands of other uses.

The science of measurement by electronics is by no means confined even to our world or to this island universe. The modern radio telescope as a matter of daily routine probes the secrets of the clouds of intergalactic matter, while the luminous stars tell the photomultiplier tube of an expanding universe.

Just as remarkable are the electronic computers that stand ready to draw conclusions from data in a matter of hours—conclusions that only a decade ago, many man-lifetimes would have been insufficient to reach.

The fascinating, exciting possibilities of electronic instrumentation are open to all through the purchase of commercial equipment. But the opportunities via this route are undoubtedly limited. The scientist who would make the most of electronic measurements must be prepared to design his own instrumentation.

It is with the hope of giving the reader an insight into the principles by which electronic instruments function that this book has been written. The text is essentially a compilation of lecture notes used by the author in a course at Purdue University. The purpose of this course was to prepare students undertaking a graduate study program to make the instruments they might need in their research work—instruments which in many cases were of a specialized type and not available from the stockroom shelf. It is impossible to anticipate the special interests of every student, but a thorough grounding in the basic principles employed in electronic instruments should prepare him to continue on his own. This is the plan followed here: to explain the features of circuitry that make typical instruments operate.

It must be emphasized that this book does *not* deal with *how to make measurements*. The reader is presumed to have this information already. The technique of using an instrument will be stressed in only a very few instances, where knowledge of "how to use" is essential to the understanding of "why it works." Likewise, stress will be laid only on the parts of an instrument that account for its unique functions. Such commonly encountered subassemblies as rectifiers, power supplies, D'Arsonval meter movements, and the like, will ordinarily be shown simply in block diagram form, if they are mentioned at all.

The reader will find this book divided into two essentially separate portions. The first twelve chapters deal with instruments to measure electrical quantities by electronic methods. The remaining chapters treat nonelectrical quantities. In this latter portion, primary emphasis is on transducers which convert the quantity in question into some electric signal that may then be measured by one of the instruments discussed earlier.

It is thought that this text will prove useful to the graduate student and the practicing engineer who are faced with the need for developing instrumentation for certain special applications. It also provides a basis for the extension or up-dating of the "measurements" program included in many undergraduate engineering curricula, provided the students have completed one year of basic electronics.

Practically every function of electronic equipment—amplification, modulation, detection, and frequency conversion to cite a few examples —is found in some type of electronic instrument. Therefore the reader will find here a comprehensive review of the subject of electronic circuits in general. The author has known some of his students to enroll for the electronic instrumentation course for exactly this reason.

In general, emphasis is placed on circuits designed to operate at relatively low frequencies, direct current to a few hundred kilocycles per second. The reason is that instruments for use in the radio frequency and microwave regions tend to be rather specialized in nature. Furthermore, many excellent texts are available dealing specifically with measurements and instruments for these portions of the frequency spectrum.

It will be noticed that the level of mathematical material varies considerably, depending on the specific topic under discussion. In dealing with a wide variety of circuits, this is inevitable. In some cases, it is necessary to use a statistical approach to a problem; at other times, a simple discussion in words will suffice to explain the operation of an instrument. Operational transform techniques, calculus, algebra, and arithmetic are liberally mixed together, to be drawn upon as one circuit or another may require. With the possible exception of statistics, it is assumed that the reader has an adequate background in mathematics so that the method of attacking a given problem may be based entirely on considerations of getting to the answer by the shortest usually traveled route.

In a number of instances, commercial instruments are used as examples to illustrate the principles involved. The author acknowledges with sincere gratitude the courtesy of the many companies who have made their data and circuit diagrams available to him. Acknowledgment of specific information will be made at appropriate points throughout the text.

Especial thanks are extended to a number of individuals who have made particular contributions to the progress of the work. Dr. Leo L. Beranek kindly offered to read the manuscript of Chapter 2, and offered a number of helpful suggestions. The completed manuscript was examined by Mr. John M. Cage, who contributed many valuable criticisms. The author also recognizes gratefully the work of several members of the secretarial staff of the Communications Department, Wayland Laboratory, Raytheon Manufacturing Company, who typed the manuscript. The girls participating in this effort were A. Fay Adams, Judith A. Corkum, Anita L. D'Amici, Mary Ellen Elliott, Theresa E. Hughes, and Laura A. White. Finally, a word of appreciation to my wife, Dorothy O. Partridge, for many an hour spent in proofreading, and for unlimited moral support.

Gordon R. Partridge

Sudbury, Massachusetts

CONTENTS

electron" effect, 75.   5-6. The input impedance to the basic peak-reading instrument, 80.

Chapter 1

WHY ELECTRONIC INSTRUMENTS?

In many scientific disciplines, the use of electronic instruments has been standard for some years. On the other hand, many workers have "discovered" the possibilities of electronic instruments rather recently, and are now in a stage of experimenting with their potentialities. Still others are wondering if there might be something in electronics that could be of use to them. It is to these newcomers in the family of electronic instrument users that this chapter is addressed. We shall try to answer briefly the very logical question, "What can they do for me?"

1-1. The advantages of electronic instruments

It must be admitted at the outset that there are relatively few measurements made by electronic instruments that could not be made by some other approach. In general, a good electronic instrument is not significantly more accurate or less expensive than a quality device of some other type designed to accomplish the same purpose. Therefore the only possible justification for electronic instruments is that they offer some particular advantage to the user—an advantage that obviously is inherent in the application of electronic techniques. These advantages include versatility, speed of response, adaptability to difficult conditions of measurement, and in most cases ease and convenience.

The extreme speed of operation is perhaps the most significant difference between electronic and nonelectronic devices. This is fundamentally because of the very low mass of the electron, which permits it to be accelerated to extremely high velocities in extremely short times. Thus measurements of rapidly occurring functions of time are relatively easy for electronic instruments, and completely impossible for mechanical indicators. A comparison between the magnetic oscillograph and the cathode ray oscillograph is a case in point. The magnetic oscillograph is basically a galvanometer designed to respond rapidly to an applied signal. The use of very small, lightweight mirrors and suspensions permits this oscillograph to operate up to frequencies of the order of a few thousand cycles per second. There was a time when such speeds were adequate, at least for studies of mechanical vibrations. But rapid advances in mechanics, especially aeronautical engineering, make it imperative to use much higher-frequency test equipment. It is known that frequency components of the order of several hundred kilocycles per second may be encountered around airfoils moving at high velocities. A mechanical galvanometer, no matter how delicate, can tell nothing of these ultrasonic vibrations.

The cathode ray oscilloscope, on the other hand, is ideal for the purpose. Its electron beam is its only moving part, and this is virtually massless. Even a modest oscilloscope is capable of operation to a few hundred kilocycles, and a first-class laboratory model will faithfully reproduce signals with frequency components up to thirty megacycles or more.

The really spectacular speeds available in electronic instrumentation play a striking role in the atomic energy field. Many atomic reactions must be studied on a one-shot basis, and the time available for their study is often of the order of millimicroseconds. Suppose, for example, that a gamma ray and a neutron are produced in a given reaction, and it is essential to detect the simultaneous production of these two particles. The gamma ray, being an electromagnetic wave, will reach a detecting device sooner than the heavier and slower neutron. But the difference in time of arrival is extremely small, and the test apparatus must be able to record it. That is, there must be both a rapid response and a very short resolving time so that one particle may be detected almost immediately after the other.

Versatility is another feature very valuable in electronic instruments. Take a basic electronic counter, for example. The same instrument, with minor changes in the input circuitry, may be made to record either events per unit time, or time interval. The former function might be used, for example, in tachometry. A crystal-controlled clock turns the counting circuits on, keeps them on for some definite time such as one second, and then stops the counting. A transducer coupled to the rotating shaft by any of several methods delivers a pulse to the counter for each rotation of the shaft. The counter therefore displays the number of revolutions that occurred during the one-second interval the counting process operated. Furthermore, by using a high-frequency clock, the accuracy may be made almost as high as desired. A one-megacycle clock would permit control of the counting interval within one microsecond, while a ten-megacycle clock would hold the interval with an accuracy of one-tenth microsecond! Moreover, by the use of electronic techniques, tachometry is possible with absolutely no mechanical loading on the shaft. A phototube, for example, might be used if a stripe of black paint were placed on the shaft to provide a change in reflected light intensity for each revolution. If greater accuracy is required, ten stripes could be painted, giving ten pulses for each revolution and increasing the accuracy by a full order of magnitude. Another system that might be used is to magnetize the shaft in a direction perpendicular to its axis of rotation. Then an induction pickup similar to those of tape and wire recorders can be placed close to the shaft, and will give two pulses for each revolution as the north and south poles in the magnetized shaft alternately sweep by.

The same electronic counter could be used to measure the frequency of mechanical vibration by connecting a strain gage to the vibrating member. It can be used to measure the frequency of an electric signal even more easily, since no transducer is required: the source of voltage is simply connected directly to the input terminals.

This same piece of equipment can count the pulses generated by its own internal clock. If the counting is started and stopped by external signals, the resulting count is an accurate measure of the time between the two events. Used in this fashion, the counter is known as a *time interval meter*. The accuracy is as good as the frequency of the crystal clock, which is of the order of one part in ten million to one part in a hundred million. The resolution, which is to be distinguished from the accuracy, is plus or minus one count.

Suppose, for example, that an electronic counter is used to measure the time of flight of a bullet over a 100-foot testing path. The counting is started when the bullet breaks a fine wire near the gun muzzle, and stops when it breaks a second wire 100 feet away. If the counter counts its own ten-megacycle clock pulses during this time, and the resulting count is, say, 500,000, then we know the time of flight of the bullet was 49,999.9, 50,000.0, or 50,000.1 microseconds, since the counter may be in error by plus or minus one count. These times may further vary by about one part in 10^7 because of variations in the clock frequency with temperature or age of the crystal. Allowing for this, the correct answer might be between 49,999.8 and 50,000.2 microseconds, which comes down to a variation of eight parts per million.* Incidentally, the bullet need not lose any energy breaking the wires. Phototubes could replace the wires at the beginning and end of the test range, and the bullet would then have to interrupt only a beam of light.

Versatility is almost unlimited in electronic instrumentation. The signal from a strain gage might be displayed on a cathode ray oscilloscope, recorded on magnetic tape for future analysis, counted with an electronic counter, or measured for amplitude with an electronic voltmeter. The strain gage, in turn, might be attached to a pipe, the elongation of which is a measure of pressure; or to a cantilever beam to determine the force therein; or to a specimen undergoing tensile testing to measure microdisplacement as the piece stretches. Strain gages have even been cemented to the human body to study the motion of the muscles. Thus this one transducer makes possible mechanical, hydraulic, and biological measurements, to name but a few. And the results may be displayed in a variety of ways, as the application may demand.

Another outstanding feature of electronic instruments is their adaptability to the control of systems. Before anything can be controlled, it must be measured. And if the measuring system delivers an output in the form of an electric signal, it is particularly adaptable to automatic control functions. The output may be in the form of an *analogue*, such as a voltage proportional to the position of a milling cutter. Or this voltage might be quantized by any of various sampling and encoding techniques to obtain *digital* information for use in punched card or similar devices. Any servomechanism may be thought of as an instrumentation problem if one cares to take that point of view. For in the final analysis, no feedback system can operate if there is not some sort of measurement of the deviation of the output from the commands of the input.

Automatic control is one very obvious example of *feedback*. However, it is by no means the only application of feedback in electronic instrumentation. In addition to minimizing the error between the

* Comparable precision in laying out the test range would require the hundred feet to be measured to an accuracy of 0.01 inch.

output and input signals of a system, feedback may be used to control input and output impedances, modify the frequency response or phase characteristics, or change the transient performance of systems. Chapter 4 discusses these properties of feedback circuits in more detail; in addition, numerous examples of the application of feedback will be found throughout the text.

The possibility of using electronic instruments as telemetering systems in dangerous or inaccessible places is fairly obvious. There are many glamorous examples, such as research rockets, unmanned satellites, or inside atomic piles. The instruments can survive in temperatures, atmospheres, or atomic fields that would kill a person. There are also many cases in which it is convenient to use remote indicating instruments, even though it would be possible to station an observer in the given location. For example, studies have been made of freight car shipments to find the causes of damage in transit. A person *could* sit in a boxcar to measure impact shocks when the car is humped or coupled, and he could watch for superficial damage to merchandise. But in many ways such a test would be unrealistic. The car would ordinarily be packed as tightly as possible during an actual shipment, and there would be no empty room for an observer. Furthermore, it is often more important to learn what happens *inside* a shipping carton than to look for damage on the outside. Shipments of fragile articles, in particular, may or may not arrive safely in spite of the appearance of superficial damage to the outside of the carton. An accelerometer or strain gage packed inside a barrel of crockery would shed far more light on the problem than could be obtained in any other way.

The growth of "automation" opens vast new possibilities for electronic control and therefore electronic instrumentation in industrial applications. Fully automatic factories must be equipped with centralized control facilities to channel the output of subassembly operations into final assembly, keep inventory, locate failures in any of the machines, and realize the advantages of reduced personnel.

Individual machines equipped with feedback control form the lowest level of the automatic production pyramid. Each of these machines will have its own instrumentation problems. A linear differential transformer, for example, might rest against a bar of round stock to measure and control the reduction in diameter as the bar is cut in a lathe. Or a magnetic strain gage automatically pressed into contact with an enameled steel panel could reveal if the coating of enamel is of the correct thickness, and drop the panel onto a conveyor for a second trip through the spraying booth if the paint is too thin.

It must be emphasized that automatic production is not new. Since the industrial revolution, there have been machines that would accomplish a given operation without operator supervision. But these were "open loop" devices. Their action went in only one direction, so to speak. As long as everything operated correctly, they were fine. But if something went wrong, there was no way for the machine to know. For example, if a punch press was supposed to stamp square holes, and a corner chipped off the punch, the holes from then on would be trapezoidal in shape. Many pieces might be ruined before the difficulty was found. In the modern concept of automation, such a machine would have feedback from its output (the finished pieces) to tell it when it makes a mistake or otherwise give it instructions. In our punch press example, a photocell might be placed beside the press to measure the amount of light coming through each newly stamped hole. If the punch breaks, the hole becomes too small, the amount of light is reduced, and a signal from the photocell stops the punch. Only one piece is ruined. Note this is not just a scheme for automatic inspection, because the inspection process is *coupled to the punch itself*. It is a simple but bona fide feedback control operation, with a signal from the output returned to the input. The important point, as far as this text is concerned, is that *an electronic instrument is involved*.

The remainder of this chapter will be devoted to some examples of complete electronic instrumentation systems. They will not be explained in detail at this point, although many of the circuits and transducers are discussed in later chapters. Rather, these examples are intended to suggest to the engineering and production personnel who read them ways in which electronic instruments might be used in their business.

1-2. Some examples of electronic instrumentation systems

(a) *Nondestructive Inspection of Metals (1)*. Suppose a rolling mill operator desires a continuous inspection of the thickness of a metal sheet. It is also required to mark the general area on the sheet in which any imperfections are discovered.

A system meeting these requirements is shown in Fig. 1-1. It consists of an x-ray tube mounted above the moving sheet of metal. Beneath the sheet is an "active" transducer. This consists of a pellet of cadmium sulfide with wire leads attached to it much like a small composition resistor. It is a property of cadmium sulfide that its resistance

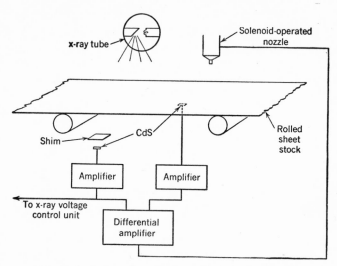

Fig. 1-1. Automatic x-ray inspection of rolled sheet.

changes with exposure to x-rays. Therefore, if a cadmium sulfide resistor is connected in series with a constant current source and exposed to x-rays having a time-varying component (usually 60 cycles), an alternating voltage will be developed across the cadmium sulfide. The intensity of the x-rays is a function of the thickness of the metal through which they pass before reaching the transducer. There is also a "reference" transducer, as nearly identical as practical to the "active" unit, but screened from the x-ray source by a shim of specified composition and thickness. This transducer likewise has an alternating voltage appearing across its terminals in the presence of 60-cycle modulated x-rays.

The two 60-cycle voltages developed by the transducers are compared in a differential amplifier. If the rolled sheet varies in thickness or composition from the reference shim, an unbalance voltage is developed in the differential amplifier. This may be amplified and used to open a solenoid-controlled nozzle that sprays paint on the imperfect section of sheet.

The use of two transducers with a reference shim offers two definite advantages. First, if the thickness of rolled sheet is to be changed, it is necessary only to insert a new shim of the desired thickness. This becomes the standard to which the next production lot is compared. Second, and more important, if the intensity of the x-ray source varies, the two transducers will be affected in about the same degree. The absolute values of the voltages reaching the differential amplifier will both change in the same way, and there will be no net error signal appearing in the output of the amplifier. Thus a line voltage fluctuation (for example) will not cause an erroneous squirt of paint. Furthermore, any change in the x-ray intensity at the reference transducer may be fed back to a line-voltage control unit and restore the x-radiation to the value at which the equipment is designed to operate.

We might note that a very similar scheme is used to measure and control the amount of tobacco packed into cigarettes (2). In cigarette inspection, beta rays are used, since these relatively weak particles are largely absorbed by even as light and porous a material as shredded tobacco; x-rays would be substantially unaffected by a cigarette.

It is most important to realize that the measuring system just described is easily adapted to process *control* as well. A variation in the thickness of the metal strip could be fed back to control the rolling mill itself; likewise, variations in tobacco density can be corrected automatically through feedback methods. In fact, *control* would ordinarily be the real reason for employing devices such as we have described. Measurement is simply the first step in initiating the control action.

(b) *Physical Analysis of Materials.* As another example of electronic instrumentation at work, suppose we consider this problem: a producer of industrial alcohol must determine the percentage of water and methanol in a given mixture. This must be done continuously and instantaneously as the mixture flows through a pipe.

The first step in solving any such problem is to determine properties of methanol and water that will affect the mixture. One such set of properties might be the dielectric constants of the two substances. For pure water, the dielectric constant is 78 at a frequency of one megacycle per second; for methanol, it is 31 (3). Assuming the dielectric constant of a mixture is directly related to the proportions of methanol and water, the dielectric constant of the mixture as a function of the per cent methanol would be as shown in Fig. 1-2.

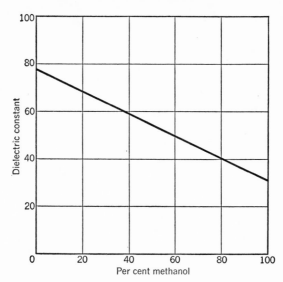

Fig. 1-2. Dielectric constant of methanol-water mixture.

This curve suggests that an analysis of the mixture could be per-formed as shown in Fig. 1-3. The alcohol-water combination flows through a glass pipe with metal plates on both sides. The capacitor thus formed is used as the tuning capacitor in an oscillator, such as the Hartley oscillator shown in the figure. The frequency of the oscillator is therefore a measure of the constituents in the mixture. The oscillator is followed by an amplifier tuned to a frequency somewhat higher than would be produced if the percentage of methanol were the desired value. Between the oscillator and amplifier is a clipper that converts the out-put of the oscillator to square waves having an amplitude independent of that of the original sinusoidal oscillations. This is done to prevent

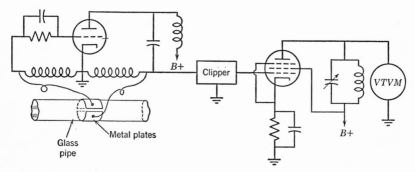

Fig. 1-3. Instrumentation for analyzing methanol-water mixture.

changes in the amplifier output as a result of varying radio frequency losses in the alcohol-water mixture that would affect the amplitude of oscillation. Finally, a vacuum tube voltmeter indicates the voltage developed across the tuned circuit, which is a function of the percentage of methanol. A typical characteristic is shown in Fig. 1-4, which also

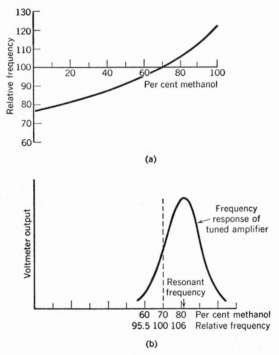

Fig. 1-4. (a) Relative frequency of oscillation. (b) Voltmeter indication as a function of frequency. Per cent methanol shown for comparison.

indicates the relative frequency of oscillation, taking 70 per cent methanol as 100. Note the implication that 70 per cent methanol is the desired mixture, for the voltmeter indication drops too low to be read accurately below 60 per cent. Above 82 per cent the tuned amplifier response curve drops down again, creating the possibility of an ambiguous indication if the percentage of alcohol should become much too high.

The frequency of oscillation could also be read directly by one of the frequency-measuring instruments discussed in Chapter 9. This

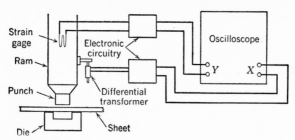

Fig. 1-5. Equipment for displaying stress-strain diagram of a punching operation.

would be another method of developing a complete instrument based on the capacitance transducer of Fig. 1-3.

(c) *A Study of Equipment Performance.* The examples already given were drawn from the area of process measurement and control. But electronic instruments are just as useful in research, design, and development. Suppose, for instance, the research laboratory of a machine tool company wishes to find the total work required to punch a hole in sheet stock with a punch press (4). Since work is the integral of force times distance, this measurement involves the determination of two variables: force and displacement. If the former can be plotted as a function of the latter, the area under the resulting curve is the work.

A device that displays the force-distance diagram is shown in Fig. 1-5. The force exerted on the punch is measured by a strain gage cemented to the ram, while the distance the punch moves is given by the displacement of the core of a differential transformer. The two variables are displayed on a d-c cathode ray oscilloscope, resulting in a picture similar to that in Fig. 1-6. This chart was produced in a punch

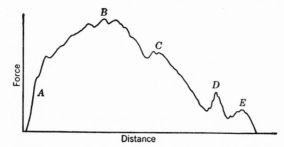

Fig. 1-6. Typical diagram produced by the instrument in Fig. 1-5.

press with insufficient clearance between the punch and die. In region A, the metal follows Hooke's law. Regions B, C, and D are primary, secondary, and tertiary shear. The peak at E represents the force necessary to eject the cut blank from the sheet. The total work is the area under the curve of Fig. 1-6. It could be determined with a planimeter from a drawing or photograph. Or, with considerable added circuit complexity, analog computer techniques could be employed to perform the integration simultaneously with the displaying of the data.

(d) *Electronic Optical Comparator.* Still another example of electronic instruments at work is shown in Fig. 1-7. This illustrates a

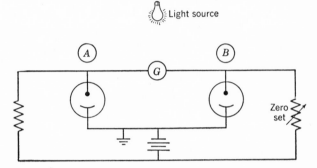

Fig. 1-7. A phototube optical bridge.

method for comparing the light transmission of two objects, A and B, indicated as circles above the photocells. The photocells are connected in a bridge, with a galvanometer between them. This arrangement has the advantage that small variations in the source intensity will affect both photocells the same way, and so if the light transmission of the two objects is the same, the bridge will remain balanced. If only one photocell were employed, a change in the source intensity would be interpreted as a change in the optical density of the object being measured.

There are several applications of this principle. One is in the calibration of lenses. Suppose a lens of known f.8 opening is used as object A, and a gray photographic "wedge" is moved across hole B until it admits approximately the same light to its photocell as does the f.8 lens. This is indicated by the galvanometer deflection approaching zero. A final balance is achieved by adjusting the zero-set potentiometer. Then the standard lens is removed, and the lenses to be calibrated are placed one by one in hole A. The iris in each new lens is adjusted until the bridge is balanced, as shown by a null of the galvanometer. The iris setting at the null point is then the same as that of the standard lens, or $f.8$.

Another application of this same technique could be the study of air pollution. Say it is desired to determine quantitatively the amount of dust entering a house or store in 24 hours. This might be done as follows: Place two pieces of clear glass in the optical bridge, and reduce the light intensity until it is certain the photocells are operating well within their linear characteristics. This could be verified by a switch that transfers the galvanometer from its position across the bridge to a position in series with one of the photocells. The galvanometer is then reconnected as a null detector, and the zero set adjusted for the null. Now remove one of the glass plates and leave it in the dusty location for the desired length of time. When this period has elapsed, the plate is replaced in the optical bridge. If the coating of dust is not extremely heavy, the bridge will be thrown only moderately out of balance, and the galvanometer needle will remain on scale. The scale could be calibrated in relative "dustiness" units.

A more elegant scheme, but one more complex mechanically, is suggested in Fig. 1-8. This employs a single photocell, thereby eliminating completely any possibility that drift between the two photocells of our previous circuit could introduce an error.

The principle of operation is as follows: A collimated beam passes through two sets of prisms, producing two separate beams. One beam passes through a standard gray wedge and a calibrating wedge, while the other passes through a calibrating wedge and the specimen. Both beams then strike mirrors and are reflected to the cathode of a photocell. A rotating shutter is placed between the two light paths in such a manner that only one path can reach the photocell at a given time. The output of the photocell is displayed on a cathode ray oscilloscope, resulting in a trace of two approximately trapezoidal patterns side by side, each pattern corresponding to one of the light paths. Initial calibration is achieved by adjusting the calibrating wedges until the two patterns are the same height (the specimen and standard gray wedge are removed during this operation). Then the specimen and gray wedge are inserted, and the latter adjusted until the two oscilloscope traces are again the same height. The optical density of the specimen is read directly from the scale on the standard wedge.

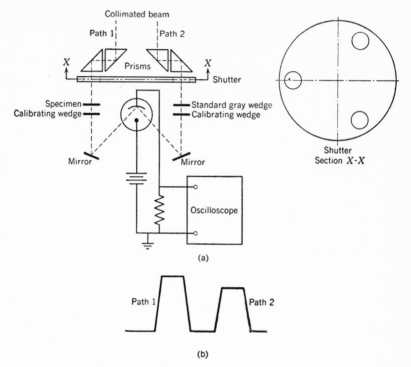

Fig. 1-8. Another type of optical comparator.

1-3. Conclusion

In this chapter, we have endeavored to show what may be gained by the use of electronic instruments, and to suggest a few possible applications for electronic instruments in practice. Only a handful of examples has been given, but it is hoped they may have awakened the reader's imagination. It is difficult to conceive of a process in manufacturing or research that could not in some way employ electronic instrumentation to advantage.

The subject of actual measuring techniques will not be treated in much more detail until the second section of this book. There we shall study the transducers and circuits that make up complete instruments for the measurement of nonelectrical quantities. But since most transducers give some sort of electric signal or change some sort of electrical parameter, it will be necessary for us to devote some time to the problem of measuring purely electrical quantities. Accordingly, the next chapters deal with such matters as the measurement of voltage, current, frequency, power, phase angle, and circuit parameters. These topics are of direct interest to those working in the electrical industry. To others, they are a necessary preliminary to understanding how complete electronic instrumentation systems may be developed.

REFERENCES

1. John F. Howell, "Automatic Metal Gauging Using X-Rays," *Proc. Natl. Electronics Conf.*, vol. 8 (1952), p. 121. See also George M. Ettinger, "A Differential X-Ray Absorption Gauge of High Sensitivity," *Proc. Natl. Electronics Conf.*, vol. 8 (1952), p. 113.
2. E. Harrison, Jr., "Beta Gage Controls Cigarette Machine," *Electronics*, vol. 9, no. 11 (Nov. 1956), p. 144.
3. *Reference Data for Radio Engineers*, 4th ed. (New York, International Telephone and Telegraph Corp., 1956), pp. 68, 70.
4. Robert A. Grimm, "A Stress-Strain Indicator" (Master's Thesis, Purdue University, August 1951).

Chapter 2

THE SIGNIFICANCE OF VOLTAGE
MEASUREMENTS

With the possible exceptions of cathode ray oscilloscopes, oscillators, and signal generators, the vacuum tube voltmeter is probably the most widely used of all electronic instruments. It seems appropriate, therefore, to start with a discussion of the types of electronic voltmeters, emphasizing the way in which they respond to signals of various waveforms. The study of specific voltmeter circuits will be deferred to the next chapter.

It is a fairly common practice among engineers to select whatever vacuum tube voltmeter happens to be available on the laboratory shelf, and proceed to write down its readings. Frequently this is a perfectly satisfactory procedure, especially if only *relative* measurements are desired. An example might be in the measurement of linear amplifier gain, where the input and output are voltages of substantially the same waveform. On the other hand, with any signal other than a pure sine wave, a very serious error may be present in the *absolute* meter indication, depending on the meter circuitry and the waveform of the voltage to be measured. This chapter will discuss the interpretation of the readings of three basic types of voltmeters as they are used to measure sine waves, white noise, and combinations of inharmonically related sine waves. The three circuits to be treated are those which respond to the rms value of the unknown, the average value, and the peak value. The discussion will follow to a large extent that given by Beranek (1).

2-1. Some properties of noise

For the purposes of this chapter, it is not necessary to go deeply into the theory of noise. The type of noise considered here is so-called "random white noise," i.e., a signal whose amplitude varies in a random way as a function of time, and whose energy content is uniformly distributed throughout the entire frequency spectrum. Noise of this type is produced in a number of ways in electronic equipment. One of the most common is thermal noise produced by the random motion of electrons in resistors.

Another is the "shot" noise caused by electrons moving through an électron tube. Although one usually thinks of such electron flow as a steady current, it consists, in reality, of discrete particles of charge (the electrons) crossing the tube in random quantities from time to time. Thus if we were able to count the electrons arriving at the anode of a tube during very short periods of time, say 10^{-12} second or so, it would

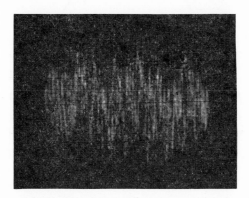

Fig. 2-1. Photograph of an oscilloscope trace showing white noise.

be found that the number arriving in any given interval would vary greatly from one interval to another. One of the best ways of producing approximately random white noise is based on a greatly exaggerated shot effect that occurs when a gas diode is placed in a magnetic field. The presence of many particles, positive ions as well as electrons, moving not only under the influence of an electric field, but rotating in the magnetic field as well, is a good guarantee of obtaining the random arrival of charge at the anode necessary to produce noise. Figure 2-1 shows an oscillogram of the output of such a gas diode noise generator.

In order to determine the manner in which an electronic voltmeter responds to noise, it is necessary to find certain properties of the noise signal, such as its rms and average values. Our problem is most readily handled by the statistical approach, and starts with the *normal prob-*

ability curve shown in Fig. 2-2. This curve plots the *probability density* $P(x)$, of some event x taking place. For example, if we are investigating narrow pulses of current that may have amplitudes anywhere between $-\infty$ and $+\infty$, but are known to follow the normal probability curve,

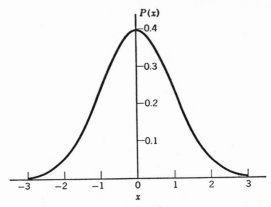

Fig. 2-2. The normal probability curve.

then the *decimal fraction* of the total number with amplitudes between x and $x + \Delta x$ is $P(x)\, \Delta x$. Obviously, the decimal fraction of the total number with amplitudes between $-\infty$ and $+\infty$ must be 1.000, or identically unity; that is to say, *the area under the normal probability curve is unity*.

In order to determine the average, rms, or any other quantity pertaining to the probability curve, it is necessary to know the equation for this curve. It appears in several forms, but the one that will be used here is

$$P(x) \;=\; \frac{1}{\sigma\sqrt{2\pi}}\,\epsilon^{-x^2/2\sigma^2} \tag{2-1}$$

where x is the amplitude of any arbitrary pulse of noise, and σ is a quantity known as the "standard deviation." We shall soon find a more interesting and meaningful interpretation of σ as it applies to electrical quantities.

We are now in a position to determine the average and rms values of a signal of the type represented by Eq. (2-1), in which x might be the amplitude of voltage or current varying in a random manner. It should be pointed out that since the amplitudes of x may be both positive and negative, the true average value is zero; therefore, when one speaks of the "average" value of noise, a full-wave-rectified situation is implied, just as when one refers to the average value of a sine wave.

Also it must be emphasized very strongly that the normal probability curve is *not a function of time*, but rather an index of the relative number of noise pulses that have an amplitude in the neighborhood of x. Bearing this in mind, the average value of a function of the form of Eq. (2-1) is

$$x_{av} = \frac{\int_{-\infty}^{+\infty} xP(x)\, dx}{\int_{-\infty}^{+\infty} P(x)\, dx} \tag{2-2}$$

That this is true may be seen by inspection, although at first glance the expression appears a little formidable. The term $P(x)\, dx$ in the numerator represents simply the fraction of pulses with an amplitude between x and $x + dx$, and multiplying $P(x)\, dx$ by x gives the appropriate weighting to the pulses in that interval. It is exactly the same process a life insurance actuary would use in calculating the average lifetime of people. He would multiply the number of those who die in their first year by 1; those who die in their second year by 2; and so on to infinity, which would be ninety-some years for all practical purposes. The only difference is that the actuary in effect replaces the integral sign by a summation symbol. He would then divide his sum by the number of people for whom he had data. In the case of Eq. (2-2), the denominator serves an analogous function, for it represents the decimal fraction of pulses in the sample of noise we are considering, and, as noted earlier, is identically equal to unity.

Since the true average value of random noise is zero, the result obtained from Eq. (2-2) will be zero, which is of little help in determining the reading to be expected from a vacuum tube voltmeter. In the electrical sense, it is more significant to give x_{av} as

$$x_{av} = 2 \int_{0}^{\infty} xP(x)\, dx \tag{2-3}$$

If Eq. (2-1) is substituted for $P(x)$, Eq. (2-3) becomes a very easily integrated expression with a value of

$$x_{av} = \sigma \sqrt{2/\pi} \tag{2-4}$$

or, approximately,

$$x_{av} = 0.798\sigma \tag{2-5}$$

The mean square value of x is found from an expression very similar to Eq. (2-2), except that x^2 is used as the coefficient of $P(x)\, dx$; thus

$$x_{mean}^2 = \frac{\int_{-\infty}^{+\infty} x^2 P(x)\, dx}{\int_{-\infty}^{+\infty} P(x)\, dx} \tag{2-6}$$

Here again the denominator is identically unity, and if Eq. (2-1) is substituted for $P(x)$, the value of Eq. (2-6) may be determined. The problem is straightforward, although a little longer, since integration by parts is necessary. The final result is

$$x_{mean}^2 = \sigma^2 \qquad (2\text{-}7)$$

so the rms value of x is simply

$$x_{rms} = \sigma \qquad (2\text{-}8)$$

The ratio of the rms value of x to the average value is $1/0.798 = 1.25$, which corresponds to 1.96 db. The vast majority of commercially available electronic voltmeters have been calibrated to indicate the rms value of a sine wave. Since the ratio of the rms to the average value of a sine wave is 1.11 (the well-known "form factor"), a meter with a circuit responsive to the average value of the input voltage must have its scale values multiplied in effect by 1.11 if it is to indicate the rms value of sine waves. This amounts to a correction factor of 0.91 db. Now suppose that such a meter, having been calibrated for a single sine wave, is applied to a source of random noise. The average value of the noise is 1.96 db below the rms value, while the meter has a built-in correction of 0.91 db. Therefore the meter indication will be too low by the difference between these numbers, i.e., 1.05 db. An error of 1.05 db corresponds to a voltage ratio of 1.13:1, so a white noise signal of 113 volts rms would be indicated by an average reading type of meter as 100 volts rms, even though the meter scale is marked "Volts, RMS" and the meter gives the correct indications on sine waves.

It should be obvious from the above example that there is a possibility of serious error if proper attention is not paid to the nature of the meter circuit and its relationship to the signal to be measured. The chance of large errors is even greater with the so-called "peak reading" types of electronic voltmeters, which will be treated in the next section.

The author wishes to state very emphatically at this point that a discussion of the errors in electronic voltmeters is not in any way to be taken as a disparagement of these devices. The modern vacuum tube voltmeters, most of which are either average or peak-reading types, have made possible measurements that were most difficult twenty years ago. The point to be made is that such errors are inherent in the circuitry, regardless of the quality or price of the instrument; and the author's objective in writing this chapter is to draw the reader's attention to these inevitable errors and emphasize the need for intelligent use of the electronic voltmeter and the proper interpretation of its readings.

2-2. Elementary peak-reading vacuum tube voltmeter

The peak-reading vacuum tube voltmeter employs internal circuitry making the indication of the device inherently a function of the *peak*, rather than the rms or average values of the unknown voltage to be measured. It is a very popular type of meter, having fairly high input

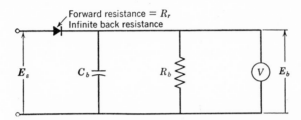

Fig. 2-3. The basic circuit of a peak-reading meter.

impedance (of the order of a half megohm or more in most cases) and good linearity. It is fairly easy and inexpensive to manufacture. The basic form of the circuit is shown in Fig. 2-3.

The action of this circuit is very simple indeed, at least as far as the general principles are concerned. An input signal voltage E_s is applied to the terminals of the instrument. The applied voltage is rectified by a tube or crystal diode having an internal resistance R_r in the conducting direction and presumably infinite resistance in the back direction. The capacitor C_b charges up to a voltage almost equal to the peak value of E_s. After this capacitor is fully charged, the voltage across it will exceed the value of E_s during most of the cycle of input voltage, and the rectifier will be nonconducting most of the time. However, some of the charge in the capacitor will be bled away by the resistor R_b, so that the indication of meter V will be slightly less than the peak value of E_s.

Meter V is here assumed to have infinite internal impedance. In practice, of course, this meter might be an ordinary D'Arsonval movement in series with the resistor R_b, and R_b in that case would be understood to include the resistance of the meter and any multiplying resistors in series with it.

In designing a peak-reading meter, it is common practice to calibrate the scale to give the rms value of an impressed sine wave. However, when the input signal is not a single sinusoid, rather large errors may be expected. Let us suppose, for example, that the input consists of a combination of inharmonically related sine waves described by the equation

$$E_s = E(\cos \omega_1 t + \cos \omega_2 t + \cos \omega_3 t + \ldots + \cos \omega_n t) \qquad (2\text{-}9)$$

where each component is of equal amplitude E, and ω_1 to ω_n represent the (angular) frequencies of the first to nth components. It is also assumed that the time constant $R_b C_b$ is very long so that the voltage E_b remains essentially constant while the rectifier is not conducting. Then the charge flowing out of the capacitor C_b per second is

$$q_{out} = E_b/R_b \qquad (2\text{-}10)$$

The charge per second flowing into the capacitor is

$$q_{in} = \int_{E_b}^{nE} \frac{(E_s - E_b)}{R_r} P(E_s)\, dE_s \qquad (2\text{-}11)$$

where $P(E_s)\, dE_s$ is the decimal fraction of the time that the voltage of the signal lies between E_s and $E_s + dE_s$. Curves of $P(E_s)$ for several different values of n are shown in Fig. 2-4, normalized in terms of the combined peak value, nE (*2*).

Since the charges entering and leaving C_b per unit time must be equal in the steady state, Eqs. (2-10) and (2-11) may be equated to each other, giving

$$\int_{E_b}^{nE} \frac{(E_s - E_b)}{R_r} P(E_s)\, dE_s = \frac{E_b}{R_b} \qquad (2\text{-}12)$$

If both sides of Eq. (2-12) are multiplied by R_r/E_b, the result is

$$\int_{E_b}^{nE} \frac{(E_s - E_b)}{E_b} P(E_s)\, dE_s = \frac{R_r}{R_b} \qquad (2\text{-}13)$$

From this expression, certain conclusions may be drawn. It is self-evident that a perfect peak-reading voltmeter will develop the full voltage nE across capacitor C_b. Then in the ideal case, $E_b = nE$, and the integral on the left-hand side of Eq. (2-13) will be zero, since both limits of integration are the same. Then if Eq. (2-13) is to be satisfied, the ratio R_r/R_b must also be zero. In practice, $R_r > 0$, and R_b is always finite, so the ideal case cannot be realized. However, the smaller this ratio can be made, the more nearly the meter will act as a true peak-

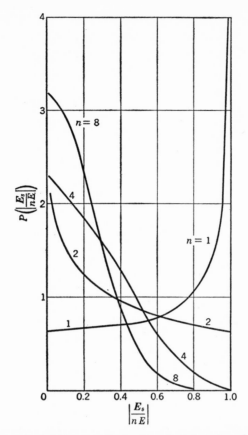

Fig. 2-4. Probability density for the absolute value of the instantaneous amplitude of a combination of n equal, inharmonically related sine waves. After Beranek (1) and Slack (2).

reading type. It follows that the ratio R_r/R_b may be taken as the figure of merit of this circuit.

The rectifier resistance is inherent in a peak-reading circuit, but any external resistance placed in series with R_r will act exactly like an increased value of rectifier resistance. Therefore in computing correction factors for a peak-reading vacuum tube voltmeter, R_r *must include the output impedance of the source of voltage to be measured.* This is a very significant fact, and has many implications. For example, not only will the output impedance of the source affect the indication of the instrument, but so will such commonly used techniques as putting a resistive voltage divider between the unknown signal and the input. In the case of commercial vacuum tube voltmeters employing voltage dividers as an integral part of their circuitry, the instrument will be calibrated to read the correct rms value of a single sine wave regardless of the range switch setting, as long as the output impedance of the signal source is relatively low. But truly spectacular errors can be made, often unknown to the user of the instrument, when peak-reading circuits are used to measure arbitrary waveforms from arbitrary source impedances, especially if a voltage divider is also present. The magnitude of an error may be difficult to determine, since it is dependent on the waveform of the signal, the source impedance, and the circuit parameters of the voltmeter itself.

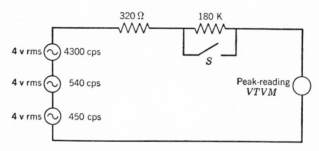

Fig. 2-5. Circuit for demonstrating error in meter indication.

An example is shown in Fig. 2-5, which shows three oscillators connected in series, with the combined output applied to a peak-reading vacuum tube voltmeter. The oscillators have an internal impedance of 320 ohms total as measured on an impedance bridge. An additional resistance of 180,000 ohms is placed in series with provisions for short-circuiting it. The case with the switch closed is analogous to measuring the output voltage from a low-impedance source such as a cathode follower. With the switch open, one might imagine the source to be a pentode amplifier. The voltmeter is a peak-reading type, with the scale calibrated to read volts rms on a single sine wave from a low-impedance source. Therefore if the voltage E_b developed in the capacitor C_b is truly proportional to the peak of the applied emf, the scale will indicate 12 volts with the three oscillators in series. The actual readings are: S closed, 10.9 volts; S open, 6.2 volts.

2-3. Corrections for peak-reading meters

In taking data with peak-reading meters, it is desirable to have at hand some information for correcting the readings to either true peak or true rms values. Curves for the two cases are presented in Figs. 2-6

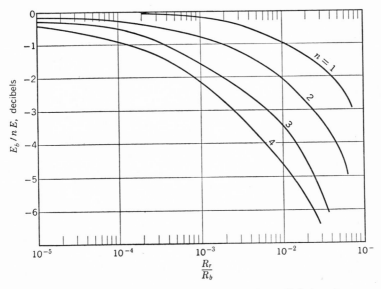

Fig. 2-6. Plot in decibels of the capacitor voltage E_b below the peak voltage of the sum of n inharmonically related sine waves. From Beranek (*1*).

and 2-7. The former gives the voltage that will be developed on capacitor C_b in decibels below the true peak value for various numbers of equal, inharmonically related sine waves. Figure 2-7 shows the difference between the meter indication and the true rms value of the signal being measured. In both figures, it is assumed that the source impedance of the signal is zero, and in Fig. 2-7, it is also assumed that the meter has *already been calibrated* to give the true rms value of a single sine wave.

If an expression of the form of Eq. (2-1) is used in Eq. (2-13), the response of the peak-reading meter to random noise may be determined. However, since the peak value of random noise is infinity, it is more meaningful to plot the results in terms of rms values directly, as has been done in Fig. 2-7.

To clarify the use of these curves, the following example is offered: Suppose four inharmonically related sine waves of equal amplitude are impressed on a peak-reading vacuum tube voltmeter in which R_r is 500 ohms and R_b is 1 megohm. The signal source has an impedance R_g of

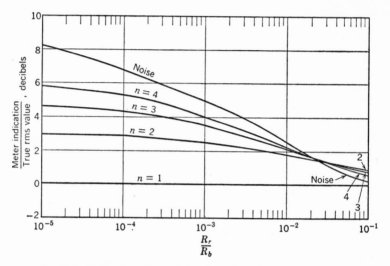

Fig. 2-7. Indication of a peak-reading meter relative to the true rms value of n equal, inharmonically related sine waves, and of white noise. Source impedance assumed zero in constructing these curves.

5000 ohms. Find the error in the meter indication relative to the true rms value of the signal if the meter has been initially calibrated to give the rms value of a single sine wave.

For the meter alone, disregarding for the moment the source impedance, $R_r/R_b = 500/1,000,000 = 5 \times 10^{-4}$. Figure 2-6 indicates that with a single sine wave as used in the factory calibration, the value of E_b will be about 0.1 db below the true peak. Since the rms value of a sine wave is 3 db below the peak, the net correction built into the meter must be 3 db − 0.1 db = 2.9 db; i.e., the scale is painted with markings 2.9 db below E_b.

Now the user of the meter has placed it in a circuit where its *effective* value of rectifier resistance is $R_r + R_g = 5500$ ohms. The ratio

$(R_r + R_g)/R_b$ is 5.5×10^{-3}. From Fig. 2-6, for this value of the ratio and $n = 4$, E_b will be 3.8 db below the true peak. Since the scale indication is 2.9 db below E_b, and E_b is itself 3.8 db too low, the meter will read 6.7 db below the *true peak value* of the four sine waves. Now the rms value of four equal waves is 9 db below their combined peak value, so the final result is that the meter indication will be *too high* by $9 - 6.7 = 2.3$ db. This should be compared with Fig. 2-7, which shows that the error would have been about 4.5 db for the same meter and signal had the source impedance R_g been zero.

It might be noted in passing that the curves in Fig. 2-7 tend to converge for relatively high values of R_r/R_b. This suggests that there is a value of R_r/R_b where the meter indication differs from the rms value by an almost constant number of decibels regardless of the value of n. This constant may be incorporated as a correction factor in the manufacture of an instrument with a large value of R_r/R_b, and an almost true rms reading device results.

2-4. Response of average-reading circuits to arbitrary signals

An average-responsive circuit connected to a source of arbitrary signals represented by a probability distribution $P(E)$ will indicate a voltage of

$$E_{av} = \int_0^\infty EP(E)\,dE \qquad (2\text{-}14)$$

where E_{av} is the average voltage, E is instantaneous amplitude, and $P(E)$ is the probability density of occurrence of an instantaneous amplitude of E in the rectified wave. The product $P(E)\,dE$ is the fraction of the time a voltage between E and $E + dE$ is present, since $P(E)$ is based upon the per cent time a voltage equal to or greater than E is present. Note that the integral of Eq. (2-14) does not have to be divided by some quantity as it would if one were finding a *time* average directly. This is because $P(E)$ already involves a time concept.

To provide an easy example of this, we shall take a simple probability function and use it to construct one of the many possible functions of time that could be represented by it. The average value of the function will be determined by graphical integration, and the value of Eq. (2-14) will be computed for purposes of comparison. The results will be identical within the accuracy of the graphical method.

Suppose that a given source of voltage delivers pulses that may have values between zero and five volts, and a probability density of occurrence given by the expression

$$P(E) = 0.08E \qquad (2\text{-}15)$$

The constant 0.08 was selected on the basis of normalizing Eq. (2-15) so that the area under the curve of $P(E)$ between the limits of zero and five will be unity, just as in Section 2-1 it was convenient to make the area under the normal probability curve equal to unity. Although Eq. (2-15) is *not* a function of time, it tells us what fraction of the time the voltage lies within the range bounded by E and $E + \Delta E$. This fraction is $P(E)\,\Delta E$, although in the remainder of this example, a percentage basis will be used in preference to a decimal fraction. Then, breaking the possible values of E into $\frac{1}{2}$ volt increments, and taking the value of E in any increment as the value at the center, we can construct Table 2-1 and determine the per cent of time that the voltage will lie within a given interval.

TABLE 2-1. CALCULATION OF THE PER CENT TIME THAT VOLTAGE LIES WITHIN THE INTERVAL E TO $E + \Delta E$

Range of voltage	ΔE	Value of E at center of range	$P(E)$ using the value of E in third column	$P(E)\,\Delta E$ expressed as per cent
0 to 0.5	0.5	0.25	0.02	1
0.5 to 1.0	0.5	0.75	0.06	3
1.0 to 1.5	0.5	1.25	0.10	5
1.5 to 2.0	0.5	1.75	0.14	7
2.0 to 2.5	0.5	2.25	0.18	9
2.5 to 3.0	0.5	2.75	0.22	11
3.0 to 3.5	0.5	3.25	0.26	13
3.5 to 4.0	0.5	3.75	0.30	15
4.0 to 4.5	0.5	4.25	0.34	17
4.5 to 5.0	0.5	4.75	0.38	19
			Total =	100%

The percentages of time that are given in Table 2-1 may be used to construct an arbitrary *function of time* that can be integrated graphically. One function is drawn in Fig. 2-8, and the integration carried out in Table 2-2.

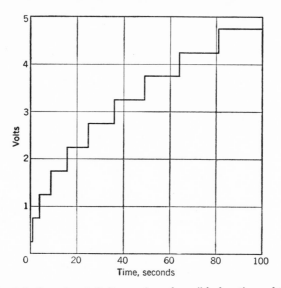

Fig. 2-8. One of an infinite number of possible functions of time having probability densities of voltage occurrence as given in Eq. (2-15).

TABLE 2-2. INTEGRATION OF THE FUNCTION OF FIG. 2-8

Interval	Duration, seconds	Voltage	Product = volt-seconds
A	1	0.25	0.25
B	3	0.75	2.25
C	5	1.25	6.25
D	7	1.75	12.25
E	9	2.25	20.25
F	11	2.75	30.25
G	13	3.25	42.25
H	15	3.75	56.25
I	17	4.25	72.25
J	19	4.75	90.25
		Sum =	332.50

An infinite number of functions of time could be constructed, all of them meeting the specifications in the table above. The one actually shown was selected as being the most obvious. The function is presumed to have a period of 100 seconds as a matter of convenience in using the percentages of Table 2-1. The average voltage is the sum of the volt-seconds divided by the period, or $332.50/100 = 3.325$ volts.

Now, for comparison, let Eq. (2-15) be substituted into Eq. (2-14) and let the result be evaluated. Since the function $P(E)$ is not defined for voltages greater than 5, the upper limit of integration is 5 rather than infinity.

$$E_{av} = \int_0^5 0.08E^2 \, dE = \frac{0.08E^3}{3} \bigg|_0^5 = 3.333 \text{ volts} \qquad (2\text{-}16)$$

This result is certainly the same as that obtained by working from the artificial function of time, and should serve to point up the implicit time relationship in the probability equation.

If one wishes to find the response of an average-responsive circuit to a number of inharmonically related sine waves, the curves of Fig. 2-4 may be used to calculate the value of E_{av} from Eq. (2-14) by graphical or numerical integration. In general, the results indicate that an average-reading vacuum tube voltmeter already calibrated to display the rms value of a sine wave, will give an indication less than 1 db lower than the true rms value of a combination of inharmonically related sine waves. The error is about $\frac{1}{4}$ db for $n = 2$, and about $\frac{3}{4}$ db for $n = 8$. We have already considered the case of the average-reading meter with an input of white, Gaussian noise.

2-5. Recapitulation

The author wishes to point out once more in concluding this chapter that the errors discussed—many of them rather serious in magnitude—are in no way a reflection on the quality or usefulness of electronic voltmeters. Such errors, like death and taxes, are inescapable and must be reckoned with on occasion. The user of electronic voltmeters should be aware of these inherent inaccuracies and know how to correct for them when the need arises. In the case of peak-responsive voltmeters in particular, he should be well acquainted with his own equipment and its internal circuit parameters.

It is obviously impossible to generalize very far regarding the response of any arbitrary meter to any possible type of signal. However, the discussion of this chapter should indicate how to approach the problem of determining the appropriate correction factor for any specific case.

Table 2-3 summarizes the errors to be expected in certain cases. Note that all the meters listed there have been calibrated to give the correct rms value of a single sine wave.

TABLE 2-3. ERRORS IN DB IN THE INDICATION OF VARIOUS TYPES
OF METERS MEASURING VARIOUS TYPES OF SIGNALS

	Average Meter	Peak Meter	Rms Meter
Sine wave	0	0	0
Combinations of inharmonic waves	Usually less than 1 db low	Several db high in most cases. See Fig. 2-7.	0
White noise	1.05 db low	Usually many db high. See Fig. 2-8.	0

REFERENCES

1. L. L. Beranek, *Acoustic Measurements* (New York: John Wiley & Sons, Inc., 1949), chaps. 10 and 11.
2. Margaret Slack, "The Probability Distributions of Sinusoidal Oscillations Combined in Random Phase," *J. Inst. Elec. Engrs.* (1946), part III, vol. 93, pp. 76-86.

Chapter 3

THE CIRCUITS OF D-C VACUUM
TUBE VOLTMETERS

Vacuum tube voltmeters may be classed in several ways, but in the opinion of the author, the most useful primary division is between d-c and a-c types. The d-c category includes instruments designed to indicate the *d-c component* of whatever signal may be under observation. Meters of the a-c type will be understood, for purposes of this book, to include all those which are *not* responsive to a d-c component of voltage. In commercial instruments, it is very common to find both a-c and d-c measuring systems included in the same package. Such instruments ordinarily employ d-c circuitry for both measurements, the a-c signals being rectified and applied to the remainder of the circuit as direct current.

Before taking up specific circuits, it might be helpful to list and discuss briefly certain factors that should be considered in the design of all electronic voltmeters, both a-c and d-c types.

3-1. Design considerations for electronic voltmeters (1)

The following list is a guide to the major points in the design of electronic voltmeters of all types:*

1. Input impedance
2. Sensitivity
3. Stability
4. Type of scale (d-c, a-c, peak, peak-to-peak, etc.)
5. Ranges available

* List quoted by permission from *Theory and Applications of Electron Tubes*, by Herbert J. Reich. Copyright, 1944. McGraw-Hill Book Co., Inc.

6. Effect of waveform upon readings

7. Portability and cost

The *input impedance* to an electronic voltmeter is one of the first points to be considered in setting design specifications. In general, it should be as high as possible. One of the main advantages of the electronic voltmeter is that its input impedance can be made high enough to avoid loading almost any circuit one might care to test. Most electronic voltmeters have an input impedance of *at least* a few hundred thousand ohms on a-c scales, and several megohms on d-c scales. The *input capacitance* is also important when signals involving high-frequency components are measured. In general, laboratory quality instruments have input impedances approximately an order of magnitude higher than those designed for sale to hobbyists, amateurs, and repairmen.'

The second design specification is the *sensitivity* of the instrument. Almost all electronic voltmeters are capable of giving full-scale indication with signals of 1 volt or more. Many instruments for *a-c* applications will deflect full scale on as little as 1 mv, and some manufacturers provide auxiliary battery-operated multiplier amplifiers to extend the range down to the order of microvolts. Thermal noise is the ultimate limiting factor in one's efforts to measure extremely small signals. It is much more difficult to measure very low *direct* voltages, but by the use of choppers to convert the small d-c signals to a-c signals, it is possible to measure direct potentials of the order of microvolts (*2*).

The term *stability* as used in conjunction with the complete instrument refers to freedom from drift in its indication. This means that an electronic voltmeter measuring a constant voltage must give the same indication hour after hour, as long as the instrument is connected to the signal. Manufacturers of instruments designed for precision work will usually include stability data in the instruction book. This is generally expressed as a drift of so many millivolts per hour after the initial warm-up time.

The word "stability" also has a connotation of freedom from oscillation, and is used in this sense by workers in the field of servomechanisms and automatic control systems of all kinds. Many electronic instruments involve feedback circuits in which the possibility of oscillation must be reckoned with, so "stability" may have either meaning as used in this book. The intended significance will be clear from the context.

By *type of scale* one means the manner in which the indication of the instrument is expressed. In d-c voltmeters, there is only one choice— volts d-c. However, with a-c reading devices, the value might be expressed in volts rms, peak, or peak-to-peak. Although of considerable importance to the user from the standpoint of convenience, the type of scale is usually a minor detail to the designer. Perhaps the main exception is in the case of instruments designed to indicate the amplitude of pulses. In this situation, the scale is calibrated in peak or peak-to-peak volts, and the internal circuitry is greatly different from that found in a-c voltmeters designed to measure the value of sinusoidal waveforms. In some cases, nonlinear scales are a convenience. In particular, logarithmic scales are often advantageous, as these result in a linear decibel indication. Since decibel readings are more often required of a-c instruments than d-c meters, the discussion of nonlinear scales has been included in Chapter 6.

The choice of *ranges* is of considerable importance to the user of the instrument. From the design standpoint, the real problem is to obtain full scale indication on the lowest voltage amplitude called for in the specifications. When this objective is met, higher voltages can be accommodated by the use of voltage divider networks at the input to the instrument. The problem is basically simple, although when a wide range of frequencies must be accommodated, it may be necessary to design frequency-compensated voltage dividers. Also, the presence of a voltage divider associated with a diode rectifier changes the apparent forward resistance of the rectifier. Therefore the value of R_r may depend on the range to which the instrument is set, and consequently the indication may be very different from one range to another when the signal under test is not a sine wave. This difficulty is fairly easy to overcome by putting a buffer amplifier, often a cathode follower, between the voltage divider and the diode.

The sixth point in the list of design considerations, that of the *effect of the waveform* upon the meter reading, has been already treated in detail in Chapter 2.

Finally, the questions of *portability and cost* must be considered. Inevitably, the tighter the first six specifications, the larger and more expensive the instrument will be. It is obviously impossible to say much of a specific nature regarding costs, and each design problem must be considered on its own merits. In general, special-purpose or laboratory instruments are designed to meet certain operating specifications, and the price must fall where it will. Instruments made for less critical applications will ordinarily be designed to include as many desirable features as possible within the allotted manufacturing cost.

3-2. The simpler d-c electronic voltmeter circuits

The most elementary possible vacuum tube voltmeter would be of the type shown in Fig. 3-1. This meets the first requirement of a vacuum tube voltmeter, i.e., high input impedance. Provided grid

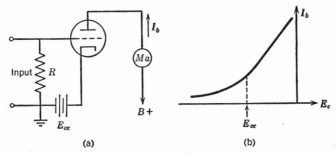

Fig. 3-1. The transfer characteristic vacuum tube voltmeter: (a) circuit of instrument; (b) a typical transfer characteristic.

direct current does not become troublesome, the resistor R may be made as large as desired. With conventional tubes, however, R could seldom be greater than 10 megohms. The direct voltage applied to the control grid is the sum of the input and the bias voltage E_{cc}. If the anode current of the tube is read from the milliammeter, the transfer characteristic of Fig. 3-1(b) will indicate the total grid voltage E_c, and from this and the known value of bias voltage the input is easily calculated. A meter of this sort is extremely crude, but does illustrate a basic principle. Among the practical objections to the circuit are the extremely serious drift that would arise from any changes in plate or bias voltages or cathode temperature, the more-or-less serious nonlinearity of the transfer characteristic, and the lack of any provision for bucking out the quiescent plate current from the milliammeter.

A so-called *inverted* circuit may be constructed in a manner similar to Fig. 3-1(a) by applying the unknown voltage to the anode and measuring the grid direct current. In this circuit, the grid would be connected to a positive voltage source; in other words, the functions of the grid and plate are interchanged. Since the transfer conductance from plate to grid is far less than that from grid to plate (the latter quantity is the familiar g_m), the inverted circuit is relatively insensitive. Therefore it may be used to measure high voltages, often of the order of kilovolts. However, there is little to commend such a scheme over the use of a conventional electronic voltmeter with suitable multiplier resistors, and all the drawbacks of drift and nonlinearity apply to the inverted circuit as much as to the prototype.

Probably the simplest circuit that could be seriously proposed for an electronic voltmeter is the cathode follower shown in Fig. 3-2. In this assembly, R_k is a load resistor, R_g is a conventional grid leak resis-

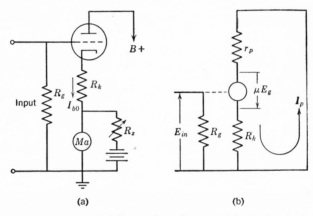

(a)   (b)

Fig. 3-2. A cathode follower d-c voltmeter: (a) the circuit, including provisions for zero set; (b) the equivalent circuit.

tor, and R_z is the "zero-set" control, which allows a bucking current to flow through the meter in opposition to the quiescent current from the tube. In this way, the meter is prevented from giving an indication in the absence of an input voltage. The size of R_z is ordinarily so much larger than the resistance of the meter movement that we may neglect any shunting effects.

The sensitivity of the circuit may be calculated from the Thévenin equivalent shown in Fig. 3-2(b). Although this is usually thought to be a concept applicable to a-c rather than d-c equivalent circuits, the reader must bear in mind that we are interested in the effects of a change in d-c levels (i.e., E_{in} changes from zero to some nonzero value). From this point of view, the problem is seen to be equivalent to *applying a step function to an a-c circuit*. We shall let E_g represent the *change* in the direct voltage between grid and cathode, and I_p the *change* in the plate direct current from the quiescent value I_{b0} to the actual current I_b that flows in the presence of input voltage. The current I_p must be determined as a function of E_{in}. The mesh equation for the circuit is

$$\mu E_g = I_p(r_p + R_k) \tag{3-1}$$

where

$$E_g = -I_p R_k + E_{in} \tag{3-2}$$

Substitute Eq. (3-2) into Eq. (3-1) and solve for I_p. The result is easily found to be

$$I_p = \frac{\mu E_{in}}{r_p + R_k(1 + \mu)} \tag{3-3}$$

A more useful measure of the sensitivity of the instrument is the ratio of I_p to E_{in}, which is designated by the letter S.

$$S = \frac{\mu}{r_p + R_k(1 + \mu)} \tag{3-4}$$

It will be noted from Eq. (3-4) that if $r_p \gg \mu R_k$, the sensitivity is approximately μ/r_p, or simply g_m. On the other hand, when $\mu R_k \gg r_p$, then S is approximately $1/R_k$. It should also be pointed out that R_k serves three functions in this circuit: (1) it fixes the d-c operating point of the tube; (2) it plays a role in determining the sensitivity; and (3) it provides enough negative feedback to eliminate nonlinearity almost completely. An example of the very excellent linearity possible with

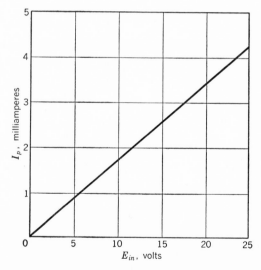

Fig. 3-3. Response of a typical cathode follower electronic voltmeter of the type shown in Fig. 3-2 (a).

such a circuit is shown in Fig. 3-3. The performance shown there was obtained from a circuit of the form of Fig. 3-2(a), using a 6J5 tube and 5000 ohms for R_k. The tube parameters were $\mu = 19.6$ and $r_p = 14,900$ ohms. The quiescent grid voltage was -13 volts. Inspection of Fig. 3-3 reveals that linear operation was obtained for input voltages up to almost twice the bias value. This is characteristic of cathode followers. The reason is that, because of the negative feedback voltage developed across R_k, the actual grid voltage E_g changes by a much smaller amount than E_{in}.

In spite of the obviously satisfactory performance exhibited by the typical circuit shown in Fig. 3-3, the simple cathode follower is not ordinarily employed for electronic voltmeters. It is not immune to drift, and the use of a bucking circuit involving a separate direct voltage source and a resistor such as R_z is awkward. Also, if an alternating voltage is picked up on the grid lead from stray fields near the instrument, a certain amount of alternating current will flow in the meter. This is not serious as long as the a-c signal does not cause distortion in the cathode follower. But if the a-c level is high enough, second-harmonic distortion will occur. It is shown in most texts in elementary electronics that such a second-harmonic current is accompanied by a so-called zeroth harmonic, or d-c component of current equal in value to the amplitude of the second harmonic (3). The D'Arsonval meter movement is responsive to this d-c harmonic, and consequently gives a false indication, based on both the alternating and direct input voltages rather than the direct voltage alone. These troubles can be eliminated almost perfectly in bridge-type d-c voltmeters, which are discussed in the next two sections.

3-3. Bridge-type d-c voltmeters, Part I

The majority of practical electronic voltmeters for d-c measurements employ one of the circuits in Fig. 3-4. The advantages of the bridge arrangement are that it is relatively simple to provide a zero adjustment by using the power supply instead of auxiliary batteries; that tendencies to drift are largely canceled, since changes in power supply or filament voltages affect both sides of the bridge in the same general way; that any stray alternating voltages in the vicinity of the instrument will be picked up by the two grid leads to approximately the same extent, and therefore zero-frequency harmonics will appear

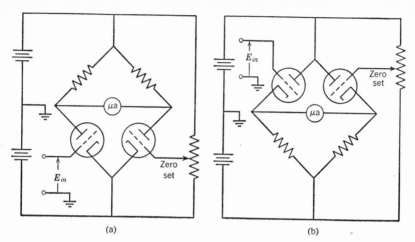

Fig. 3-4. The basic d-c voltmeter bridge circuits.

in the currents of both tubes symmetrically rather than flow in the microammeter; and finally, the bridge type instrument has good linearity.

The sensitivity is one-half that of a single-sided circuit such as the cathode follower discussed in Section 3-2. This loss of sensitivity is not an exhorbitant price for the benefits the bridge circuit offers. The reason for selecting a microammeter rather than a milliammeter for the indicating movement is not to overcome this loss of sensitivity, but rather because good practice dictates that the currents in all parts of the circuit be relatively small. This helps prevent overheating of the components and minimizes thermal drift. A meter movement of between 200 μa and 1 ma full scale is usually selected.

The circuit of Fig. 3-4(a) as it might be employed in a complete instrument is shown in Fig. 3-5. The potentiometer shown in dotted lines is used for balancing the two halves of the circuit during factory calibration and adjustment. Since we shall be concerned with the method of analyzing the circuit rather than with specific points of manufacturing techniques, it will be assumed that the two sides of the bridge are identical, and one-half of the potentiometer resistance is included in the value of R_1 on each side of the circuit. Certain obvious features, such as a d-c power supply, range switch, and multiplier resistors have been omitted. However, it might be well to point out that the multiplier circuit should not involve placing a total of more than 5 to 10 megohms resistance between the grid and ground of the left-hand

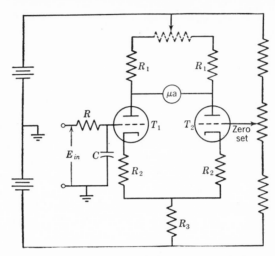

Fig. 3-5. A practical version of the prototype instrument of Fig. 3-4(a).

tube. A larger resistance is almost certain to cause trouble from grid direct currents, at least if conventional receiving-type tubes are used. The network RC serves to attenuate any a-c signals that may be super-imposed upon the direct voltage being measured. The values of R and C will usually be in the neighborhood of 100,000 ohms to 1 megohm and about 0.01 to 0.1 μf, respectively.

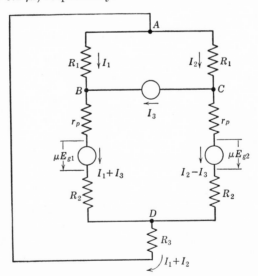

Fig. 3-6. The equivalent circuit of Fig. 3-5.

The sensitivity of the instrument may be computed from the equivalent circuit of Fig. 3-6. To simplify the problem, it is assumed that the resistance of the meter is zero. The currents I_1, I_2, and I_3 represent the *changes* from the quiescent currents as a result of applying a voltage E_{in}. The two tubes, and all other symmetrically placed circuit components on opposite sides of the bridge, are assumed identical.

Because of the assumption of zero meter resistance, points B and C must be at the same potential, so the currents I_1 and I_2 are equal, and the symbol I_1 will be used for both in writing equations. Tracing around loop BCD gives

$$\mu E_{g1} - \mu E_{g2}$$
$$= R_2(I_1 + I_3) - R_2(I_1 - I_3) + r_p(I_1 + I_3) - r_p(I_1 - I_3) \qquad (3\text{-}5)$$

The grid voltages may be written by examining the equivalent circuit in conjunction with the original one, and are seen to be

$$E_{g1} = E_{in} - R_2(I_1 + I_3) - 2I_1R_3 \qquad (3\text{-}6)$$

$$E_{g2} = -R_2(I_1 - I_3) - 2I_1R_3 \qquad (3\text{-}7)$$

If Eqs. (3-6) and (3-7) are substituted into Eq. (3-5), and the resulting expression solved for I_3, it is found that

$$I_3 = \frac{\mu E_{in}}{2[r_p + (1 + \mu)R_2]} \qquad (3\text{-}8)$$

This expression is virtually identical to Eq. (3-3) for the single-tube cathode follower circuit, except for the additional factor 2 in the denominator, indicating the sensitivity is cut in half by the bridge arrangement. This is to be expected.

When R_2 is small and r_p is large, the sensitivity from Eq. (3-8) is approximately

$$S = \mu/(2r_p) = g_m/2 \qquad (3\text{-}9)$$

This is very convenient for estimating the probable sensitivity of a circuit of this type. The fact that the quiescent direct currents are small implies that the tubes will operate in a portion of their characteristic curves where r_p is high. Furthermore, R_2 usually is small—of the order of one to two thousand ohms. Therefore the approximation made in Eq. (3-9) is often rather closely fulfilled in practice. For actual design, as distinguished from preliminary estimates, it is obviously necessary to use an exact sensitivity expression

$$S = \frac{\mu}{2[r_p + (1 + \mu)R_2]} \qquad (3\text{-}10)$$

The reader should be cautioned that this sensitivity is based on the portion of the input voltage that actually appears between the control grid and ground. It does not take into account the action of multiplier resistors and voltage dividers that are associated with the range-switching system.

Equation (3-10) implies that the sensitivity is a function exclusively of the tube parameters and resistor R_2. This is correct, but it must be remembered that the tube parameters themselves are functions of the d-c operating point, which is fixed by the resistors R_1, R_2, R_3, and the supply voltage as well.

When an operating point has been found to give approximately correct values of μ and r_p, a value of R_2 may be chosen to meet the sensitivity requirements. For final adjustments, it is desirable to provide for varying the resistors R_2 to control sensitivity directly, or else vary R_3 to control sensitivity indirectly through the effect the quiescent current has on r_p. The latter choice would be easier to reduce to practice, for varying R_2 involves changing two resistors, while R_3 is a single component. Also, since a change in R_2 gives more pronounced variations in sensitivity than a comparable change in R_3, there would be advantages from the standpoint of reducing thermal drift if the R_2 resistors could be made fixed, temperature-compensated units instead of variable resistors.

The zero-set control in Fig. 3-5 provides for adjusting for minor variations between the two tubes. Ordinarily the potential at the tap of this potentiometer will be very close to direct ground potential. It is well to place the potentiometer between two fixed resistors so the user cannot throw the bridge too seriously out of adjustment if the zero-set control is misused. As long as the zero set does not provide enough change in the bias of tube 2 to alter the operating point seriously, the sensitivity will not be affected by varying this control.

Problems involving different tube parameters or other marked lack of balance between the two halves of the bridge can be treated by the same equivalent circuit we have just analyzed, although the task becomes somewhat messy. For the moderate asymmetries usually encountered, results accurate enough for most purposes can be obtained by assuming the circuit to be symmetrical, and giving the components on each side a value equal to the average of the actual values.

One very important departure from the above analysis occurs when we do not allow ourselves the luxury of assuming zero resistance in the meter. If the meter resistance is taken as R_m ohms, analysis of the equivalent circuit shows the sensitivity to be

$$S = \frac{\mu R_1}{R_m(\mu R_2 + R_2 + R_1 + r_p) + 2R_1(\mu R_2 + R_2 + r_p)} \qquad (3\text{-}11)$$

This more exact analysis suggests the possibility of an alternate method of adjusting the sensitivity of the instrument. This consists of placing a small variable resistor in series with the meter movement.

3-4. Bridge-type d-c voltmeters, Part II

A d-c electronic voltmeter of the type shown in Fig. 3-4(b) is repeated in Fig. 3-7 for ready reference at this point. The equivalent circuit is

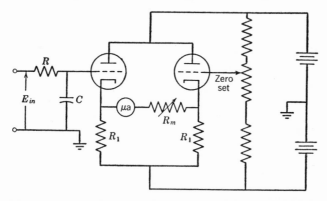

Fig. 3-7. A somewhat more detailed circuit of the bridge-type d-c electronic voltmeter first shown in Fig. 3-4(b).

shown in Fig. 3-8. As a matter of convenience, the resistance of the meter movement is lumped in with R_m. As before, the object of our study will be to determine the sensitivity of the instrument, i.e., the amount of current in the meter movement for a given voltage at the terminals marked E_{in}. Equations are written by Kirchhoff's current law for nodes A and B.

$$-g_m E_{g1} + \frac{E_A}{R_1} + \frac{E_A}{r_p} + \frac{E_A - E_B}{R_m} = 0 \qquad (3\text{-}12)$$

$$-g_m E_{g2} + \frac{E_B}{R_1} + \frac{E_B}{r_p} + \frac{E_B - E_A}{R_m} = 0 \qquad (3\text{-}13)$$

Also,
$$E_{g1} = -E_A + E_{in} \qquad (3\text{-}14)$$

$$E_{g2} = -E_B \qquad (3\text{-}15)$$

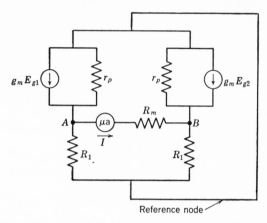

Fig. 3-8. The equivalent circuit of the instrument shown in Fig. 3-7.

If Eqs. (3-14) and (3-15) are substituted into Eqs. (3-12) and (3-13) and coefficients of E_A and E_B are gathered together, we obtain two equations in two unknowns which may be solved for the potentials E_A and E_B. The difference between these voltages may be divided by R_m to obtain the current in the meter, and from this the sensitivity is easily found. Making the substitutions for the E_g's as indicated,

$$E_A \left(g_m + \frac{1}{R_1} + \frac{1}{r_p} + \frac{1}{R_m} \right) + E_B \left(\frac{-1}{R_m} \right) = g_m E_{in} \qquad (3\text{-}16)$$

$$E_A \left(\frac{-1}{R_m} \right) + E_B \left(g_m + \frac{1}{R_1} + \frac{1}{r_p} + \frac{1}{R_m} \right) = 0 \qquad (3\text{-}17)$$

Solving for E_A and E_B and subtracting the latter from the former gives

$$E_A - E_B = \frac{g_m E_{in}}{g_m + 1/R_1 + 1/r_p + 2/R_m} \qquad (3\text{-}18)$$

If Eq. (3-18) is divided by R_m to obtain the current I, and this result in turn divided by E_{in} to obtain the sensitivity S, the final result is

$$S = \frac{g_m}{2 + R_m(g_m + 1/R_1 + 1/r_p)} \qquad (3\text{-}19)$$

In the limiting case of $R_m = 0$, the result is the very simple form

$$S = g_m/2 \qquad (3\text{-}20)$$

The values of the components ordinarily found in circuits of this type are such that for *preliminary design estimates*, the use of Eq. (3-20) is justified. For example, if $g_m = 500$ micromhos, $R_m = 600$ ohms,

$R_1 = 100,000$ ohms, and $r_p = 50,000$ ohms, the exact sensitivity calculated from Eq. (3-19) is $S = 216$ μa per volt. The approximation $S = g_m/2$ gives a sensitivity of 250 μa per volt.

Since the circuit of Fig. 3-7 has no component analogous to R_3 in the circuit of Fig. 3-5, it is not convenient to adjust the sensitivity by varying r_p or g_m through changes in the quiescent direct currents. Therefore the variable resistor R_m is placed in series with the meter to provide vernier adjustment of the sensitivity at the time of final calibration.

3-5. An example of the complete design procedure for a d-c electronic voltmeter

To illustrate the complete design process for a bridge-type d-c voltmeter, suppose we are given this problem. A voltmeter is required to give full-scale deflection for inputs of 10, 30, or 100 volts. The same instrument may be used on occasion to obtain a permanent record of voltages applied to it, in which case the meter movement will be replaced by a magnetic pen motor which requires 1 ma for full-scale pen travel. The input resistance must be 20 megohms on all ranges.

The requirement of a full-scale current of 1 ma implies the need for higher current levels in the circuit than we have previously considered desirable. However, such a situation may be met by using tubes with relatively high values of g_m, operated at the lowest feasible values of quiescent plate current to reduce heating. One suitable tube is the type

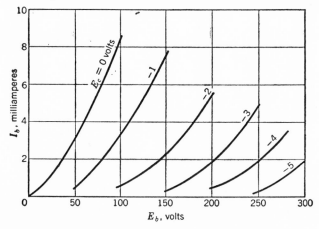

Fig. 3-9. Characteristics of the type 12AT7 tube. (Courtesy, Radio Corporation of America.)

12AT7, which has characteristics as shown in Fig. 3-9. For the prototype in our design, the circuit of Fig. 3-4(b) will be used.

Suppose that preliminary testing in the laboratory shows a 12AT7 tube can stand 3 megohms resistance in its grid circuit before grid currents present a problem. Let 1 megohm be reserved for the a-c attenuator mentioned in Section 3-3. Say it is desired to provide 20 db attenuation for 60-cycle components. A simple RC filter attenuates at 20 db per decade, so let the time constant of the filter be 1/37.7, since 37.7 is the radian frequency of 6 cycles. Then $RC = 0.0266$, and if R is 1

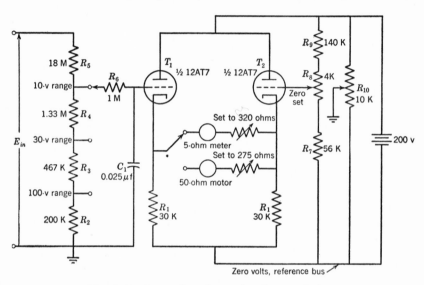

Fig. 3-10. A complete electronic voltmeter design.

megohm, C is 0.0266 μf. Probably 0.025 would be used as the nearest standard value. These components are shown as R_6 and C_1 in Fig. 3-10.

We must next correlate the required sensitivity of the instrument with the values of resistors in the input voltage divider. Let us assume as a reasonable sensitivity that 1 volt at the control grid of T_1 must produce the 1 ma of meter current. Then from Eq. (3-20), $g_m/2 = 0.001$ amp per volt, so $g_m = 2000$ micromhos. The accurate sensitivity Eq. (3-19) shows g_m must be a little higher than this, although we do not yet know the exact value. Inspection of the characteristic curves of Fig. 3-9 reveals that $g_m \cong 3000$ at an operating point $E_{b0} = 140$ volts and $I_{b0} = 2$ ma. As a starting point, let us assume that this transconductance is high enough. If subsequent results show this to be wrong, another operating point can always be selected.

Having established, at least tentatively, that 1 volt at the T_1 grid will give the desired results, the voltage divider can be designed. The most sensitive range is 10 volts, so the topmost tap on the range switch must pick off 10% of this. If the total input resistance is 20 megohms, the sum of resistors R_2, R_3, and R_4 will be 10% of 20 megohms, or 2 megohms. Then $R_5 = 20$ megohms $- 2$ megohms $= 18$ megohms. The resistance effectively in series with the grid lead is R_6 plus the parallel combination of 18 and 2 megohms. This is within the 3 megohms allowed. It is easily determined by the method just illustrated that on the 30-volt range, $R_2 + R_3 = 667,000$ ohms and on the 100-volt range, $R_2 = 200,000$ ohms. Then $R_3 = 467,000$ ohms and $R_4 = 1.33$ megohms.

Resistor R_5 should always be at least several megohms in order to provide high input impedance for a-c components that may be present in the voltage being measured. Even though the d-c instrument is not intended to be *responsive* to alternating current it would be most undesirable to have it short-circuit the time-varying components of the signals applied to it.

Now let us turn back to the bridge portion of the instrument. First of all, we must select a d-c operating point for the tubes. As suggested above, $E_{b0} = 140$ volts and $I_{b0} = 2$ ma looks promising, since here $g_m = 3000$. If a 200-volt power supply is available, and 140 volts appear across the tubes, 60 must be dropped across the R_1 resistors. Then $R_1 = 60$ v/2 ma $= 30,000$ ohms. When no voltage is applied to the input terminals, only the quiescent current will flow, and reference to Fig. 3-9 shows that the grids must be at -2 volts relative to the cathodes. The grid of T_1 is at ground potential, or $+58$ volts with respect to the reference bus of zero direct volts. The cathodes are at a potential of $+60$. This arrangement provides the required bias. The ground level is established by a tap on resistor R_{10}. A value of 10,000 ohms has been selected for this resistor, primarily so it will draw enough current to act as a bleeder on the power supply. The tap would be set to $+58$ volts as a factory adjustment. The $+58$-volt potential for the grid of T_2 is obtained from resistor R_8, which provides for ± 2 volts of adjustment to set the zero. Too much range in this control is unwise, for it gives the user an opportunity to damage the pen motor or meter movement with excess current.

The design is now complete except for the final sensitivity calculation. From Eq. (3-19),

$$S = 0.001 \text{ amp/volt}$$

$$= \frac{3000 \times 10^{-6}}{2 + R_m(3000 \times 10^{-6} + 1/30,000 + 1/20,000)} \quad (3\text{-}21)$$

The 20,000-ohm value of r_p is obtained by dividing the μ of the tube (given as 60 in the tube manual) by g_m. Solving Eq. (3-21) for R_m gives $R_m = 325$ ohms. The circuit is completed by providing a switch to give the choice of meter or motor recording. Values of 5 ohms and 50 ohms are assumed for the meter movement and the motor resistance, respectively, in which case the necessary extra resistances will be 320 ohms and 275 ohms. In practice, 500-ohm potentiometers might be used for these resistances, with the values being adjusted as the last step in factory calibration of the instrument.

One final check must be made before freezing the design. This is regarding the matter of linearity. The equations we have derived assumed small-signal operation, but the meter current in the final design is of the order of 50 per cent of the quiescent tube current, and there is good reason to question whether small signal theory applies. Investigation of this matter is most easily made by trial and error by using a sketch stripped to the absolute essentials, as shown in Fig. 3-11. It is known that after applying the input to the grid of T_1, 1 ma flows

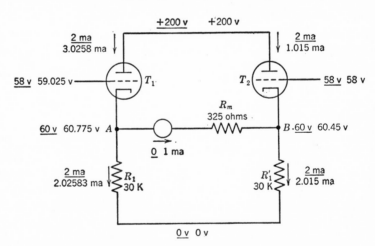

Fig. 3-11. Currents and voltages before and after applying input voltage to the bridge of Fig. 3-10. Underlined quantities are quiescent values, i.e., in the "before" category.

in the 325-ohm resistance between points A and B. It is also known that the direct voltage at the grid of T_2 is constant at $+58$. Because of the symmetrical nature of the circuit, most of the 1 ma traveling from A to B is accounted for by a reduction in the current of T_2. If the current in R'_1 increases from 2 ma to 2.015 ma, the voltage at B rises to 60.45 volts. Then the cathode-to-grid potential at T_2 becomes -2.45 volts, and the current in T_2 drops to a trifle over 1 ma, as shown by the curves of Fig. 3-9. For the sake of argument, we shall call it exactly 1.015 ma, the value it must have to satisfy Kirchhoff's current law at point B. Now the potential at point A will be that at B plus 0.325, the voltage developed by the 1 ma current in R_m. The current in R_1 is then $(60.45 + 0.325)/30,000 = 2.02583$ ma. Since 1 ma flows from A to B, the current in T_1 must be 3.02583 ma. The voltage across T_1 is still 140 for purposes of reading the curves of Fig. 3-9, and these curves show that for a plate current of 3.0+ ma, the cathode-to-grid voltage must be -1.75. But if the cathode potential has risen to 60.775 volts, the grid must *now* be at $(60.775 - 1.75) = 59.025$ volts. Since the quiescent value was 58 volts, it follows that a signal of 1.025 volts had to be applied to give the 1 ma meter current. This current should have been the result of 1 volt at the grid, so our instrument is in error by 2.5%, which is satisfactory accuracy in most equipment. As the reader noticed, this example called for micrometer-like readings of the tube curves. It is offered more to illustrate a method of *estimating* the error than to obtain an *accurate* quantitative result. Certainly a final linearity check would have to be made experimentally, but an analysis such as the one above would reveal the chances of really disastrous errors before time was spent on making a prototype instrument.

3-6. A d-c integrator (4)

We shall conclude our chapter on d-c electronic voltmeters with the description of a voltage integrating device. Although the only application of electronics *per se* in this integrator is in the use of a flip-flop circuit to control a relay, a person working in electronic instruments may sometimes have need for an integrator. The system described here employs a mechanical device for integrating, and so is not dependent on the value of RC time constants or tube parameters as is the case with the all-electronic Miller integrator.

The heart of the system is a D'Arsonval meter movement of any desired sensitivity, with the usual restoring spring removed. Consequently the movement will run as a motor with velocity just sufficient to produce a back emf equal (except for voltage drops in the coil resistance) to the voltage impressed across it. This voltage appearing as a back emf E is proportional to $N\, d\phi/dt$, where ϕ is the flux cut by the coil. Assume that the coil is constrained to rotate through a sufficiently

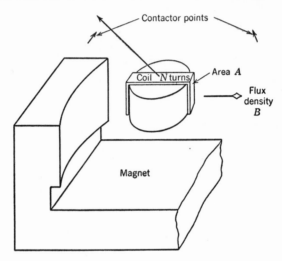

Fig. 3-12. Movement of the d-c integrator.

small angle that its vertical sides are essentially perpendicular to the direction of the flux at all times. Then the value of ϕ is BA, the symbols B and A being identified in Fig. 3-12. If the angular velocity of the coil is $d\theta/dt$, then $d\phi/dt$ is proportional to $BA\, d\theta/dt$, and therefore

$$E = kNBA \frac{d\theta}{dt} \qquad (3\text{-}22)$$

where k is a proportionality constant. Integration of Eq. (3-22) gives

$$\theta = \frac{1}{kNBA} \int E\, dt \qquad (3\text{-}23)$$

showing that the angle through which the coil moves is proportional to the time integral of the applied voltage.

Obviously, after a time the pointer will reach the end of its travel. To keep the device operating after this limit is reached, contactor points are placed at each side where the pointer will touch them at the limits of its allowable deflection. Conceivably a current could flow through the pointer and contacts to operate a reversing relay and cause the motion to start in the opposite direction. This scheme has the objection that most relays require at least several milliamperes for their operation, and such large currents might produce a slight spot welding, causing the pointer to stick for a moment and delay the reversal of the coil's motion.

To prevent this difficulty, a flip-flop circuit may be used as shown in Fig. 3-13. The current required to trigger such a circuit is negligible,

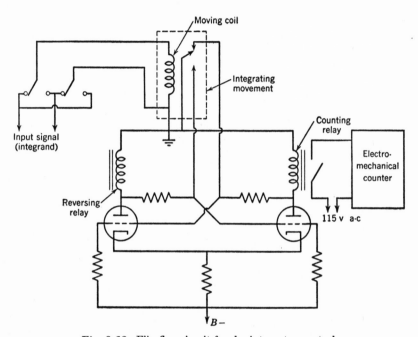

Fig. 3-13. Flip-flop circuit for d-c integrator control.

and could surely be held to the order of a few microamperes. It will be noted in the figure that one of the tubes controls the reversing relay, while the other operates an electromechanical counter. The purpose of the latter is to record the number of cycles the movement has gone through so that integration may be carried on for days if desired without the need for constant watching of the D'Arsonval movement. Thus the counter gives a coarse indication of the value of the integral, while a scale placed under the pointer will give a vernier reading.

Almost any d-c ammeter might be used in the integrator, but a sensitive movement is preferred. The time integral of *currents* may be obtained by using shunts across the input.

The use of a rectifier will permit the integration of a-c quantities. However, a word of caution should be given regarding such an application. Vacuum tube rectifiers may give trouble here, for there tends to be a small current, of the order of a few microamperes, through vacuum diodes, produced by electrons emitted with high initial velocities. It is entirely possible that such current will produce insufficient torque to overcome the static friction of the movement's bearings, and consequently would not matter. On the other hand, with a sensitive enough movement, the integral might build up a considerable error from this cause. The difficulty can be prevented by using crystal diodes or similar nonthermionic rectifiers, although these are quite nonlinear for very small input voltages, and so may contribute an error of a different type. Frequently, it is possible to amplify the a-c signals to a point where such low-level nonlinearities are effectively swamped out.

A certain amount of current must be drawn by the integrator to overcome its own frictional losses. If the voltage source has a high internal impedance, this current, though small, may cause an appreciable voltage drop and therefore a large discrepancy between the open-circuit terminal voltage of the "integrand" and the back emf of the integrator. This potential difference is a measure of the operating error. Therefore the source impedance of the integrand should be as low as possible, and in any event not appreciably greater than the resistance of the movable coil. It follows that multiplier resistors should not be placed in series with the coil as a means of adjusting the integrator sensitivity.

A commercial embodiment of this integrator is found in the Weston Model 808 Industrial Integrator. A typical application is the measurement of ampere-hours in the electrolytic refining of aluminum.

REFERENCES

1. Herbert J. Reich, *Theory and Applications of Electron Tubes* (New York: McGraw-Hill Book Company, Inc., 1944), chap. XV.
2. See Sections 7-3 and 7-4 in this text.
3. George E. Happell and Wilfred M. Hesselberth, *Engineering Electronics* (New York: McGraw-Hill Book Company, Inc., 1953), sect. 6-17.
4. R. W. Gilbert, "A Sensitive Direct Current Electrical Integrator," *Rev. Sci. Instr.*, vol. 18, p. 328, May 1947.

Chapter 4

REVIEW OF FEEDBACK

In the majority of electronic instruments, modern practice is to include a large amount of negative feedback. This has already been mentioned briefly in connection with certain of the d-c voltmeters discussed in Chapter 3. However, as we continue into a discussion of a-c voltmeters and many other instruments, an understanding of feedback will be much more essential than it was in the previous chapter. For this reason, a review of feedback will be given at this point.

4-1. The benefits of negative feedback

The type of feedback emphasized in this chapter is negative feedback, i.e., a portion of the output signal is returned to the input in such a phase as to reduce the net driving signal. While this reduces the over-all gain of a system, a number of advantages accrue that more than offset the price that must be paid in terms of a reduction in gain.

From the standpoint of instrumentation, the main advantage of negative feedback is the greatly increased stability of the system. We use the word "stability" here in the sense of meaning freedom from drift. In other words, the gain of one or more stages of an amplifier or other unit in a system can change by a relatively large amount without causing any appreciable change in the over-all performance of the system. Also, the use of negative feedback returned in series with the input signal increases the input impedance to a system and decreases its output impedance, both effects usually being very desirable in instrumentation. Still another benefit is the possible improvement in the signal-to-noise ratio of the system and the tendency of feedback to combat the effects of distortion and nonlinearities in a circuit.

4-2. The gain of a feedback amplifier

The essential parts of a feedback amplifier are shown in Fig. 4-1. Here the quantity K represents the *forward gain* of the circuit, and the

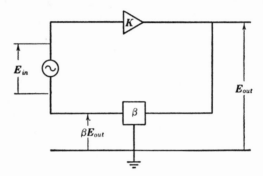

Fig. 4-1. The basic feedback circuit.

block marked β is the feedback path. The quantity β is defined as the ratio of the voltage returned to the input to the output voltage. It will be seen from the figure that the total voltage applied to the input of the amplifier is $E_{in} + \beta E_{out}$. The output voltage is equal to the input times the forward gain, or

$$E_{out} = K(E_{in} + \beta E_{out}) \tag{4-1}$$

When Eq. (4-1) is solved for E_{out}, we obtain

$$E_{out} = \frac{KE_{in}}{1 - \beta K} \tag{4-2}$$

and the gain is
$$G = \frac{E_{out}}{E_{in}} = \frac{K}{1 - \beta K} \tag{4-3}$$

This is the net gain of the over-all system. The product βK is a very important quantity known as the *loop gain*.

Two important points should be noted from Eq. (4-3) at this time. One is that if βK is of such an amplitude and phase angle as to increase the magnitude of the denominator, the value of G will be less than K. This case is negative feedback. If the amplitude and phase angle of βK reduce the magnitude of the denominator, then G is greater than K and a condition of positive feedback exists. This scheme is sometimes used to obtain unusually high gain from an amplifier, but is of little practical consequence in most types of instrumentation. The second point to note is that when K is very large, in particular approaching infinity as a limit, then

$$\text{Lim } G = -1/\beta \qquad (4\text{-}4)$$
$$\scriptstyle |\beta K| \to \infty$$

Thus, when the forward gain is high enough, the net gain G depends only on the value of β. Since the β network can be made from precision components with temperature compensation or other refinements, it follows that the value of G can be made as constant as desired. The practical importance of this statement is impossible to overstress. It means, in effect, that the amplifiers and other major active networks used in instrumentation systems may be made essentially independent of any changes that might occur in the tubes, transistors, and other individual active elements.

4-3. The constancy of gain

To implement the conclusion just reached, let us determine a quantitative measure of the amount by which negative feedback combats variations in G. We shall start by obtaining the derivative of G with respect to K.

$$\frac{dG}{dK} = \frac{1}{(1 - \beta K)^2} \qquad (4\text{-}5)$$

Then

$$dG = \frac{dK}{(1 - \beta K)^2} \qquad (4\text{-}6)$$

If the left- and right-hand sides of Eq. (4-6) are divided, respectively, by the left- and right-hand sides of Eq. (4-3), the result is

$$\frac{dG}{G} = \frac{1}{1 - \beta K} \frac{dK}{K} \qquad (4\text{-}7)$$

The quantity dK/K may be thought of as the *fractional change* in K, or as a matter of convenience, a per cent change. Likewise, dG/G is the per cent change in G. It will be seen that the change in G is less than the change in K by the factor $1/(1 - \beta K)$. For example, if $1 - \beta K = 10$, a 20 per cent change in K would cause only a 2 per cent change in G. The effects of larger changes in K are shown in Fig. 4-2, where G is plotted as a function of K for various values of β. When $\beta = 0.02$, for example, K could drop from 10,000 to 400, a change of a factor of 25, with only 10 per cent change in the value of G.

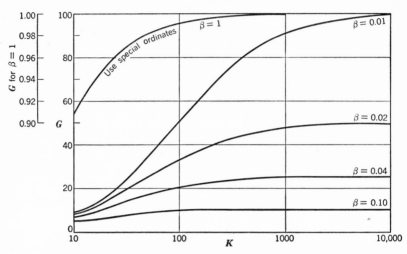

Fig. 4-2. Net gain G as a function of forward gain K for various values of β. For negative feedback, either K or β must be considered a negative number so the quantity $-\beta K$ is positive.

4-4. The effect of feedback on input impedance

A comparison of the input impedance to a system with feedback and without feedback may be made from a study of the circuit of Fig.

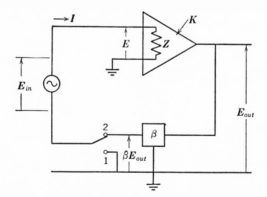

Fig. 4-3. A circuit for determining input impedance.

4-3. With the switch in position 1, the input impedance, E_{in}/I, will obviously be Z; i.e., without feedback, $Z_{in} \equiv Z$.

Now let the switch be moved to position 2. In this case, the voltage appearing across Z is

$$E = E_{in} + \beta E_{out} \tag{4-8}$$

But since $E_{out} = KE$, Eq. (4-8) may be written

$$E = E_{in} + \beta KE \tag{4-9}$$

Solving Eq. (4-9) for E gives

$$E = \frac{E_{in}}{1 - \beta K} \tag{4-10}$$

The current I is equal to E/Z, or

$$I = \frac{E_{in}}{(1 - \beta K)Z} \tag{4-11}$$

From Eq. (4-11), one may obtain the ratio E_{in}/I which is the input impedance. This is seen to be

$$\frac{E_{in}}{I} = Z_{in} = Z(1 - \beta K) \tag{4-12}$$

The result of negative feedback, then, is to *increase the input impedance* by the factor $(1 - \beta K)$. Since high input impedance is a design objective in many electronic instruments, this is a most useful result.

4-5. The effect of feedback on output impedance

The effects of feedback on output impedance may be determined from the circuit of Fig. 4-4. In this drawing, V represents the open-

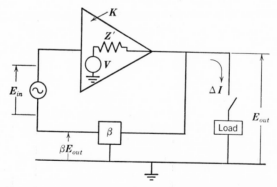

Fig. 4-4. A circuit for determining output impedance.

circuit output voltage, and Z' represents the impedance in series with this voltage source. In other words, V and Z' are the Thévenin equivalent of the output stage of the amplifier. If no feedback were present, then closing the switch to the load would cause the current ΔI to flow, giving a change in output voltage of

$$\Delta E_{out} = -\Delta I Z' \qquad (4\text{-}13)$$

The negative sign indicates that an increase in current will lead to a reduction in output voltage, and the output impedance of the amplifier without feedback is obviously Z'.

When feedback is present, the change in E_{out} will travel around the loop formed by the β network and K, giving a change in V. Then with feedback,

$$\Delta E_{out} = \Delta V - \Delta I Z' \qquad (4\text{-}14)$$

Also, $$\Delta V = K(\beta \, \Delta E_{out}) \qquad (4\text{-}15)$$

and substituting Eq. (4-15) into (4-14) gives

$$\Delta E_{out} = K\beta \, \Delta E_{out} - \Delta I Z' \qquad (4\text{-}16)$$

If Eq. (4-16) is solved for E_{out}, the result is

$$E_{out} = \frac{-\Delta I Z'}{1 - \beta K} \qquad (4\text{-}17)$$

A comparison between Eqs. (4-17) and (4-13) shows that the change in output voltage with feedback is less than the change for the no-feedback case by a factor of $1 - \beta K$. In other words, the *feedback reduces the output impedance* by the factor $1 - \beta K$.

4-6. Effect of negative feedback on noise and distortion

The action of feedback in improving the signal-to-noise ratio may be studied from the circuit shown in Fig. 4-5. Here E_n represents a source of noise. We shall use the word "noise" in a very broad sense

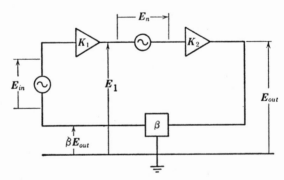

Fig. 4-5. A circuit for studying the effect of feedback on noise.

here. It might be true noise, i.e., a random disturbance, or possibly power supply hum or harmonics of the input signal produced as a result of nonlinearity in amplifier K_1. It is best to think of E_n as simply a spurious signal that has crept into the system.

The analysis is most easily handled by assuming at the start that $E_{in} = 0$, and examining the fate of E_n alone. It is seen from inspection of the figure that

$$E_{out} = K_2(E_1 + E_n) \qquad (4\text{-}18)$$

But $$E_1 = K_1\beta E_{out} \qquad (4\text{-}19)$$

Substitution of Eq. (4-19) into Eq. (4-18) gives

$$E_{out} = K_2(E_n + K_1\beta E_{out}) \qquad (4\text{-}20)$$

The solution for E_{out} from Eq. (4-20) is

$$E_{out} = \frac{K_2 E_n}{1 - \beta K} \qquad (4\text{-}21)$$

where $K = K_1 K_2$, the total forward gain. Without the feedback, the output due to the noise source would be

$$E_{out} = K_2 E_n \qquad (4\text{-}22)$$

so the effect of feedback is to reduce the noise output voltage by a factor of $1 - \beta K$. It should be noted, however, that the larger K_2 is, the worse the noise output will be, whether there is feedback or not. In other words, *the earlier in the system the noise occurs, the more trouble it will cause. Noise appearing at the input itself (effectively in series with E_{in}) will not be combated by feedback at all.*

To see whether the signal-to-noise *ratio* is improved by negative feedback, assume that an input voltage is now present as well as the noise. Then the output voltage will be the sum of the contributions due to signal and noise, or

$$E_{out} = E_{in}\left(\frac{K}{1 - \beta K}\right) + E_n\left(\frac{K_2}{1 - \beta K}\right) \qquad (4\text{-}23)$$

The signal-to-noise ratio at the output is the first term of Eq. (4-23) divided by the second, or

$$\frac{S}{N} = \frac{K}{K_2}\frac{E_{in}}{E_n} = K_1\frac{E_{in}}{E_n} \qquad (4\text{-}24)$$

For purposes of comparison, consider next the noisy amplifier without feedback shown in Fig. 4-6. Here the output voltage is

$$E_{out} = E_{in}K_1'K_2 + E_n K_2 \qquad (4\text{-}25)$$

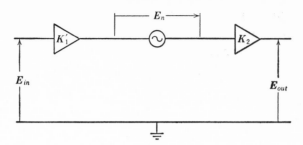

Fig. 4-6. A noisy amplifier without feedback.

so the signal-to-noise ratio is

$$\frac{S}{N} = K_1' \frac{E_{in}}{E_n} \tag{4-26}$$

However, to provide a fair comparison, the two amplifiers must have the same net gain G, so this requires that

$$K_1'K_2 = \frac{K_1K_2}{1 - \beta K} \tag{4-27}$$

Then
$$K_1' = \frac{K_1}{1 - \beta K} \tag{4-28}$$

and substituting Eq. (4-28) into Eq. (4-26) gives

$$\frac{S}{N} = \frac{K_1}{1 - \beta K} \frac{E_{in}}{E_n} \tag{4-29}$$

Comparison between this expression and Eq. (4-24) shows the signal-to-noise ratio is better by the factor $1 - \beta K$ in the amplifier with feedback, assuming the noise receives the same amount of amplification (K_2) in the two systems before reaching the output, and assuming further that the gain G is the same in both cases. It is the *increased gain between the input and noise source* (K_1K_1') that improves the signal-to-noise ratio rather than the feedback *per se*. But without the feedback, we would not have this beneficial extra.

4-7. Shunt feedback

It has been assumed heretofore in this chapter that the fed-back signal is returned *in series* with the input voltage. However, this is not invariably the case. Feedback may be returned in shunt with the input signal, in which case it produces somewhat different results. We shall not go into the matter deeply, but it is useful to consider at least one example.

The circuit of Fig. 4-7 illustrates a resistor R_f feeding back part of the output voltage of an amplifier to the input. The source has an internal impedance R_g, which for simplicity we assume purely resistive.

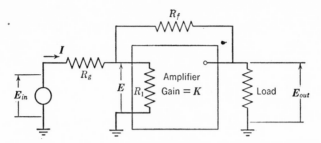

Fig. 4-7. An amplifier with feedback in shunt with the input.

The input impedance to the amplifier without feedback is represented by R_1; we shall show presently that the effective input impedance due to the feedback is *less* than R_1. Also, we may determine the gain of the system, i.e., the ratio of E_{out}/E_{in}, where E_{in} is the open-circuit voltage of the signal generator.

The Kirchhoff current equation for the node at the junction of R_g, R_f, and R_1 is

$$\frac{E - E_{in}}{R_g} + \frac{E - E_{out}}{R_f} + \frac{E}{R_1} = 0 \qquad (4\text{-}30)$$

But $$E = E_{out}/K \qquad (4\text{-}31)$$

Substitute Eq. (4-31) into Eq. (4-30) and solve for the ratio E_{out}/E_{in}. The algebra is straightforward, and the result is

$$\frac{E_{out}}{E_{in}} = \frac{KR_1R_f}{R_1R_g(1 - K) + R_f(R_1 + R_g)} \qquad (4\text{-}32)$$

If R_f approaches infinity, i.e., the feedback is reduced and ultimately disconnected, Eq. (4-32) degenerates to

$$\frac{E_{out}}{E_{in}} = \frac{KR_1}{R_1 + R_g} \qquad (4\text{-}33)$$

It is seen that no matter what value R_f takes, Eq. (4-32) is less than Eq. (4-33) because of the additional contribution of $R_1R_g(1 - K)$ in the denominator of Eq. (4-32). Therefore shunt feedback reduces the gain of the amplifier just as does series feedback.

The current I may be determined by routine algebra, and is given by

$$I = E_{in} \frac{R_f + R_1(1 - K)}{R_1 R_g(1 - K) + R_f(R_1 + R_g)} \qquad (4\text{-}34)$$

The input impedance Z_{in} is

$$Z_{in} = \frac{E_{in}}{I} - R_g \qquad (4\text{-}35)$$

Substitution of Eq. (4-34) into Eq. (4-35) leads to

$$Z_{in} = \frac{R_1 R_f}{R_f + R_1(1 - K)} \qquad (4\text{-}36)$$

The limiting value of Z_{in} as R_f becomes infinite (no feedback) is

$$\lim_{R_f \to \infty} Z_{in} = R_1 \qquad (4\text{-}37)$$

Equation (4-36) shows that with feedback, Z_{in} is always *less than* R_1. Thus the effect of shunt feedback is to *reduce* the input impedance. This is exactly opposite to the results obtained with series feedback.

Series feedback is more common than shunt feedback. However, there are many practical applications of shunt feedback in so-called *operational* amplifiers. An example is the Miller integrator discussed in Section 15-3 of this text. The Miller integrator employs a capacitor instead of a resistor in the position of R_f in Fig. 4-7. As we have just established, shunt feedback reduces the input impedance of the amplifier. When the shunt feedback path takes the form of a capacitor, the lowered input impedance is manifest as an apparent increase in the size of this capacitor. Thus the Miller integrator effectively places a large capacitor between the right-hand terminal of R_g and ground. With sufficient gain in the amplifier, a feedback capacitor of a few microfarads may be made to look like an appreciable part of a farad, and results in an integrator with a very long time constant.

4-8. The stability of a feedback system

Reference to Eq. (4-3) shows that if $\beta K \equiv 1$, the gain of the amplifier becomes infinite. In this event, any input signal will presumably be amplified to an infinite voltage. A more useful point of view, however, is to assume that zero input voltage will give a finite output. This implies that the system will manufacture its own input, leading to a condition known as *instability*. To predict whether a system will be unstable, a number of possible tests may be employed.

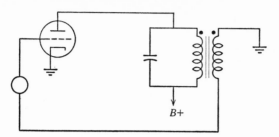

Fig. 4-8. A questionable feedback amplifier to be tested for stability.

One test is to write the equations for the system and examine the positions of the poles. If any pole has a positive real part, the feedback circuit is unstable. As an example, consider the circuit of Fig. 4-8. Without the source of signal voltage, this would be the circuit of a

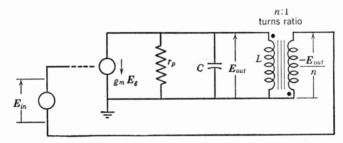

Fig. 4-9. The equivalent circuit of Fig. 4-8.

tuned-plate oscillator. A circuit known to be unstable has been intentionally selected for an example in order to show how the instability is made evident by mathematical tests. Figure 4-9 shows the equivalent circuit. We may write the equation for the output voltage and solve this for gain. By Kirchhoff's current law,

$$\frac{E_{out}}{r_p} + \frac{E_{out}}{sL} + E_{out}sC + g_m E_g = 0 \qquad (4\text{-}38)$$

But

$$E_g = \frac{-E_{out}}{n} + E_{in} \qquad (4\text{-}39)$$

where n is the transformer turns ratio. The minus sign in Eq. (4-39) is due to the sense of the transformer windings. If the polarity of either winding were reversed, the circuit would become stable. Substitute Eq. (4-39) into (4-38) and solve for the ratio E_{out}/E_{in}, which is the gain G.

$$G = \frac{-\mu sL}{s^2 LC r_p + sL - \mu sL/n + r_p} \qquad (4\text{-}40)$$

If the transformer turns ratio n approaches infinity, the circuit reduces to one with no feedback, and the value of G in this case becomes equal to the forward gain K. Thus

$$K = \lim_{n \to \infty} G = \frac{-\mu s L}{s^2 L C r_p + s L + r_p} \tag{4-41}$$

This expression for K may be worked into Eq. (4-40) with some relatively easy manipulation, giving

$$G = \frac{\dfrac{-\mu s L}{s^2 L C r_p + s L + r_p}}{1 - \left(-\dfrac{1}{n}\right)\left(\dfrac{-\mu s L}{s^2 L C r_p + s L + r_p}\right)} \tag{4-42}$$

Expressed in this form, K and β are readily picked out. The value of K has already been given in Eq. (4-41); β is seen from the denominator of Eq. (4-42) to be $-1/n$. We shall refer back to Eq. (4-42) in considering Nyquist's criterion. For the present, let us turn our attention to the denominator of Eq. (4-40).

If the denominator of Eq. (4-40) is solved for values of s that make the denominator equal zero, i.e., the poles of the function, it is found that

$$s = \frac{-L + \mu L/n \pm \sqrt{(L - \mu L/n)^2 - 4 L C r_p^2}}{2 L C r_p} \tag{4-43}$$

For the usual values of r_p, the quantity under the radical will be negative, leading to a $j\omega$ component in the poles of s. The test of stability, however, is based on the real part, which is

$$\Re e\, s = \frac{-L + \mu L/n}{2 L C r_p} \tag{4-44}$$

This will be positive if μ/n is greater than unity. In this case, the circuit is unstable. As a matter of fact, it is not necessary that the real part of the pole be positive; a value of exactly zero is sufficient to cause instability.

Still another test for stability is the *Nyquist criterion*. The theoretical justification for the Nyquist criterion is developed in a number of references, including many of those listed in the bibliography at the end of this chapter. There are certain ins and outs in the application of this test for stability; these fine points are covered in the material cited in the bibliography. But briefly, the argument is this:

If $1 - \beta K = 0$, the system is unstable. Therefore instability will occur when $\beta K \equiv 1$. In this case, a steady-state oscillation develops.

If $\beta K > 1$, the system not only oscillates, but the amplitude of oscillation increases until limited by nonlinearities or the electrical or mechanical failure of a component.

If we plot the quantity βK and the plot touches or encircles the critical point $1 + j0$ (or in polar coordinates, $r = 1$, $\theta = 0$), the system is shown to be unstable. This test must be used with some discretion. For example, the vector representing βK may sweep past the critical point in a clockwise direction at one frequency, and in a counterclockwise direction at a different frequency. These two crossings cancel each other, and there is no net encirclement. Thus such a Nyquist plot would represent a stable system even though it appears at first glance that the critical point is enclosed not only once but twice.

Suppose we apply the Nyquist criterion to Fig. 4-8. Let $\mu = 100$, $n = 50$, $L = 1$ h, $C = 10^{-8}$ f, and $r_p = 100,000$ ohms. From Eq. (4-42), βK is

$$\beta K = \frac{j2\omega}{-\omega^2 \times 10^{-3} + 10^5 + j\omega} \tag{4-45}$$

This function is plotted in Fig. 4-10, with values of ω indicated at certain discrete points on the locus of βK values. Note that the critical

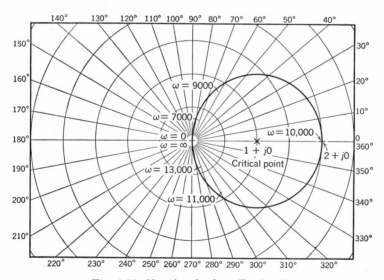

Fig. 4-10. Nyquist plot from Eq. (4-45).

point is encircled as we expected, since the system was intentionally set up to be unstable.

4-9. Conclusion

The purpose of this chapter has been to give a brief review for the reader who is already acquainted with feedback principles, and to suggest to the novice some of the benefits that feedback will give. There has been no intention of treating feedback systems in detail, nor of even including practical examples, for many will appear in subsequent chapters. The reader desiring more information on feedback circuits is referred to almost any textbook on electronics published since World War II, or any text in the field of servomechanisms and automatic control systems. A few examples are listed below:

REFERENCES

1. Bode, H. W., *Network Analysis and Feedback Amplifier Design* (Princeton: D. Van Nostrand Company, 1945).
2. Ahrendt, William R. and Taplin, John F., *Automatic Feedback Control* (New York: McGraw-Hill Book Company, Inc., 1951).
3. Cage, John M., *Theory and Application of Industrial Electronics* (New York: McGraw-Hill Book Company, Inc., 1951). See especially Chapters 4 and 5.
4. Chestnut, Harold and Mayer, Robert W., *Servomechanisms and Regulating System Design* (New York: John Wiley & Sons, Inc., 1951).
5. Brown, Gordon S. and Campbell, Donald P., *Principles of Servomechanisms* (New York: John Wiley & Sons, Inc., 1948).
6. Truxal, John G., *Automatic Feedback Control System Synthesis* (New York: McGraw-Hill Book Company, Inc., 1955).

Chapter 5

A-C ELECTRONIC VOLTMETERS—I

The electronic voltmeter for measuring alternating voltage is one of the most important of all types of electronic instruments—quite possibly the most important of all if the number in use is taken as a criterion. Our discussion of the a-c voltmeter is divided into two chapters, the first dealing with elementary circuits, and the second with the more elaborate types, most of which use a generous amount of negative feedback.

5-1. Some basic principles and elementary circuits (1)

With the exception of the slide-back type of instrument, the a-c voltmeter usually employs some type of rectification for converting the signal in question to a direct voltage. A number of different types of rectification may be employed. The most common are small-signal and large-signal plate detection, diode rectifiers, and grid detection, which is essentially a type of diode rectification.

It is well known that a signal applied to the control grid of a tube will cause a current of substantially the same waveform to flow in the plate circuit when operation is Class A. However, the current that flows will ordinarily be somewhat distorted because of nonlinearities in the transfer characteristic of the tube. The distortion is made evident by the production of a number of harmonics of the input frequency components. For our purposes, the harmonic of greatest interest is the so-called zeroth harmonic, which consists of a direct current equal in magnitude to the peak value of the second-harmonic current. A D'Arsonval movement in series with the anode of the tube will therefore show a slight change in current as soon as an alternating voltage is applied to the control grid. The greater this alternating voltage, the greater will be the distortion, and therefore the greater the change in the d-c current. Thus it is possible to measure the amplitude of an alternating voltage by the indication of a d-c meter in series with a tube operating in Class A. An instrument employing this principle is said to use *low-bias plate detection.*

This system of measuring an alternating voltage is of academic interest only. The amount of change in the plate current is relatively small for a given input voltage, and therefore the sensitivity of the circuit is very low. Also, the relationship between the meter indication and the input voltage is far from linear. Better results can be obtained by using *high-bias plate detection*, in which the tube is biased exactly to cutoff. A circuit of this type is shown in Fig. 5-1. The only difference

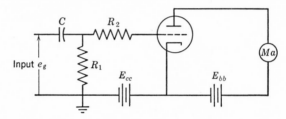

Fig. 5-1. The circuit of a plate-detection vacuum tube voltmeter.

between this and the low-bias case is in the value of E_{cc}, which is appreciably greater in the high-bias case. The network CR_1 serves to block out any direct voltage that may be present in the input signal, while R_2 is a resistor to limit the grid current in the event that the input should be larger than expected and drive the grid positive.

Let us assume that the plate current in the tube is exactly zero in the absence of an input voltage, due to the Class B operating point. It will also be assumed that the plate current is given by the expression

$$i_b = g_m e_g \qquad (5\text{-}1)$$

If the input voltage e_g is a sinusoidal signal,

$$e_g = E_{max} \sin \omega t \qquad (5\text{-}2)$$

and the average plate current will be

$$I_{bav} = \frac{1}{2\pi} \int_0^\pi g_m E_{max} \sin \omega t \, d\omega t \qquad (5\text{-}3)$$

The limits of integration are between zero and pi because, due to the Class B operation, the tube will pass no current during the negative half cycle of the input voltage. Therefore the integral between π and 2π will contribute nothing to the answer. Evaluating the integral of Eq. (5-3), we obtain

$$I_{bav} = \frac{g_m E_{max}}{\pi} \qquad (5\text{-}4)$$

and therefore E_{max} is $\qquad E_{max} = \frac{\pi I_{bav}}{g_m} \qquad (5\text{-}5)$

Since the rms rather than the peak value is ordinarily desired, both sides of Eq. (5-5) may be divided by $\sqrt{2}$, giving

$$E_{rms} = \frac{\pi I_{bav}}{\sqrt{2}\, g_m} \qquad (5\text{-}6)$$

From Eq. (5-6), the calibration may be calculated for any specific circuit so that the scale of the milliammeter may be marked to read directly in volts.

There are two really serious objections to this instrument. The first, and most disturbing, is that the relationship given in Eq. (5-1) does not hold when the tube is near cutoff. For very small values of e_g, the plate current bears more nearly a square law relationship to the input voltage. This causes a relatively serious nonlinearity in the meter indication, and means that Eq. (5-6) is valid only for relatively high values of plate current. Since g_m will vary with the age of the tube, it may be difficult to keep an accurate calibration.

The second difficulty is characteristic of any instrument using a half-wave rectified signal as the basis of an average reading. If the top and bottom halves of the input waveform differ in shape, the indication on the meter may depend on which way the input leads are connected to the voltage source. This effect is known as "turnover." It is not present in full-wave rectifier instruments, and may be compensated for fairly well in half-wave rectifier types by reading the voltage with the leads first one way, then the other, and taking the correct answer as the average of the two.

The tendency of the current to vary with the square of the voltage at small signal levels has been proposed as a basis for making a true rms reading electronic voltmeter. While the idea is not bad in principle, it is most unsatisfactory in practice. The reason is that there is no definite dividing line between square law and linear operation. As a matter of fact, with extremely small input voltages the relationship between current and voltage is approximately a $\frac{5}{2}$ power law. Obviously, square law action will occur over only a very limited range of input voltages. Moreover, since the shape of the transfer characteristic depends on the age and previous history of the tube, the applied voltages, filament temperature, etc., the user of an instrument employing square law operation for obtaining rms values could never be entirely sure that operation *is* square law at the particular time he takes a reading.

Another elementary circuit for measuring alternating voltages is shown in Fig. 5-2. The principle involved is obvious from an examina-

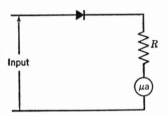

Fig. 5-2. A diode rectifier type of average-responsive circuit.

tion of the drawing. The calibration of the instrument is obtained very quickly if one recalls that the ratio of rms to average values in a sine wave is 1.11. However, with a half-wave rectifier, this factor is doubled, so the average voltage is 2.22 times the rms value. Then the current in the meter will be

$$I_{dc} = \frac{E_{rms}}{2.22R} \tag{5-7}$$

or to obtain the rms voltage in terms of the current, one may use the expression

$$E_{rms} = 2.22 I_{dc} R \tag{5-8}$$

Certain assumptions are implicit in the discussion leading to Eq. (5-8). These are that the rectifier has linear volt-ampere characteristics and that the forward resistance is negligible compared to R while the back resistance is infinite. Usually the value of R will be relatively large, a fact which helps to overcome the effects of nonlinearity in the rectifier. An instrument employing the circuit just discussed would be simple and inexpensive, but has the very serious disadvantage of taking appreciable current from the source under test. A value of R large enough to provide a respectable input impedance will require a meter of extraordinary sensitivity and therefore of extraordinary fragility. For example, if it is desired to obtain full-scale indication for an input of 10 volts rms, with R equal to 2 megohms, the corresponding full-scale current from Eq.

(5-7) would be only 2.25 μa! Actually, the principle shown in Fig. 5-2 is employed in a number of excellent electronic voltmeters, but invariably in conjunction with amplifiers to act as buffers between the rectifier assembly and the input signal. Since the half-wave rectifier is subject to error from turnover, full-wave bridge-type rectifiers are usually used in practice.

5-2. The slide-back principle

One system that offers certain advantages in applications requiring unusual precision is shown in Fig. 5-3. The input signal is applied, and

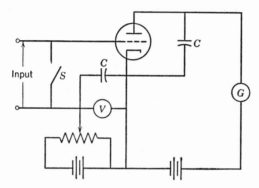

Fig. 5-3. The slide-back voltmeter. Capacitors C are for bypassing a-c signals around the meters.

the tap on the potentiometer is adjusted until the deflection of the galvanometer is just barely detectable. The signal is then disconnected, the short-circuiting switch is closed, and the tap is reset, making the bias more negative until again the galvanometer barely deflects. The difference between the voltmeter readings in the two cases is equal to the peak value of the applied voltage.

The advantages of the system are that there is absolutely no loading effect upon the signal source other than the input capacitance, and that the voltmeter V derives its current from an independent power supply. Therefore this meter may be of the low-impedance, high-power type sometimes used as a secondary standard. This variety of meter often comes equipped with a vernier on the scale, permitting readings accurate to three significant figures. The slide-back instrument may be constructed with a self-balancing feature incorporating a servomotor to drive the slider, the motor being controlled by the amplified voltage developed in a resistor used in the anode circuit in lieu of a galvanometer.

5-3. The grid-detection principle

The grid-detection circuit was developed rather early in the history of radio for the demodulation of amplitude modulated signals. It may

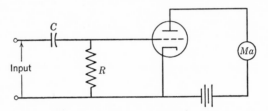

Fig. 5-4. The grid-detection instrument.

be used without change as an electronic voltmeter. It will be seen from the circuit shown in Fig. 5-4 that no provision is made for fixed bias. Therefore the anode current will normally be quite high. When an input signal is applied, the capacitor C will charge through the grid and cathode acting as a diode to a voltage essentially equal to the peak value of the a-c signal. This voltage then becomes a d-c bias, resulting in a new reading on the milliammeter. The circuit is of the peak-responsive type, although the meter will ordinarily be calibrated in volts rms. Essentially two separate functions are performed by the tube: first, it acts as a diode rectifier; and second, in conjunction with the anode portion of the circuit, it serves as a transfer-characteristic instrument similar to the type first discussed in Section 3-2. Like the basic transfer-characteristic instrument, it is subject to marked nonlinearity, drift, and loss of calibration. It is discussed here largely as a matter of historical interest, and because it is a simple prototype of the modern peak-responsive circuits with which we shall be concerned for the remainder of this chapter.

5-4. The modern peak-responsive instrument

The majority of present-day electronic voltmeters incorporate a circuit substantially equivalent to the one shown in Fig. 5-5. There are as many variations as there are manufacturers. This is, of course, a peak-

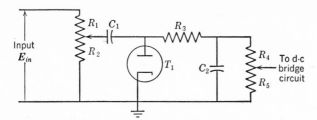

Fig. 5-5. The basic rectifier assembly of a peak-responsive a-c electronic voltmeter.

responsive type of circuit. It is undoubtedly the most common from the standpoint of the quantity of instruments sold.

The action of the circuit is basically very simple, although the mathematical analysis may become very involved when all factors are considered. An input voltage is applied at the position indicated, and a certain fraction of this, depending on R_1 and R_2, is applied to capacitor C_1. The diode T_1 permits the capacitor to charge to approximately the peak value of the voltage appearing across R_2. The network R_3C_2 serves as a filter to remove the ripple voltages that may be present, and the essentially pure direct current that remains is then applied to voltage divider R_4R_5 which is part of the range-switching assembly, together with R_1R_2. The actual measurement is made by a d-c bridge circuit of the type discussed in Section 3-3 or 3-4. If a d-c component is present in E_{in}, then C_1 will acquire a charge equal to the direct voltage across R_2, and of such polarity that the algebraic sum of these two voltages is zero. Therefore the circuit will not be affected by direct current at the input.

No attempt will be made to state exact values of the circuit components, as these vary greatly from one instrument to another. However, typical values might make the sum of R_1 and R_2 about one to two megohms, the sum of R_4 and R_5 about twice this, and R_3 a few hundred thousand ohms. The values of C_1 and C_2 would usually be of the order of tenths microfarad. Almost any diode will be suitable for the rectifier; in fact, a crystal diode with high back resistance and adequate inverse voltage rating might be used rather than a tube.

The information given in Chapter 2 is sufficient to explain most of the important points regarding the action of the circuit, if we can determine the values of R_r and R_b. For this purpose, the circuit of Fig. 5-6 is useful. In this circuit, the input voltage divider has been replaced by an equivalent resistor consisting of R_1 in parallel with R_2. The apparent

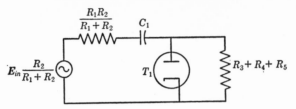

Fig. 5-6. The Thévenin equivalent of the circuit of Fig. 5-5.

size of the input voltage is also reduced, as shown. The forward resistance of the diode is usually small compared with that of the Thévenin equivalent circuit, so for all practical purposes,

$$R_r = \frac{R_1 R_2}{R_1 + R_2} \tag{5-9}$$

The resistance through which C_1 must discharge is

$$R_b = \frac{R_1 R_2}{R_1 + R_2} + R_3 + R_4 + R_5 \tag{5-10}$$

From these two expressions, the numerical value of the ratio R_r/R_b may be found very easily, and the performance of the instrument determined from Fig. 2-6 or 2-7. On the most sensitive ranges in a given instrument, the tap on the input multiplier may be at the very top of the voltage divider assembly, making $R_1 = 0$. In this case, Eq. (5-9) would not apply, and R_r would be simply the forward resistance of the diode. The value depends on the specific tube or crystal rectifier employed, but will ordinarily be between 100 and 1000 ohms. Both Eqs. (5-9) and (5-10) assume the output impedance of the voltage source to be zero. If the source impedance is greater than zero, its value must be added to *both* Eqs. (5-9) and (5-10).

The use of a resistive voltage divider directly across the input terminals is fairly common in moderate-priced instruments, but has a very definite disadvantage in the fact that changing ranges will usually change the value of R_r/R_b. The most annoying consequence of this is that when measuring a waveform other than a pure sinusoid, the readings of the instrument will not, in general, be the same if made on different ranges.

Example: An instrument employing the circuit discussed above is to be used to measure the value of the sum of two equal inharmonically related sine waves each of which has a value of 14.14 volts rms. The output impedance of the signal source is 5000 ohms. The forward resistance of the diode is 500 ohms. $R_3 + R_4 + R_5 = 4$ megohms. With the range switch in the most sensitive position, $R_1 = 0$ and $R_2 = 1$ megohm. After changing ranges, $R_1 = R_2 = 500,000$ ohms. Determine the indication of the instrument on the two ranges.

On the most sensitive range, $R_r = 5000 + 500 = 5500$ ohms, and $R_b = 4,005,000$ ohms. Then $R_r/R_b = 1.37 \times 10^{-3}$. From the curve for $n = 2$ in Fig. 2-7, the reading of the instrument will be 2.4 db above the true rms value, or 2.4 db above 20 volts. This corresponds to an indication of 26.4 volts, assuming the instrument is calibrated to read the correct rms value of a single sine wave.

On the less sensitive range, $R_r = 250,000 + 5000 + 500 = 255,500$ ohms, and $R_b = 250,000 + 4,000,000 + 5000 = 4,255,000$ ohms. Then $R_r/R_b = 6.00 \times 10^{-2}$. Figure 2-7 shows the instrument will read 1 db above the true rms value. This corresponds to 22.4 volts. Therefore on the low-sensitivity range, the reading of the meter will differ by 4 volts from the one obtained on the high-sensitivity range. The discrepancy would be even worse if a larger variation in the ratio R_r/R_b were encountered, or if the input waveform were more complicated. Various ways to avoid this difficulty will be suggested in connection with the more elaborate instruments treated in Chapter 6.

5-5. The "fast electron" effect

In spite of the universal assumption made in introductory courses in electronics that electrons are emitted with zero initial velocity, the more sophisticated reader will realize that this is not so. The electrons emitted with high initial velocities are able to cross a tube against an opposing field and deposit a negative charge on the anode. In circuits of the type we have just discussed, this may be a serious problem. If we refer back to the circuit of Fig. 5-5, it will be seen that the electrons with nonzero initial velocity may travel from the cathode of T_1 to the anode and develop a negative potential there. Eventually, capacitor C_1 will charge to a steady-state voltage of some magnitude E and such polarity as to oppose the fast electrons. Such electrons as do cross against the opposing field will return to ground through the assembly of R_3, R_4, and R_5. Ordinarily about 1 volt will be developed by this fast electron effect, which is a large voltage indeed to have in such close proximity to the input of the d-c bridge circuit. In fact, 1 volt will often be larger than the voltage required for full-scale deflection of the meter. It might be argued that the problem is really of no consequence, since appropriate adjustment of the zero-set control on the opposite side of the d-c bridge could cancel out the voltage E. However, the fast electron effect is very sensitive to cathode temperature, and so any fluctuation in the heater voltage will cause an appreciable change in the magnitude of E. The zero-set control would have to be continuously monitored to prevent annoying drift in the instrument.

Near the end of this section, two schemes will be shown for eliminating the trouble caused by the fast electrons. First, let us look briefly into

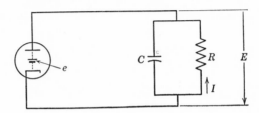

Fig. 5-7. Circuit for analyzing the fast electron effect.

the mathematics of the problem, since it is an easy and interesting little example of the use of statistical distributions in engineering. A circuit for studying the fast electron effect is shown in Fig. 5-7.

The net voltage opposing the flow of electrons from cathode to anode in the diode is $E + e$, where E is the voltage across the capacitor, and e is the contact potential, if any, between the cathode and anode. The sign of e will depend on the relative positions of the anode and cathode materials in the electrochemical series. The magnitude will usually be of the order of a few tenths of a volt.

The Fermi-Dirac law for the statistical distribution of electron velocities indicates the relative amount of current (i.e., number of electrons) that can cross a tube against an opposing voltage (2). This law may be stated for our purposes as

$$\frac{I}{I_0} = \epsilon^{-(E+e)q_0/kT} \tag{5-11}$$

where I is the current able to cross the tube, I_0 is the current that would flow in a short circuit between anode and cathode, q_0 is the magnitude of the charge of the electron (1.6×10^{-19} coulomb), k is Boltzmann's constant (1.38×10^{-23} watt-sec per degree Kelvin), and T is the cathode temperature in degrees Kelvin. The current I must be equal to E/R.

From this fact, and Eq. (5-11), we may say

$$\frac{E}{R} = I_0 \epsilon^{-(E+e)q_0/kT} \tag{5-12}$$

For a given vacuum tube voltmeter circuit, one usually knows R and would like to find E. This presumes a good deal of knowledge regarding

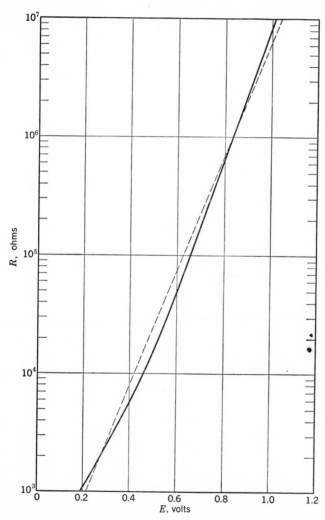

Fig. 5-8. The relationship between resistance R and voltage E developed by the fast electron effect. Solid curve: experimental data for a type 6H6 diode. Dashed curve: typical theoretical prediction, assuming $e = 0$, $I_0 = 2.5$ ma, and $T = 1200°$ K.

the temperature of the cathode and the current I_0—knowledge which is not usually available. Furthermore, Eq. (5-12) cannot be solved directly for E. It is necessary to obtain an expression for R as a function of E, working the problem backward, so to speak. The function in question is

$$R = \frac{E}{I_0 \epsilon^{-(E+e)q_0/kT}} \tag{5-13}$$

A plot of the relationship between R and E is shown in Fig. 5-8, which was obtained assuming $e = 0$, $I_0 = 0.0025$ amp, and $T = 1200°$K. For comparison, a plot of R and E is given on the same figure for experimentally determined data, using one-half of a 6H6 diode operating at rated filament voltage.

The temperature-dependence of E is not very obvious, since I_0 is related to temperature through Dushmann's equation for emission from cathodes. This equation is

$$I_0 = aAT^2\epsilon^{-b_0/T} \tag{5-14}$$

where a is a proportionality constant, dependent on cathode area and also on the fact that the space charge immediately adjacent to the cathode will send back most of the emitted electrons; A and b_0 are constants of the cathode material; and T is temperature in degrees Kelvin. For oxide-coated cathodes of the type usually found in small diodes, $A \cong 0.01$ amp/cm^2/deg K^2 and $b_0 \cong 10,000°$K. Equation (5-14) may be substituted into Eq. (5-13) to obtain a single expression involving R, E, and T. However, a general solution for E as a function of T is no more possible than one for E as a function of R. If desired, a family of curves could be plotted for R as a function of E for different values of T, and from these curves, which would be similar to Fig. 5-8, the change in E with temperature for a given R may be determined. However, it is doubtless easier and probably much more accurate in a given case to obtain experimental data giving E as a function of filament voltage. Two such curves for the same 6H6 diode as in Fig. 5-8 are plotted in Fig. 5-9. The values of R are 100,000 ohms and 5 megohms. To take a concrete example from Fig. 5-9, suppose the filament voltage were to drop by approximately 5 per cent, from 6.3 volts to 6.0 volts. The value of E would decrease from 0.96 to 0.92 volt for the case of $R = 5$ megohms. Since most peak-responsive instruments are designed to give full-scale deflection for a direct voltage of between 0.5 and 1.0 volts, the change of 0.04 volt in the value of E would cause a drift in the meter indication of between 4 and 8 per cent. This assumes that

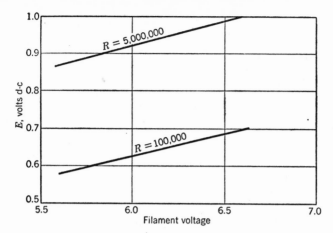

Fig. 5-9. Variations of E with filament voltage for two different values of R. The value of 5 megohms is approximately typical of commercial practice.

the original 0.96 volt had been compensated by the zero-set control. Otherwise the meter would be driven to or beyond full-scale indication by this voltage alone.

Two methods for compensating for the fast electron effect are shown

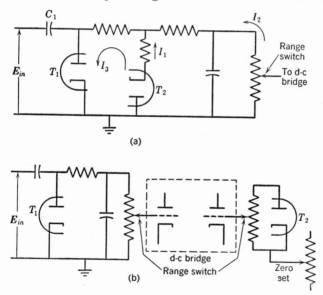

Fig. 5-10. Two circuits for compensating for the fast electron effect: (a) compensation on same side of d-c bridge; (b) compensation on opposite sides of bridge.

in Fig. 5-10. Both methods employ a second diode, so connected that the high initial velocity electrons from the second tube travel in such a direction as to neutralize those from the first tube. In part (a) of the figure, tubes 1 and 2 provide a closed path for each other's fast electrons, so that the electrons travel as a circulating current I_3 rather than developing an unwanted direct voltage across the range switch assembly. This method has the objection of providing an additional discharge path for the voltage developed on capacitor C_1, effectively reducing R_b. These two discharge paths are indicated by currents I_1 and I_2. The method of Fig. 5-10(b) overcomes this difficulty by putting the compensating tube on the other side of the bridge. In both methods, it is desirable to employ a duodiode tube for T_1 and T_2 so that both tubes will be heated by a common filament and therefore be affected the same way by line voltage fluctuations.

5-6. The input impedance to the basic peak-reading instrument

An *estimate* of the input impedance may be made very easily from the circuit of Fig. 5-5. If the frequency is high enough so that capacitor C_2 is essentially a short circuit (this is usually the case in practice), the input resistance *neglecting the action of the diode* will be

$$R_{in} = R_1 + \frac{R_2 R_3}{R_2 + R_3} \tag{5-15}$$

A more accurate determination of input impedance is difficult in the extreme. The input impedance is defined as the rms value of E_{in} divided by the rms current drawn by the instrument from the source of voltage being measured. The action of the diode is to cause a sharp pulse of current to be drawn near the top of each positive half cycle, which increases the rms current and reduces the input resistance. Since the problem becomes one of dealing with nonlinear components, an easy solution is not possible.

Figure 5-11 shows the waveform of current drawn by a typical instrument, together with the voltage across its terminals. The charging current appears as a wide spike at the top of the current cycle, accompanied by a very noticeable clipping of the voltage. An accurate determination of the rms input current would require the calculation of the angles in electrical degrees at which the charging current starts and stops. An attempt to carry this process through leads to equations

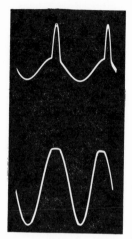

Fig. 5-11. Current (top) and voltage (below) at the input of a peak-reading vacuum tube voltmeter. Note the surge of current required to keep capacitor C_1 charged, and the clipping this causes in the waveform of the voltage being measured.

which can only be solved graphically (*3,4*). For purposes of estimating, the input resistances might be taken as somewhere between 70 and 90 per cent of the value obtained from Eq. (5-15). The input *impedance* will be even less than the input *resistance* because the input capacitance to the instrument is in shunt with the input terminals.

In the circuit we have been discussing, where the voltage divider R_1R_2 appears directly at the input terminals, the input impedance will not be constant on all ranges. On the high-voltage ranges, R_1 is large and R_2 small, with the result that the input impedance increases as the instrument is switched to progressively less sensitive ranges, putting more resistance in series with the diode.

REFERENCES

1. Myron C. Selby, "High-Frequency Voltage Measurement," *National Bureau of Standards Circular 481* (September 1, 1949). (For sale by Superintendent of Documents, U.S. Government Printing Office, Washington 25, D.C., 20 cents.) This booklet does not emphasize electronic instruments in particular, but does have a great deal of material on certain basic types of electronic voltmeters and certain extremely high-precision measuring techniques.

2. Karl R. Spangenberg, *Vacuum Tubes* (New York: McGraw-Hill Book Company, Inc., 1947), p. 25.

3. George E. Happell and Wilfred M. Hesselberth, *Engineering Electronics* (New York: McGraw-Hill Book Company, Inc., 1953), sect. 14-7.

4. Truman S. Gray, *Applied Electronics* (New York: John Wiley & Sons, Inc., 1954), chap. 6, art. 9.

Chapter 6

A-C ELECTRONIC VOLTMETERS—II

The instruments discussed in this chapter differ from those in Chapter 5 primarily in their more elaborate circuitry. Many of them operate on similar principles, but all have in common the advantages of negative feedback that were lacking in the circuits of the previous chapter. Three commercial instruments will be treated as examples: the Hewlett-Packard Model 400D, the Ballantine Model 300, and the Reed Diotron. We shall also discuss certain special characteristics that can be obtained from nonlinear circuit components; in particular, logarithmic characteristics that result in linear decibel scales.

6-1. The input circuit

Many modern electronic voltmeters employ special input circuits to give improved high-frequency performance and increased input impedance. These circuits are the compensated voltage divider and the cathode follower buffer amplifier.

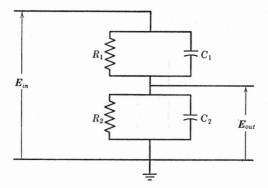

Fig. 6-1. Compensated voltage divider.

83

The compensated voltage divider is a network designed to yield an output equal to a certain fraction of the input *independent of frequency*. The circuit is shown in Fig. 6-1. Here the capacitance C_2 represents the input capacitance of the tube or other components connected across resistor R_2, together with such stray capacitance as may be present between the top of R_2 and ground. It may be shown (*1*) that if $C_1R_1 = C_2R_2$, then

$$\frac{E_{out}}{E_{in}} = \frac{R_2}{R_1 + R_2}$$ (6-1)

at all frequencies.

Usually the value of C_2 will have to be found experimentally. This may be done by raising the frequency of E_{in} until E_{out} drops to $1/\sqrt{2}$ times its d-c or low-frequency value. If this frequency is f_{ht}, then

$$C_2 = \frac{1}{2\pi f_{ht}R_{eq}}$$ (6-2)

where R_{eq} is the value of R_1 in parallel with R_2. (It will be noted that f_{ht} is the same as the upper half-power frequency of an amplifier with stray capacitance C_2 and a resistance between plate and ground of R_{eq}.) With the value of C_2 thus determined, C_1 is easily found from the relationship

$$C_1 = \frac{C_2R_2}{R_1}$$ (6-3)

The idea of employing a cathode follower as the first stage in an instrument (immediately following a compensated voltage divider in many cases) is fairly obvious. It has the advantages of providing a high, constant input impedance; isolating the instrument from the source of

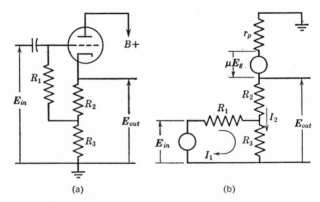

Fig. 6-2. The cathode follower—an alternative form to that of Fig. 3-2: (a) actual circuit; (b) equivalent circuit.

signal to be measured; and, in the case of peak-responsive instruments employing a diode rectifier, presenting a low output impedance to the diode, thus keeping R_r small. The simplest type of cathode follower has been discussed briefly in Section 3-2. Another version, which usually gives appreciably higher input impedance, is shown in Fig. 6-2.

The complete analysis of this circuit is not difficult, and is given in most texts on elementary electronics. The problems of finding gain, output impedance, and input impedance are readily solved by determining the currents I_1 and I_2. The input impedance is

$$Z_{in} = E_{in}/I_1 \tag{6-4}$$

The gain is
$$G = \frac{E_{out}}{E_{in}} = \frac{I_1 R_3 + I_2(R_2 + R_3)}{E_{in}} \tag{6-5}$$

The output impedance may be found by considering open-circuit voltage and short-circuit current at the output. The result is

$$Z_{out} = \frac{gain}{g_m} \tag{6-6}$$

The equations for determining I_1 and I_2 will be set up here, and the method of solution outlined. From the equivalent circuit,

$$E_{in} = I_1(R_1 + R_3) + I_2 R_3 \tag{6-7}$$

$$\mu E_g = I_1 R_3 + I_2(r_p + R_2 + R_3) \tag{6-8}$$

Also,
$$E_g = -I_2 R_2 + I_1 R_1 \tag{6-9}$$

Next substitute Eq. (6-9) into Eq. (6-8), solve the pair of equations (6-7) and (6-8) for I_1 and I_2, and substitute the expressions for current into Eqs. (6-4) to (6-6). The final results are

$$Z_{in} = R_1 + R_3 + \frac{\mu R_1 R_3 - R_3^2}{r_p + (\mu + 1)R_2 + R_3} \tag{6-10}$$

$$gain = \frac{\mu(R_1 R_2 + R_1 R_3 + R_2 R_3) + r_p R_3}{(\mu + 1)(R_1 R_2 + R_1 R_3 + R_2 R_3) + r_p(R_1 + R_3)} \tag{6-11}$$

For typical values of circuit parameters, Eq. (6-11) almost invariably simplifies to

$$gain = \frac{\mu}{\mu + 1} \tag{6-12}$$

within slide rule accuracy.

As an example, let us calculate some typical properties of this type of cathode follower. Suppose that the following circuit parameters are given: $R_1 = 500,000$ ohms, $R_2 = 1000$ ohms, $R_3 = 50,000$ ohms, $\mu = 60$,

$r_p = 15,000$ ohms, and $g_m = 4000$ micromhos. Then from Eqs. (6-6), (6-10), and either (6-11) or (6-12), the quantities of interest are found to be $Z_{in} = 12.45$ megohms (note this is more than 20 times as large as R_1), $gain = 0.984$, and $Z_{out} = 246$ ohms.

Both the compensated voltage divider and the cathode follower are sufficiently common that the user of an instrument should be familiar with them, and the designer should be prepared to welcome them as old friends. The cathode follower, in particular, is highly desirable any time an instrument is to be isolated from the signal it is to measure, and its use is by no means confined to electronic voltmeters.

6-2. The Hewlett-Packard Model 400D Voltmeter

The Hewlett-Packard Model 400D voltmeter has been selected for discussion in this chapter because it serves as an example of an average-responsive circuit employing full-wave rectification, and because it illustrates the use of negative feedback. (The negative feedback principle is shown in other instruments in this chapter also.)

Figure 6-3 illustrates the instrument basically in block diagram form, although details have been added for the feedback system. The input

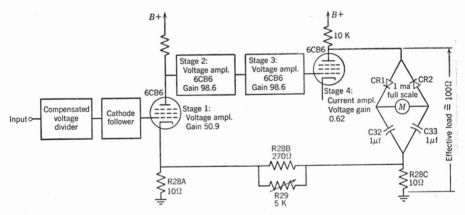

Fig. 6-3. Block diagram of the Hewlett-Packard 400D vacuum tube voltmeter, including details of the feedback system. (Courtesy, Hewlett-Packard Co.)

consists of a compensated voltage divider, followed by a cathode follower. Both of these have been discussed earlier in this chapter, and we shall not consider them in detail here. The heart of the system consists of three stages of voltage amplification (stages 1, 2, and 3), and one stage of current amplification (stage 4). The voltage gain of stage 4 is less than unity, as shown on the figure. However, its value is important in the calculation of forward gain and loop gain.

The tubes, all type 6CB6, are operated under conditions such that g_m is about 6200 micromhos. The gains of the four stages are 50.9, 98.6, 98.6, and 0.62, respectively. The load on stage 4 consists of the full-wave rectifier assembly, a 10-ohm resistor R28C, and about 300 ohms in shunt with R28C. The effective load resistance is about 100 ohms. The forward gain is the product of the individual stage gains, or

$$K = 50.9 \times 98.6 \times 98.6 \times 0.62 = 306{,}000 \qquad (6\text{-}13)$$

The feedback factor β is the ratio of the voltage returned to the cathode of stage 1 to that at the anode of stage 4. Ten per cent of the output appears across R28C, and $\frac{10}{280}$ of this appears across R28A, assuming the shunting effect of R29 across R28B is negligible. Then

$$|\beta| = 0.1 \times \frac{10}{280} = 0.00357 \qquad (6\text{-}14)$$

Actually, β is set slightly higher by R29, to about 0.003828. The loop gain is

$$|\beta K| = 0.003828 \times 306{,}000 = 1171 \qquad (6\text{-}15)$$

The net gain is $$G = \frac{306{,}000}{1 + 1171} = 261 \qquad (6\text{-}16)$$

Now let us see what these numbers tell of the over-all performance of the instrument. Suppose that the gain K drops to 96,820 due to a 25% drop in g_m of each tube. Then βK becomes 370.64 and G drops to 96,820/371.64, or 260.52, a decrease of about 0.2 per cent. Obviously, the calibration of the instrument can be expected to hold very well over a wide range of variations in tube parameters.

The value of β is increased by reducing the apparent size of R28B. Therefore the value of G may be decreased by lowering R29. This variable resistor serves as the calibrating control for all ranges of the instrument, since the input range switch reduces all full-scale input voltages to the same value (about 0.85 mv rms) at the grid of stage 1.

The voltage gain of 261 between stage 1 and the rectifier assembly means that for 0.85 mv at the input, 0.22 volt appears at the junction of $CR1$ and $CR2$. The impedance between this point and ground is about 100 ohms, so a current of 2.22 ma rms flows into the rectifiers. This divides into two parts, half flowing to ground via the meter and $C33$, and the other half via $C32$ during the positive half cycle. In the negative half cycle, $C32$ and $C33$ discharge, the current in $C32$ passing through the meter on this occasion; $CR1$ conducts during the positive half cycle, and $CR2$ during the negative. Thus the combination of diodes and capacitors is equivalent to a full-wave bridge, except it is only 50 per cent efficient, since half the current flows in a capacitor not associated with the meter. Consequently, the effect on the meter is the same as a current of 1.11 ma rms full-wave-rectified. The meter direct current is then 1 ma, which causes full-scale deflection.

The individual amplifier stages are relatively conventional, operating in general on the principle that wide bandwidth is obtained by using amplifiers with low plate load resistances and high g_m tubes. Shunt peaking inductance is used in one of the four stages. In addition, lead networks are included in the interstage couplings to stabilize the closed loop system against oscillation.

The accuracy of the instrument is specified to be within ±5% of full-scale value over a frequency range of 10 cycles to 4 megacycles. The accuracy is even better over somewhat narrower bandwidths. Like any average-responsive voltmeter, the 400D is subject to the errors discussed in Chapter 2 when the input signal is not sinusoidal.

6-3. The pentriode amplifier $(2,3)$

One very interesting type of amplifier sometimes used in electronic voltmeters is the *pentriode*. We shall analyze this circuit because it provides a novel way of obtaining wide bandwidths, around 2 megacycles, without the use of compensating circuits. Also, it affords an opportunity to study some often-neglected tube parameters associated with the screen grid of a tube.

Figure 6-4 shows a typical pentriode stage. At low frequencies, the circuit acts like a cross between the pentode and triode, and from this property receives its name. Between the low- and high-frequency regions there is a so-called "crossover" range.

The physical action of the circuit is as follows: at high frequencies, where the by-pass capacitors are effective, the only load on the tube is R_1, since the 560,000-ohm resistor to the right offers negligible shunting action. The gain is then

$$K_{hi} = -g_m R_1 \qquad (6\text{-}17)$$

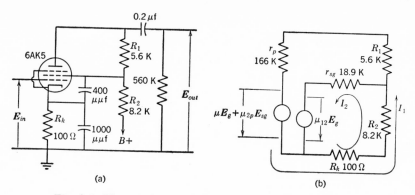

Fig. 6-4. The pentriode amplifier: (a) actual circuit; (b) equivalent circuit.

At low frequencies, where the by-pass capacitors are not effective at all, the resistors R_2 and R_k introduce negative feedback at the screen grid and cathode and so tend to reduce the gain. However, resistor R_2 is *also part of the plate circuit*, and its action in this position is to raise the gain. By proper design, the two effects can be made to cancel each other, giving the same gain at low frequencies as at high. The circuit eliminates both the shunt peaking coil often used to improve high-frequency performance, and the large capacitors often found in circuits for low-frequency compensation.

Zeidler and Noe (*3*) discuss the circuit from the design point of view. Their paper is essential reading for those seeking to construct a pentriode amplifier. For our purposes, in order to illustrate the effects of tube parameters other than the conventional μ, r_p, and g_m, an analysis is somewhat more instructive than a design problem. This analysis will be carried out for the low-frequency case with the aid of Fig. 6-4(b). The high-frequency case is very simple, and is covered adequately by Eq. (6-17).

To examine the performance of the circuit when the by-passing is inoperative, the following definitions will be required:

$$\mu_{12} = \frac{\partial e_{sg}}{\partial e_g}\bigg|_{i_{sg} \text{ constant}} \tag{6-18}$$

$$\mu_{2p} = \frac{\partial e_b}{\partial e_{sg}}\bigg|_{i_b \text{ constant}} \tag{6-19}$$

$$r_{sg} = \frac{\partial e_{sg}}{\partial i_{sg}}\bigg|_{e_g \text{ constant}} \tag{6-20}$$

In this list, e_{sg} is screen grid voltage, i_{sg} is screen grid current, e_b is plate voltage, i_b is plate current, and e_g is grid voltage.

From the equivalent circuit, the following equations may be written:

$$\mu E_g + \mu_{2p} E_{sg} = I_1(R_k + R_1 + R_2 + r_p) + I_2(R_k + R_2) \qquad (6\text{-}21)$$

$$\mu_{12} E_g = I_1(R_k + R_2) + I_2(R_k + R_2 + r_{sg}) \qquad (6\text{-}22)$$

Also,
$$E_g = -(I_1 + I_2)R_k + E_{in} \qquad (6\text{-}23)$$

$$E_{sg} = -(I_1 + I_2)(R_k + R_2) \qquad (6\text{-}24)$$

The output voltage is

$$E_{out} = -(I_1 + I_2)R_2 - I_1 R_1 \qquad (6\text{-}25)$$

If Eqs. (6-23) and (6-24) are substituted into Eqs. (6-21) and (6-22), two equations are obtained which can be solved for I_1 and I_2.

$$I_1(R_1 + R_2 + \mu_{2p}R_2 + R_k + \mu R_k + \mu_{2p}R_k + r_p)$$
$$+ I_2(R_2 + \mu_{2p}R_2 + R_k + \mu R_k + \mu_{2p}R_k) = \mu E_{in} \qquad (6\text{-}26)$$

$$I_1(R_2 + R_k + \mu_{12}R_k) + I_2(R_2 + R_k + \mu_{12}R_k + r_{sg}) = \mu_{12} E_{in} \qquad (6\text{-}27)$$

The expressions for I_1 and I_2 may then be substituted into Eq. (6-25) to obtain the output voltage, and the gain is easily determined. It approaches μ_{12} as a theoretical limit.

An algebraic solution is not difficult, but the resulting equations are rather long, and in a given problem it will usually be convenient to introduce numerical values at this point. For the 6AK5 tube at the d-c operating point employed in this circuit, the tube parameters are

$$\mu = 675, \qquad r_p = 166{,}000 \text{ ohms}$$

$$\mu_{12} = 29.1, \qquad r_{sg} = 18{,}900 \text{ ohms}$$

$$\mu_{2p} = 19.6, \qquad g_m = 4040 \text{ micromhos}$$

Substitution of these values, together with those of the other circuit components, into Eqs. (6-26) and (6-27) gives

$$I_1 = 1.38 \times 10^{-3} E_{in}$$

and
$$I_2 = 4.59 \times 10^{-4} E_{in}$$

From these and Eq. (6-25), the low-frequency gain is found to be

$$K_{lo} = -22.8$$

Numerical evaluation of Eq. (6-17) for the high-frequency case gives

$$K_{hi} = -22.6$$

It is seen that the gains are almost identical in the low- and high-frequency cases. An analysis of the crossover region is more involved than the low-frequency analysis, since the effects of the capacitors must be taken into account. The problem is a straightforward one, in that the capacitors may be drawn in their proper places in Fig. 6-4(b), and the analysis carried out by the usual techniques. However, the author does not feel that enough is to be learned going through the treatment to justify the very considerable labor involved.

6-4. The Ballantine Model 300 Voltmeter

The Ballantine Model 300 voltmeter has been selected for discussion since it provides another example of the use of negative feedback, and because it derives some unusual properties from its particular value of the ratio R_r/R_b.

The circuit of the instrument, neglecting input multipliers, power supplies, and the like, is shown in Fig. 6-5. For purposes of analyzing

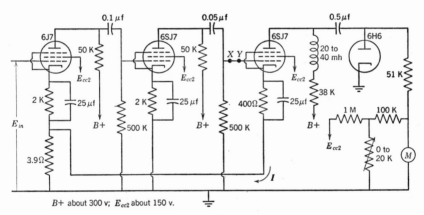

Fig. 6-5. The Ballantine Model 300 voltmeter, somewhat simplified. (Courtesy, Ballantine Laboratories, Inc.)

the circuit, we shall look first of all into the matter of the loop gain, and then into the action of the measuring circuit proper. The ratio of R_r/R_b is so close to unity that this voltmeter is essentially an average-responsive type.

In order to compute the loop gain, it is first necessary to determine the values of the tube parameters. For the 6J7 tube and the first 6SJ7, laboratory measurements on six tubes each of the appropriate type at the operating point used in this instrument gave average values of $g_m = 1150$ micromhos and $r_p = 2.53$ megohms. In the case of the second

6SJ7, the average tube parameters are g_m = 1920 micromhos and r_p = 206,000 ohms.

The loop gain will be determined by imagining the connection between points X and Y in the grid of the last 6SJ7 to be removed, and a signal of 1 volt rms applied between Y and ground. It will be assumed that the frequency is low enough so that the effects of the peaking coil in the anode circuit of this tube need not be considered, and that once the 0.5μf capacitor is charged, no further current will be taken by the diode. This last assumption is rather untenable, but is made in order to avoid considering the nonlinear behavior during a few electrical degrees each cycle.

The voltage gain of the last 6SJ7 stage is equal to g_m times the total shunt impedance between anode and ground. This includes r_p in parallel with the 38,000-ohm and 51,000-ohm resistors. (The meter resistance is presumed to be negligible.) Since r_p = 206,000 ohms, the net value of the shunt resistance is 19,700 ohms. Then

$$k = -g_m R_{sh} = -0.001920 \times 19,700 = -37.8 \qquad (6\text{-}28)$$

The lower-case k is used here to distinguish the stage gain from the total forward gain K. For 1 volt applied at point Y, the voltage developed at the anode will be -37.8 volts, and the current I is

$$I = \frac{-37.8}{R_L} = -0.00173 \text{ ampere} \qquad (6\text{-}29)$$

where R_L is the load resistance of 21,800 ohms consisting of the 38,000-ohm and 51,000-ohm resistors in parallel. This current flowing in the 3.9-ohm resistor will develop a voltage of -6.76 mv.

Since the plate resistance is high in the first two tubes, the value of R_{sh} in these stages is 50,000 ohms in parallel with 500,000 ohms or 45,500 ohms. Then the gain per stage is

$$k = -g_m R_{sh} = -0.001150 \times 45,500 = -52.4 \qquad (6\text{-}30)$$

The voltage at X is

$$E_X = -6.76 \text{ mv} \times (52.4)^2 = -18.5 = \text{loop gain } \beta K \qquad (6\text{-}31)$$

The loop gain and voltage are the same, since it was assumed that 1 volt was applied at point Y. Variations in circuit or tube parameters will be effectively reduced by a factor of 19.5, i.e., $1 - \beta K$.

Now let the loop be closed by rejoining points X and Y. The output impedance of the last tube becomes

$$Z_{out} = \frac{r_p}{1 - \beta K} = \frac{206,000}{19.5} = 10,600 \text{ ohms} \qquad (6\text{-}32)$$

This is in parallel with the 38,000-ohm resistor, so the resulting impedance driving the rectifier is $R_r = 8300$ ohms. The value of R_b is the 8300-ohm resistance of R_r in series with the 51,000-ohm resistor, or 59,300 ohms. Therefore

$$R_r/R_b = 8.3/59.3 = 0.140 \tag{6-33}$$

At first glance, this looks like an extremely high value, and indeed it would be if there were any intention of obtaining a meter indication proportional to the true peak value of any arbitrary signal that is applied. However, if the reader will refer back to Fig. 2-7, it will be noted that for this value of the ratio, the meter indication will be within *1 db of the true rms value* for any combination of equal inharmonically related waves between 1 and 4 in number. As a matter of fact, this instrument reads within approximately 1 db of the true rms for values of n as high as 10. This is a very remarkable feature. The same principle could, of course, be incorporated into peak-responsive circuits of the simpler type discussed in Chapter 5.

Another convenient feature of this voltmeter, and certain others as well, is the inclusion of a front panel connection to the output of the internal amplifiers. This permits inspection of the input signal waveform without the additional loading of an oscilloscope directly across the source. It also allows the instrument to be used as a preamplifier for small signals. Furthermore, by inspecting the waveform within the instrument, one may be sure there is no clipping or other distortion. This is a wise precaution when measuring signals having a high peak-to-average ratio.

6-5. An RMS Responsive Circuit: The Reed Diotron (4)

In the final analysis, the one infallible indication of the rms value of a voltage or current is the heating action it can produce. In applications where a fragile instrument of low input impedance can be tolerated, the thermocouple meter is still frequently used. It gives a true rms indication, but the scale is greatly compressed at the low end, and the thermocouple burns out on very small overloads. Another approach based on the heating effect of a current is found in the Reed Diotron circuit, shown in Fig. 6-6.

The action of the circuit is as follows: An a-c signal is applied to the filament of a diode via a cathode follower. This increases the temperature of the filament, and causes the emission to increase. The anode

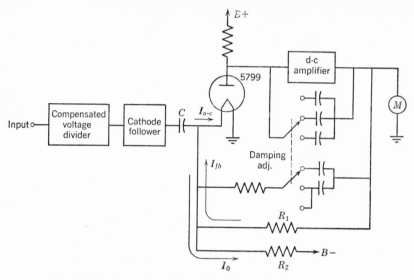

Fig. 6-6. Basic configuration of the Diotron instrument. (Courtesy, Reed Research, Inc., Washington, D.C.)

voltage is high enough so that the diode is virtually temperature saturated; i.e., practically all emitted electrons are drawn across the tube. A true case of temperature saturation would be equivalent to an infinite internal impedance looking back into the tube, since the plate current would be independent of external circuitry. As we look back toward the diode from the d-c amplifier, there appears to be a shunt resistance of about 1 megohm. Therefore operation is not wholly in the temperature-saturated state, but it is convenient to consider it so to simplify our thinking.

When the filament emission increases with an a-c input, the 5799 plate current likewise increases, and the anode potential drops. The d-c amplifier responds with a feedback current I_{fb} that flows in opposition to a constant d-c heating current, I_0. This reduces the filament heating current to offset the added heating from the a-c input. In effect, the Diotron circuit is a feedback system for holding a fixed value of filament emission.

The actual measurement is made by the meter M, which indicates the changes in I_{fb} in response to the a-c input. Resistors R_1 and R_2 are simplified representations of more elaborate resistor networks, shown in detail in the paper by Campbell. These are large enough to keep I_{ac}

almost entirely in the 5799 filament. The filament direct currents are blocked from the input portion of the circuit by capacitor C.

Now since the regulating action of the circuit involves keeping the filament temperature constant, it follows that the sum of the d-c and a-c filament power contributions must be constant. Thus

$$I_{dc}^2 R + I_{ac}^2 R = \text{constant} \tag{6-34}$$

where R is the filament resistance and I_{dc} is $I_0 - I_{fb}$.

Suppose we divide both sides of Eq. (6-34) by R, and let R be included in the constant. Then

$$I_{dc}^2 + I_{ac}^2 = k^2 \tag{6-35}$$

where k^2 is another constant. It is convenient to have a squared quantity on the right-hand side purely for subsequent mathematical manipulations. From Eq. (6-35),

$$\frac{I_{dc}}{k} = \left(1 - \frac{I_{ac}^2}{k^2}\right)^{1/2} \tag{6-36}$$

The instrument is so designed that I_{ac} is small compared with I_{dc}, and therefore small compared with k. Hence Eq. (6-36) may be represented as the first two terms of the series expansion for the square root of unity minus a small quantity. Thus

$$\frac{I_{dc}}{k} \cong 1 - \frac{1}{2}\frac{I_{ac}^2}{k^2} \tag{6-37}$$

or

$$I_{dc} \cong k - (1/2k)I_{ac}^2 \tag{6-38}$$

Equation (6-38) shows that I_{dc} varies as the *square* of I_{ac}. Obviously, only the contribution to I_{dc} made by I_{fb} can vary, as I_0 is fixed. Since I_{fb} is controlled by the d-c amplifier, the meter indicating the d-c amplifier output gives a reading proportional to I_{ac}^2. Inasmuch as power is proportional to the square of the alternating current, it follows that the Diotron meter has a linear power scale as long as the assumptions involved in reaching Eq. (6-37) are valid. The deviation from a linear power scale is only 0.8 per cent if I_{ac} is as large as 45 per cent of I_{dc}.

There are two feedback paths supplementing the path through R_1. One is a capacitor from the output of the d-c amplifier to its input. The second is an RC series circuit between the d-c amplifier output and the filament of the 5799 tube. The latter provides damping of the feedback loop in order to obtain optimum stability and speed of response. The former reduces the bandwidth for a-c signals sufficiently to prevent the feedback loop from following temperature changes in the 5799 filament. This tube has a very small filament with a short thermal time constant. With low-frequency input signals, it can actually vary in temperature during an individual a-c cycle. If this fluctuation were amplified by the feedback circuit, it would introduce extra heating power that would not be indicated by the d-c meter M. Obviously these networks are operative only for a-c components in the feedback loop, since they contain series capacitors. Both of these supplementary feedback paths are adjustable by varying the series capacitance with the switch marked "Damping Adj."

The loop gain of the feedback system is of the order of 100,000. This varies somewhat during operation because the filament of the diode is part of the closed loop, and the "gain" of this component, which is the change in plate current per unit change in filament power (di_b/dp_{fil}), is a function of the filament power. Since in practice the filament power is held essentially constant by the feedback system, the nonlinear nature of the filament is not a serious problem.

The very large value of loop gain means that the circuit is virtually immune to any drift caused by variations of amplifiers within the loop. It also means that changes in the 5799 plate current will be only about 1 part in 100,000 as large as if I_{ac} were applied in the absence of feedback. While the filament emission is not linearly related to the filament power, it is nevertheless obvious that a very considerable reduction in changes of filament power must also result. This provides excellent protection against burnout of the diode. As a matter of fact, the normal operating point of the filament is at only 12 per cent of the burnout power. If necessary, added protection could be obtained by designing the input cathode follower to saturate at a "safe" level for the diode.

6-6. Methods of obtaining nonlinear indications—I

It sometimes happens that for one reason or another, a linear relationship between input voltage and deflection of a meter is not desired. This is especially true in such fields as telephony and acoustics, where a decibel scale is useful. A linear decibel scale is equivalent to a logarithmic voltage scale, so some instruments are designed to produce a meter deflection proportional to the *logarithm* of the input signal.

One very straightforward way to achieve this result is shown in Fig. 6-7. This illustrates a D'Arsonval meter movement with the pole

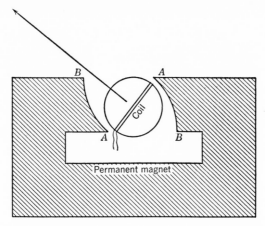

Fig. 6-7. A D'Arsonval movement for nonlinear indications.

faces machined in such a way that the air gap increases as the pointer moves from left to right. By a proper design of air gap length as a function of angular rotation, a logarithmic indication can be obtained. While the basic idea is rather obvious, the detailed design of such a magnetic system is far from easy, and since it lies outside the main line of interest in this book, we shall not pursue the matter further.

Another method for obtaining logarithmic indications is sketched in block diagram form in Fig. 6-8 (*5*). The circuit is a closed loop system which keeps the output of the amplifiers substantially constant in spite of variations in the input signal level. The d-c voltage E_{c3} on the third grid of a pentagrid tube varies the gain of this stage to perform the regulating action. In turn, E_{c3} is derived from the output of the amplifier chain. By suitable design, the variation in E_{c3} can be made proportional to the logarithm of the input voltage. This is easily proved.

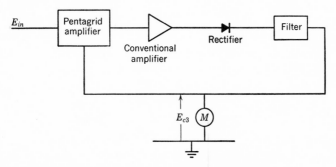

Fig. 6-8. Block diagram of a logarithmic circuit.

Assume that the pentagrid amplifier gain varies according to the law

$$K = k\epsilon^{bE_{c3}} \tag{6-39}$$

where k and b are simply proportionality constants. The output from the amplifier is then

$$E_{out} = E_{in}k\epsilon^{bE_{c3}} \tag{6-40}$$

If the voltage E_{out} were held absolutely constant by the feedback system, solution of Eq. (6-40) for E_{c3} would give

$$E_{c3} = -\frac{1}{b}\ln\frac{kE_{in}}{E_{out}} \tag{6-41}$$

Since E_{out} is presumed to be almost constant, it will be seen that the voltage on the third grid is a function only of the *logarithm of the input voltage* and certain constants of the circuit.

The method of reducing this principle to practice will be illustrated by means of an example. For this purpose, consider the circuit of Fig. 6-9, which uses a 6L7 tube as the variable-gain pentagrid stage,

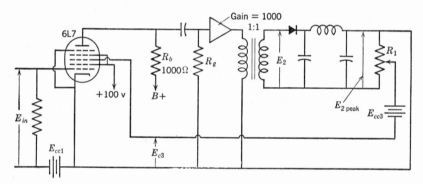

Fig. 6-9. A circuit to produce an output voltage E_{c3} proportional to the logarithm of E_{in}.

and has additional fixed gain of 1000. It will be assumed for simplicity that the voltage across potentiometer R_1 is equal to the peak value of E_2, and that R_g is large enough to have negligible shunting effect on R_b. Then the voltage E_2 will be

$$E_2 = g_mR_b \times 1000 \times E_{in} \tag{6-42}$$

If g_m is read *directly in micromhos*, it will be seen that

$$E_2 = g_mE_{in} \tag{6-43}$$

since the product $1000R_b = 1,000,000$ in this particular example.

The next step in designing the logarithmic circuit is to plot the value

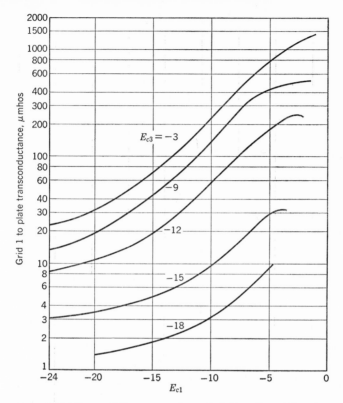

Fig. 6-10. Type 6L7 average characteristics. $E_f = 6.3$ volts. Plate volts = 250. Screen volts (E_{c2} and E_{c4}) = 100. Grid 1 to plate transconductance as a function of signal grid (grid 1) voltage for various values of control grid (grid 3) voltage. (Courtesy, Radio Corporation of America.)

of $E_{2\ peak}$ as a function of E_{c3} for various values of E_{in}. This is done with the aid of the characteristic curves of the tube, shown in Fig. 6-10. For example, if a fixed bias of -15 volts is used on grid number one ($E_{cc1} = -15$), the g_m of the 6L7 will be 70 micromhos when $E_{c3} = -3$ volts. Then if the peak value of E_{in} is 0.1 volt, $E_{2\ peak} = 70 \times 0.1 = 7.0$. This is marked as point A on Fig. 6-11. Similarly, a number of other points are determined for different values of E_{c3} when $E_{in\ peak} = 0.1$, and a curve is drawn for this value of input voltage. Other curves are obtained in exactly the same manner for values of $E_{in\ peak} = 0.2, 0.4, 0.8,$ and 1.0 volt. All are plotted in Fig. 6.11.

The next step is to derive a line such as the one marked "rectifier characteristic." The *intercept* of this line on the E_{c3} axis is determined by

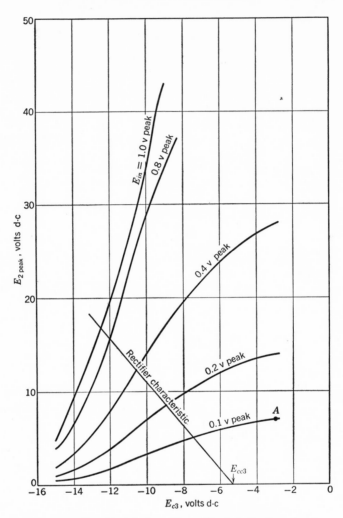

Fig. 6-11. Graphical design of logarithmic indicating circuit.

the fixed bias voltage E_{cc3} in Fig. 6-9. Its *slope* is fixed by the setting of the tap on R_1. Obviously, the slope is restricted to values such that

$$\frac{\Delta E_{c3}}{\Delta E_{2\,peak}} \leqq 1.00 \tag{6-44}$$

This simply means that the voltage at the tap of R_1 could never exceed the total voltage across R_1.

The only possible operating points for the over-all circuit are at the intersections of the rectifier characteristic and the family of curves for

$E_{in\ peak}$. Suppose, for example, that somehow operation of the circuit took place at point A in Fig. 6-11. Then an input of 0.1 volt peak would be associated with a value of $E_{c3} = -3$ volts, and $E_{2\ peak}$ would be 7.00 volts. The slope of the rectifier characteristic, as defined by Eq. (6-44), turns out to be 0.461. That is, 46.1% of the voltage developed across R_1 contributes to the value of E_{c3}. The remainder of E_{c3} is made by E_{cc3}. Now in this example, if $E_{2\ peak} = 7.00$ volts, the components of E_{c3} are

$$E_{c3} = (-0.461 \times 7.00) - 5.3 = -8.53 \text{ volts} \qquad (6\text{-}45)$$

But if $E_{c3} = -8.53$, the gain of the pentagrid stage would drop to such an extent that $E_{2\ peak}$ could not possibly be 7.00 volts for an input of 0.1 volt peak, so operation at A could not occur.

It is necessary only to try a number of different choices for slope and intercept until a rectifier characteristic is found that leads to a *linear* increase in the value of E_{c3} for a *geometric* increase in E_{in}. This is the test of logarithmic operation. In the present example, the value of E_{c3} increases by 1.5 volts each time the input is doubled. Probably the easiest way to make sure logarithmic readings will be obtained is to plot the values of E_{c3} (read from the intersections of the rectifier characteristic with the $E_{in\ peak}$ family of curves in Fig. 6-11) as a function of $E_{in\ peak}$,

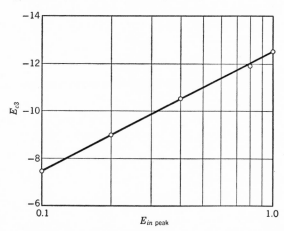

Fig. 6-12. Voltage E_{c3} as a function of E_{in} for the circuit described in Figs. 6-9 and 6-11.

using semilogarithmic paper. If the result is a straight line, the effort has been successful. An example is shown in Fig. 6-12.

A circuit of the type just discussed offers the possibility of getting logarithmic action over approximately 1 to $1\frac{1}{2}$ decades in most cases.

The range may be extended by placing two or more variable gain amplifier stages in cascade. If it is desired to display the logarithmic indication on a conventional meter, the voltage E_{c3} will be measured by a d-c voltmeter. In all probability, the meter will be calibrated so that the scale indication is -20 for an input of 0.1 volt, corresponding to the fact that $20 \log_{10} 0.1 = -20$. The point corresponding to a 1-volt input would be marked "0 db." The instrument could be adjusted for reading other decade ranges (1 to 10, 10 to 100, etc.) by a range switch at the input terminals. In practice, it is usually easier to use a special D'Arsonval movement as in Fig. 6-7 if the display of the measured quantity on a conventional meter is desired.

Systems that produce a logarithmic output by their electronic rather than mechanical characteristics are especially useful in conjunction with the vertical deflection amplifiers of cathode ray oscilloscopes. One important application is in sound-spectrum analyzers, which display on the face of a cathode ray tube a plot of sound energy in decibels as a function of frequency. These analyzers are discussed in more detail in connection with frequency measurements in Chapter 9.

6-7. Methods of obtaining nonlinear indications—II

One attractive scheme for obtaining special functions of output vs input is to use purely passive circuit components. Such an arrangement is ordinarily appreciably less expensive and troublesome to construct than active circuits employing some feedback principle. By the same token, it lacks the advantages inherent in any feedback circuit.

One method of obtaining a logarithmic response employs the exponential relationship between current in a diode and the *negative* potential applied to its anode. The starting point for examining this phenomenon is Eq. 5-11, repeated here as a matter of convenience.

$$\frac{I}{I_0} = \epsilon^{-(E+e)q_0/kT} \tag{6-46}$$

If this equation is solved for E, the result is

$$E = -\left(e + \frac{kT}{q_0} \ln \frac{I}{I_0}\right) \tag{6-47}$$

It is seen from this expression that E is a linear function of the logarithm of I, and therefore a circuit using current as an input and the voltage between anode and cathode as an output will act logarithmically. Such

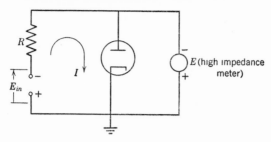

Fig. 6-13. A circuit for obtaining logarithmic output as a function of input. Note that reference directions of E_{in} and I are chosen to correspond to the notation of Eqs. (6-46) to (6-48). The actual d-c polarity of E_{in} must be with the positive side grounded.

a device is shown in Fig. 6-13. The input impedance to the voltmeter should be very high, of the order of hundreds of megohms. The resistor R likewise should be large in order that the input voltage may be converted to the equivalent of the constant current source.

As in the case of the fast electron effect (see Section 5-5), an actual problem is best approached by working backward, i.e., assuming values of the ratio I/I_0 and computing the values of E_{in}. By way of an example, assume $e = 0$, $T = 1000°K$, and $I_0 = 2.5$ ma. For different values of the current ratio, the value of E is easily determined from Eq. (6-47). However, the value of E_{in} is

$$E_{in} = -E + IR \tag{6-48}$$

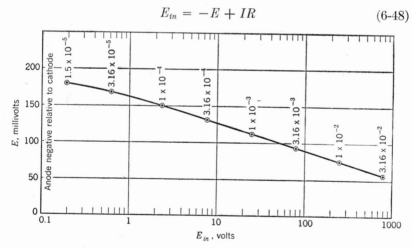

Fig. 6-14. Plot of E as a function of E_{in} for typical constants in the circuit of Fig. 6-13. Numbers beside points are values of the ratio I/I_0.

The voltage E is plotted as a function of E_{in} in Fig. 6-14, assuming a value of 10 megohms for R. A logarithmic relationship will be seen to prevail over a range of several decades. The departure at the left-hand side of the curve is due to the presence of $-E$ in Eq. (6-48). The relatively small values of E are something of a disadvantage, as they require that the voltmeter must not only have a high input impedance, but also be about an order of magnitude more sensitive than run-of-the-mill meters.

The effects of contact potential may be very pronounced in a practical situation, leading to appreciably larger voltages than were found in this example. Also, as the potential between anode and cathode approaches zero (i.e., the anode ceases being negative and starts to become positive with respect to the cathode), the operation will change from logarithmic to the familiar Child's law of electron tubes. Furthermore, any inhomogeneities in the cathode surface will result in a serious departure from the desired logarithmic response because of local differences in contact potential. Meagher and Bentley (6) suggest that this difficulty may be overcome by using a multigrid tube with the grids positive by about 20 to 90 volts. This accelerates the electrons and brings them to a region between the plate and the last grid, where they are decelerated by the opposing voltage on the plate and form a virtual cathode. This virtual cathode will still exhibit the exponential distribution of electron velocities, but is free of contact potential effects.

Still another method of obtaining nonlinear relationships between input and output is the "multiar" circuit (7). This circuit can simulate a wide variety of functions, and is by no means limited to logarithmic operation. It is shown in Fig. 6-15. As long as all the diodes are biased beyond cutoff, the output voltage is equal to, or directly proportional

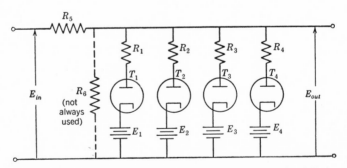

Fig. 6-15. The multiar circuit. (Courtesy, Hewlett-Packard Co.)

to the input. When the output reaches the value of E_1, tube T_1 will start to conduct, and the *slope* of the output vs input curve, assuming R_6 is omitted, will be

$$\frac{dE_{out}}{dE_{in}} = \frac{R_1}{R_1 + R_5} \tag{6-49}$$

When the output reaches the value of E_2, then T_2 will conduct, and the slope will then be

$$\frac{dE_{out}}{dE_{in}} = \frac{R_{12}}{R_{12} + R_5} \tag{6-50}$$

where R_{12} represents the value of R_1 in parallel with R_2. In the basic form shown, the multiar circuit can produce only curves that are concave down, and in no case can the slope dE_{out}/dE_{in} exceed unity. Diodes and bias batteries may be reversed in polarity in order to operate on negative as well as positive input voltages. In Brunner's paper (7), an example is given of synthesizing a sinusoid from a triangular wave, as done in the Hewlett-Packard Low-Frequency Function Generator.

A somewhat simpler case will be used here to illustrate the design

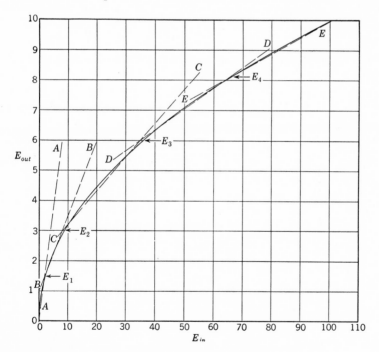

Fig. 6-16. Graphical design of a multiar circuit for taking square roots.

procedure. Say that a multiar circuit is desired to give an output equal to the square root of the input voltage for inputs from 0 to 100 volts. The first step is to sketch the *desired* output curve, as is done in Fig. 6-16, solid line. Next the curve is *approximated* with straight-line segments, lines *AA*, *BB*, *CC*, *DD*, and *EE*. As many segments as desired may be used, if one is willing to go to a sufficient number of diodes and bias supplies. The points where segments intersect indicate the values of bias voltages, which are read from the E_{out} axis. In this case, they are $E_1 = 1.5$ volts, $E_2 = 3.0$ volts, $E_3 = 6.0$ volts, and $E_4 = 8.1$ volts.

Next the slopes of the lines will be found. The slope of line *AA* is $dE_{out}/dE_{in} = 0.735$. Then $R_6/(R_5 + R_6) = 0.735$. The value of R_5 may be picked arbitrarily. It should be moderately large to avoid presenting too low an input impedance to the source. A value of 100,000 ohms might be suitable. Then solving for R_6 gives $R_6 = 377,000$ ohms. The slope of line *BB* is equal to $R_{61}/(R_5 + R_{61})$, where R_{61} is the value of R_1 in parallel with R_6. Measurement of the slope on Fig. 6-17 shows it to have the value 0.25, and from this the value of R_{61} is found to be 33,000 ohms. Knowing that $R_6 = 377,000$ ohms, the value of R_1 is readily found to be 36,500 ohms. By similar methods, the values of R_2, R_3, and R_4 are found to be 20,200, 18,800, and 24,300 ohms, respectively.

The example we have just considered assumed that the diodes operated as switches; i.e., they either conducted perfectly or not at all. In practice, this is not quite true, and slightly different values of the resistances may be required to obtain the desired response. In the author's experience, it is often easiest to calculate approximately what the resistances should be and then complete the design experimentally, using the calculated values as starting points from which further adjustments may be made.

REFERENCES

1. Cruft Laboratory, Harvard University, *Electronic Circuits and Tubes* (New York: McGraw-Hill Book Company, Inc., 1947), p. 29.
2. Frederick E. Terman, William R. Hewlett, Charles W. Palmer, and Wen-Yuan Pan, "Calculation and Design of Resistance-Coupled Amplifiers Using Pentode Tubes," *Trans. AIEE*, vol. 59 (1940), p. 879.
3. H. M. Zeidler and J. D. Noe, "Pentriode Amplifiers," *Proc. I.R.E.*, vol. 36 (1948), p. 1332. See also U. S. Patent 2,566,508.

4. R. D. Campbell, "The Diotron . . . An Aid to RMS Instrumentation," *Electronics*, vol. 23, July 1950, p. 93.
5. Stuart Ballantine, "Variable-mu Tetrodes in Logarithmic Recording," *Electronics*, vol. 2, January 1931, p. 472.
6. Ralph E. Meagher and Edward P. Bentley, "Vacuum Tube Circuit to Measure the Logarithm of a Direct Current," *Rev. Sci. Instr.*, vol. 10, November 1939, p. 336.
7. Robert H. Brunner, "A Low-Frequency Function Generator," *Electronics*, vol. 25, December 1952, p. 114.

Chapter 7

ELECTROMETER TUBES AND CIRCUITS

An electrometer is a device for measuring extremely small quantities of charge. This charge may be in motion, as a minute current; or it may be stored, as in a capacitor, and make its presence known by an electromotive force. Thus whether an electrometer is considered a current or voltage measuring device depends a good deal on one's point of view and on the way the electrometer is used in a given application.

A "pure" electrometer is inherently an electrostatic instrument. Once it acquires its initial charge, it does not act as a load upon the circuit in which it is inserted. The gold-leaf electroscope is an example of a virtually perfect electrometer. Electric charge is applied to a ter-

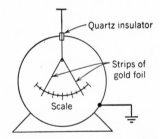

Fig. 7-1. The gold-leaf electroscope.

minal on the case of the instrument. The electrons, being small particles of like charge, repel one another and try to get as far apart as possible. Consequently, they flow to the sheets of gold leaf, causing these sheets to repel each other and bend apart as shown in Fig. 7-1. An indication of the amount of charge is obtained by noting the separation between the leaves.

When used in the manner just described, the electroscope is basically a voltmeter. This is because charge has been injected on a "one shot" basis, producing a voltage

$$E = Q/C \qquad (7\text{-}1)$$

where Q is charge in coulombs, C is capacitance in farads between the gold leaf assembly and the grounded case of the instrument, and E is the potential difference in volts.

On the other hand, the electroscope could be connected to a circuit in which an extremely small current flows, so that charge is accumulated over an extended period of time. The amount of time required for the leaves to spread a given distance is measured, and the current is computed from

$$I = Q/T \qquad (7\text{-}2)$$

where I is average current and T is the time through which the measurement was conducted. The electroscope is now basically an ammeter. Note that it has not changed; only our viewpoint is different. The same situation prevails regarding *electronic* electrometers: they may be voltage, current, or charge-measuring devices depending on the way we interpret their readings.

7-1. Principles of electrometer tubes (1)

Unlike the gold-leaf electroscope, an electrometer using vacuum tubes is not truly electrostatic. The question then is how closely it should approach this condition to merit the name "electrometer." For our purposes, we shall consider a tube to be suited for electrometer service if the input grid has a leakage resistance not less than 10^{16} ohms and a grid direct current in the neighborhood of 10^{-15} ampere. These requirements also indicate the orders of magnitude of current that electrometers are called upon to measure, from about 10^{-15} to 10^{-10} ampere. The higher current range tends to merge with the ratings of the most sensitive conventional galvanometers.

There are three necessary features in a d-c electrometer circuit. These are (1) high input resistance; (2) an indicating device to display the value of the measured quantity; and (3) such additional gain as may be needed to link the input with the output indicator. The input resistance to the over-all circuit will ordinarily be significantly less than the 10^{16} ohms leakage resistance demanded of the tube itself. Something around 10^{10} to 10^{14} ohms would be typical. The output indicator will usually be a microammeter in basic electrometer circuits. In more elaborate electrometers, such as those discussed later in this chapter, almost any type of display could be used. Very little can be said in a general way about the requirements for additional gain, as these will depend on the level of the expected input signal and the amount of power required to operate the chosen output system.

The most basic electrometer circuit is shown in Fig. 7-2. It is seen to be the same as the transfer-characteristic voltmeter of Fig. 3-1. Indeed, the only difference is in the choice of tubes and the extra care required for mechanical and electrical design in the electrometer circuit.

It would appear from the circuit of Fig. 7-2 that high transconductance would be essential to give a reasonable output current, es-

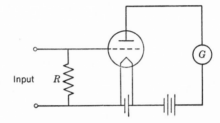

Fig. 7-2. The elementary electrometer circuit.

pecially in view of the extremely low-level input signals. However, high transconductance is associated with large plate current, and a large plate current tends to be accompanied by high grid current. Hence high transconductance is not an unmixed blessing. It is especially important, whatever the actual value of g_m may be, that it remain constant to minimize annoying drift.

As with any d-c amplifier, drift is indeed one of the main problems in electrometers. The need for well-stabilized plate supplies is self-evident. But unlike receiving tubes, the filament circuit of electrometer tubes is of great importance also. In so far as possible, the electron emission and the plate current should be invariant with filament current over a moderate range on both sides of the rated filament current value. Ideally, $dI_b/dI_{fu} = 0$, where I_b is plate current and I_{fu} is filament heating current. A plot of plate current as a function of filament current is shown in Fig. 7-3. A similar curve for a hearing aid type of tube with filamentary cathode is included for comparison. Note that the slope of the curve for the electrometer tube is only about one-third as great as that of the hearing aid tube in the vicinity of rated filament current. It is also desirable that the filament have a low temperature coefficient

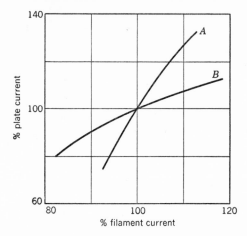

Fig. 7-3. Variation of plate current with filament current in (a) a hearing aid tube and (b) an electrometer tube. (From Victoreen, Reference 1.)

of resistance. The filament is frequently a part of the network of resistors that sets the d-c operating points. A change in the filament resistance may throw the over-all circuit badly out of balance.

The filaments are mounted so as to have minimum contact area with the rest of the tube assembly. This helps prevent variations in thermal losses if the tube is disturbed mechanically. The filament is operated at temperatures where no visible glow can be detected in order to avoid photoemission from other electrodes. The filaments are ordinarily aged at the factory for 100 hours or thereabouts before sale in order to stabilize their emission properties.

The presence of gas in the tube has marked influence upon the grid current. Even with the best possible vacuum, there is enough gas to cause troublesome ionization. This difficulty may be avoided by operating with plate potentials well below the gas ionization voltage. Supply potentials of 4 to 6 volts are common.

In d-c instrument tubes, the filament is part of the network of resistors that determine the over-all operation. Therefore it should ideally have a zero temperature coefficient of resistance. In practice, the change of filament resistance from cold to hot is about 5 per cent. Electrometer tubes should be allowed to operate for 30 to 60 minutes before any measurements are made. This allows thermal equilibrium to be reached in all components. Perhaps more important, the residual gas "cleans up" somewhat during this time, and the rate of gas evolution from hot electrodes comes into equilibrium with the rate of cleanup. Also, during this time any charges that may have accumulated on the tube envelope have an opportunity to leak off or come into some sort of equilibrium condition.

According to published data, the grid current in the Victoreen VX series of electrometer tubes varies with plate voltage approximately as

$$I_g = mE_b^5 \tag{7-3}$$

where m is a constant of the order of 4×10^{-19}, I_g is the grid direct current in amperes, and E_b is the plate voltage in volts. For a fixed plate voltage, grid current increases very rapidly as the grid voltage approaches zero. When the control grid is more negative than about -1.5 volts, the grid current is approximately constant at 4.5×10^{-15} ampere for a plate voltage of 6 volts. In the General Electric GL5740/FP54 electrometer tube, the grid current becomes essentially constant at about 1×10^{-15} ampere for grid voltages more negative than -3.5 volts.

Leakage currents must be avoided very carefully. Insulators in electrometer circuits should preferably be quartz, and the tube should be mounted in an air- and light-tight enclosure with a dessicant. Capacitors in the grid circuit should have dielectrics of pure polystyrene or quartz, with leakage resistance of the order of 10^{17} ohms.

There seem to be two schools of thought on the tube envelopes themselves. Some hold that a graphite coating (such as Aquadag) over most of the envelope helps reduce surface charge effects. Others prefer to keep the entire surface of the envelope absolutely clear. In either case, glass areas must be kept scrupulously clean, free of grease, fingerprints, and lint.

Switches should be avoided because of their capacitance to ground, which may introduce long time constants in the circuit. A capacitance of only 5 $\mu\mu$f becomes a little frightening if it is accompanied by a resistance of 10^{15} ohms! Furthermore, switches may introduce contact potentials.

Whenever possible, electrometers should be used in a shielded room.

7-2. Practical electrometer circuits

The majority of electrometer circuits are either elaborations of the elementary design of Fig. 7-2, or based on the d-c vacuum tube voltmeter

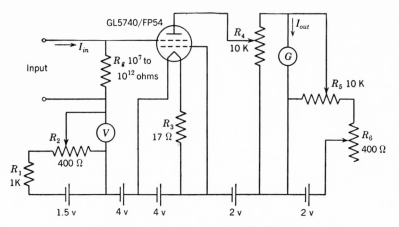

Fig. 7-4. The one-tube electrometer circuit. (Courtesy, General Electric Company.)

of Fig. 3-4(a). The tubes may be either triodes or tetrodes. Tetrodes are preferable because their static characteristics are better for low plate-potential operation in the usual type of circuit.

Figures 7-4 and 7-5 show in detail the circuits of single tube and

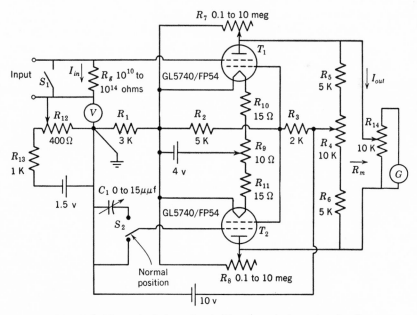

Fig. 7-5. Two-tube balanced or bridge-type electrometer circuit. (Courtesy, General Electric Company.)

bridge-type electrometers (2). Both of these employ tetrode tubes. The circuits would be similar with triodes, but of course there are no screen grids, and there would be some differences in operating potentials and component values.

The single-tube circuit employs the slide-back principle first mentioned in Chapter 3. A measurement is made as follows: disconnect the input from the circuit under test, set voltage V to zero, and balance the galvanometer with the coarse and fine adjustments, R_5 and R_6, so that the output current I_{out} is zero. Then apply the input signal and set the slide-back control R_2 until the galvanometer is again nulled. Then the voltage V is equal to the voltage $I_{in}R_g$, and since R_g is a known resistor in a given case, the value of I_{in} can be readily calculated.

Resistor R_4 is a sensitivity control. For maximum sensitivity, the tap is set to the top of this resistor, and for minimum sensitivity and maximum protection to the galvanometer, it is moved to the bottom. Assuming the maximum sensitivity setting, the performance of the circuit is defined mathematically as follows:

$$g_m = \frac{\partial i_b}{\partial e_g} \cong \frac{\Delta I_{out}}{\Delta I_{in} R_g} = \frac{kd}{I_{in} R_g} \tag{7-4}$$

where i_b and e_g are the plate current and grid voltage, and k and d are the galvanometer sensitivity in amperes per millimeter and deflection in millimeters, respectively. The current amplification is

$$K_I = \frac{\Delta I_{out}}{\Delta I_{in}} = g_m R_g \tag{7-5}$$

Equation (7-5) shows the desirability of making R_g as large as possible. Remember that increasing g_m is usually a self-defeating process, since the grid current rises for larger values of g_m.

The two-tube circuit, being a bridge, is less sensitive to small variations in supply voltages. In fact, such variations may be rendered ineffective over a limited range by proper adjustment of the circuit parameters. Specifically, resistors R_4, R_7, and R_8 may be set so that variations in plate supply voltage will not change the balance of the galvanometer. Likewise, R_9 should be adjusted to make the galvanometer null independent of moderate voltage variations in the filament supply. Resistor R_4 is actually responsible for the initial null balance, while R_7 and R_8 serve to minimize the effects of varying plate potential. However, all four adjustments (R_4, R_7, R_8, and R_9) may have to be made more or less simultaneously, and the optimum adjustment reached by a series of successive approximations. Resistor R_{14} is the galvanometer sensitivity control, serving the same purpose in this circuit that R_4 does in Fig. 7-4.

The inherently greater stability of the bridge arrangement makes possible the use of appreciably larger values of R_g. An advantage of about two orders of magnitude may be gained in the grid resistor over the one-tube circuit. The over-all sensitivity, however, is reduced by a factor of 2 in the bridge. Consequently, an increase in R_g by a factor of 100 will result in a net sensitivity increase of 50 times.

The analysis of Section 3-3 applies exactly to this circuit. It is necessary only to interpret the symbols there in terms of the notation in Fig. 7-5. If we assume identical tubes, and for convenience assume R_4 is exactly center-tapped so that

$$R_5' = R_5 + 0.5R_4 = R_6 + 0.5R_4$$

then the current gain is

$$K_I = \frac{I_{out}}{I_{in}} = \frac{\mu R_5' R_g}{R_m(R_5' + r_p) + 2r_p R_5'} \tag{7-6}$$

where R_m is the resistance looking into the galvanometer with its sensitivity control R_{14}. Equation (7-6) is derived by inspection from Eq. (3-11). Note, however, that the useful sensitivity may be much less than given by Eq. (7-6), since this equation does not include the effect of R_{14} on the galvanometer. The galvanometer and output currents will be the same only if the tap on R_{14} is at the top, and the galvanometer resistance is substantially zero compared with R_{14}.

A method for measuring extremely small currents consists of floating the control grids. The grid of T_2 is connected to capacitor C_1, and resistor R_g is open-circuited. The tap on R_{12} is grounded. Then C_1 is adjusted until the galvanometer ceases to drift. This shows that the voltages developed by grid currents in the two tubes, as they charge their respective grid-to-ground capacitances, are equal, and that the bridge configuration is balancing out the effects of grid current.

Now allow current to flow to the grid of T_1. The input capacitance at this electrode will then charge at a different rate from that at the grid of T_2, and the galvanometer will start to drift again. Assume that R_{14} is set for maximum sensitivity.

$$\frac{dI_{out}}{dt} = \frac{g_m}{2} \frac{de_g}{dt} = \frac{g_m}{2} \frac{I_{in}}{C_{in}} \tag{7-7}$$

so
$$I_{tn} = \frac{2C_{in}}{g_m} \frac{dI_{out}}{dt} \tag{7-8}$$

Example: A galvanometer has a sensitivity of 10^{-10} ampere per milli-meter, and drifts at a rate of 1 mm per second. Here $C_{tn} = 6$ $\mu\mu f$, and $g_m = 20$ μmhos (a typical value in electrometer tubes). Then $I_{tn} = 6 \times 10^{-17}$ ampere. With extreme care, currents as low as 5×10^{-18} ampere may be detected—only 31 electrons per second!

A concluding caution: Electrometer tubes are expensive and must be treated with great respect. Momentary overloads, especially a "high" plate voltage of 15 or 20 volts, can be ruinous to their properties. Every precaution mentioned at the start of this chapter is essential if satisfactory results are to be achieved. The watchmaker's skill, the surgeon's cleanliness, and the patience of Job are vital ingredients of a good electrometer. Finally it should be emphasized that tubes not de-signed for electrometer service cannot be used as substitutes. Even when operated at greatly reduced filament voltage and with plate po-tentials around 4 to 6 volts, typical receiving tubes have grid currents of the order of 10^{-10} ampere.

7-3. Chopper electrometers

We have already discussed two essentially different principles of electrometer design: the mechanical electrometer, of which the gold leaf electroscope is an example; and the vacuum tube electrometer. There is still a third family of electrometers: namely, instruments employing chopper techniques to convert extremely small d-c signals to alternating current for subsequent amplification.

The principle of a chopper is extremely simple, as the sketch in Fig. 7-6 shows. A vibrating reed, represented as a switch in the drawing, alternates between two resistors. The voltage to be measured is mo-mentarily applied across one, during which time no signal is present on the other. Therefore, as the switch moves back and forth, a square wave of voltage appears at the electrometer input. The plate circuit contains a resistor rather than a galvanometer, and the square wave of voltage developed across this resistor is the input to subsequent amplifier stages. These are often tuned to the frequency of the vibrating reed in order to employ narrow bandwidths and eliminate all noise energy except that

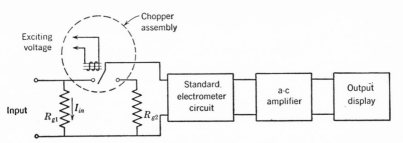

Fig. 7-6. The basic chopper electrometer system.

which falls close to the frequency of the chopper. Such tuned amplifiers must have a wide enough pass band to include any a-c components in the input signal. For example, if the input consists of a d-c signal with 5-cycle a-c components superimposed on it, the bandwidth of the tuned circuits must be at least 10 cycles, centered about the chopper frequency. The frequencies most commonly used for choppers are 60, 400, and 1000 cycles.

At this point, now that all three classes of electrometers have been at least mentioned, it might be useful to draw some comparisons among them. The sensitivity of mechanical electrometers is limited by thermal agitation of the electrons. In the vacuum tube electrometer, it is limited by both thermal agitation and shot noise as far as purely theoretical considerations go. In practice, the problem of drift is usually much worse than noise. Also the tube electrometer may be influenced by stray fields. Chopper electrometers are subject to thermal and shot noise. However, gradually changing supply potentials in their associated amplifiers is no problem, because a-c rather than d-c amplification is employed. Instead, the chopper introduces a different form of drift, namely, random variations in the contact potentials at the switching points.

The advantages of the vacuum tube electrometer over the mechanical type are: (1) it requires less skill to set up for use (we assume the electrometer has already been constructed, and the problem is simply one of connecting it into the circuit being tested); (2) it is far more rugged; and (3) the output may be displayed on an electric meter. Chopper electrometers have the advantages of the vacuum tube type with the additional very significant benefit that direct-coupled amplifiers are eliminated. Many commercial instruments employ chopper techniques. Examples are found in chart recorders made by the Brown Instrument Division of Minneapolis-Honeywell and the Leeds and Northrup Co.

Choppers are also available as separate components for equipment design and construction.

7-4. The dynamic condenser electrometer

An especially elegant form of chopper is the dynamic capacitor electrometer reported by Palevsky, Swank, and Grenchik (*3*). This operates on the principle that if charge is placed on a capacitor and the capaci-

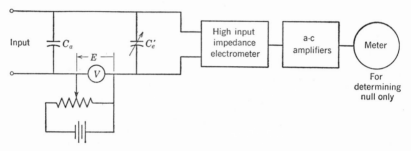

Fig. 7-7. The manually balanced dynamic capacitor electrometer.

tance is varied by mechanical vibration of the plates, an alternating voltage will appear across the capacitor. Figure 7-7 illustrates the basic circuit, arranged for manual operation. We shall also discuss a self-balancing arrangement shortly.

(a) *Manual Balancing.* In the figure, C_e' is the dynamic capacitor, and C_a is a capacitor of known value. The latter quantity includes the output capacitance of the circuit connected to the instrument. The notation is that of Palevsky. If the voltage E is set to zero and a charge Q is delivered to the input terminals, this charge will divide up between C_e' and C_a in the following proportions:

$$Q_e = \frac{QC_e'}{C_e' + C_a} \tag{7-9}$$

$$Q_a = \frac{QC_a}{C_e' + C_a} \tag{7-10}$$

Since charge is placed on C_e' and the plates of C_e' are made to vibrate, a voltage will appear at the input of the electrometer.

Now suppose the voltage E is made a nonzero value. Then from the standpoint of the voltage source E, the capacitors C_e' and C_a are in series (they were in parallel as seen by the input), and each capacitor will acquire the same charge, namely,

$$Q' = E \frac{C_e' C_a}{C_e' + C_a} \tag{7-11}$$

Let E be varied until the charge on C_e' from this source is equal and opposite to that placed there by the input. Then C_e' will have no net charge, and a null will appear at the electrometer output. This means that $Q' + Q_e = 0$, or

$$E \frac{C_e' C_a}{C_e' + C_a} + Q \frac{C_e'}{C_e' + C_a} = 0 \tag{7-12}$$

Solving Eq. (7-12) for E gives

$$E = -Q/C_a \tag{7-13}$$

Therefore E is proportional to the *initial charge* placed on the system. The position of C_a in the denominator of Eq. (7-13) shows the importance of keeping this capacitance small to obtain high sensitivity.

The electrometer itself is not used in an active way in the measurement of charge. It is simply a null indicator. The actual measurement is made with a rugged, low-impedance voltmeter connected to read the voltage E.

The above discussion implies that the potentiometer controlling voltage E would be adjusted by hand. It is also possible to use the amplified output voltage to drive a small servo motor, which automatically moves the potentiometer to a null position. This method is used in a number of instruments, including the Brown and the Leeds and Northrop.

(b) *Automatic Balance.* Instead of using a potentiometer to balance the circuit to a null, a feedback method may be used to obtain a voltage proportional to Q. This approach is shown in Fig. 7-8. The amplifier A

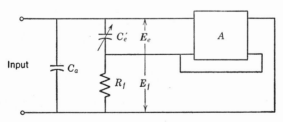

Fig. 7-8. The feedback-balanced dynamic capacitor electrometer.

includes both alternating voltage gain stages and a phase-sensitive rectifier so that the feedback voltage E_f is in the form of direct current, even though E_e, the input voltage from the dynamic capacitor, is alternating. By definition,

$$E_f = -AE_e \tag{7-14}$$

the negative sign indicating that the fed-back voltage must be of such polarity as to oppose the input charge. Then E_e must also be interpreted in a somewhat special way. If we suppose that the plates of the dynamic capacitor are always made to vibrate at a fixed frequency and constant amplitude, then the *alternating voltage* E_e will be proportional only to the *d-c charge* Q_e and the capacitance C'_e of the dynamic capacitor at rest. The proportionality constant we shall assume to be lumped in with the amplifier gain A, so E_e is defined here as

$$E_e = Q_e/C'_e \tag{7-15}$$

The anomaly of dividing a d-c charge by a capacitance and obtaining an rms voltage should cause the reader no trouble as long as it is borne in mind that the proportionality constant, known as the *conversion efficiency*, has been included elsewhere.

Now let us analyze the operation of the system of Fig. 7-8. The voltage E_f is developed through amplification and rectification of E_e. The original charge placed on the system at the input terminals we shall call Q_{eQ}, and the charge contributed by the feedback system Q_{ef}. By analogy with Eqs. (7-9) and (7-11), these charges are

$$Q_{eQ} = \frac{QC'_e}{C'_e + C_a} \tag{7-16}$$

where Q is the total charge from the input source, and

$$Q_{ef} = \frac{E_f C'_e C_a}{C'_e + C_a} \tag{7-17}$$

The total charge on C'_e is the sum of these two contributions.

$$Q_e = Q_{eQ} + Q_{ef} = \frac{C'_e(Q + E_f C_a)}{C'_e + C_a} \tag{7-18}$$

Also, as defined above

$$E_f = -AE_e = -A(Q_e/C'_e) \tag{7-19}$$

Substitute Eq. (7-18) into the last term of Eq. (7-19) and solve for E_f.

$$E_f = -\frac{A}{1 + A} \frac{Q}{C_a + C'_e/(1 + A)} \tag{7-20}$$

Equation (7-20) shows that E_f is a linear function of Q. Since amplifier A may be designed to deliver any desired amount of d-c power, the voltage E_f may be read with a low-impedance D'Arsonval meter.

(c) *The Input Capacitance.* Equation (7-18) may be put into the form

$$Q_e = \frac{C_e' \, [Q - (AQ_e/C_e')C_a]}{C_e' + C_a} \tag{7-21}$$

If this is solved for Q_e, we obtain

$$Q_e = Q \, \frac{C_e'/(1 + A)}{C_a + C_e'/(1 + A)} \tag{7-22}$$

Also, $$Q_a = Q - Q_e = \frac{QC_a}{C_a + C_e'/(1 + A)} \tag{7-23}$$

Equations (7-22) and (7-23) show that the input charge divides as if there were two capacitors in parallel of capacitance C_a and $C_e'/(1 + A)$. Therefore the effective capacitance to the right of the input terminals is

$$C_{in} = C_a + C_e'/(1 + A) \tag{7-24}$$

Only C_e' is reduced in magnitude, since C_a lies without the feedback loop.

(d) *Freedom from Drift with Changing Gain.* As in the simple feedback circuits studied in Chapter 4, the performance of this electrometer system is largely independent of the forward gain, provided this gain is relatively large. This may be proved by differentiating Eq. (7-20) with respect to A.

$$\frac{dE_f}{dA} = \frac{-Q(C_e' + C_a)}{[C_e' + C_a(1 + A)]^2} \tag{7-25}$$

Divide both sides of Eq. (7-25) by E_f and multiply both sides by A. Substitute Eq. (7-20) for E_f on the right-hand side. This leads to

$$\frac{dE_f}{E_f} = \frac{dA}{A} \, \frac{1}{1 + A} \, \frac{C_e' + C_a}{C_a + C_e'/(1 + A)} \tag{7-26}$$

If we assume that $C_e'/(1 + A) \ll C_a$, Eq. (7-26) simplifies somewhat to

$$\frac{dE_f}{E_f} = \frac{dA/A}{1 + A} \left(1 + \frac{C_e'}{C_a}\right) \tag{7-27}$$

Equation (7-27) may be interpreted as showing that the percentage change in E_f is proportional to $1/(1 + A)$ times the percentage change in A. If A is very large initially, the value of A may vary a good deal without introducing appreciable error in E_f. (Since all the voltage E_f

is fed back, this circuit is represented by the case of $\beta = 1$ in Fig. 4-2. The quantity A in this discussion is therefore equal to the quantity $-\beta K$ of Chapter 4.)

(e) *Circuit Noise.* The theoretical limit to the usefulness of this electrometer is the random noise appearing in various portions of the input circuit. This may be investigated with the aid of the detailed drawing of the input assembly in Fig. 7-9.

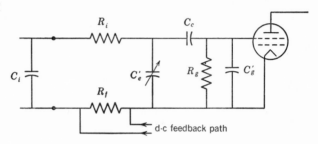

Fig. 7-9. The complete input circuit.

In this drawing, C_i represents the capacitance of the source of charge under measurement, C_c is a coupling capacitor for blocking direct current from the electrometer tube grid, C_g' represents the input capacitance to the electrometer tube, and R_i is an input buffer resistor to help prevent the capacitance C_i from shunting C_e'. Proper isolation by this resistor requires that

$$R_i C_e' \gg 1/f_e \qquad (7\text{-}28)$$

where f_e is the frequency of the vibrating capacitor. Likewise, if R_g is not to shunt C_e' to any appreciable extent, it is required that

$$R_g C_e' \gg 1/f_e \qquad (7\text{-}29)$$

The value of C_c is usually made about the same as that of C_e' when the latter is at rest.

One effect of the added circuit components is to increase the apparent capacitance of the variable capacitor from C_e' to a new value.

$$C_e = C_e' + C_c \qquad (7\text{-}30)$$

This is because the right-hand plate of C_c eventually reaches ground potential *for direct current* as C_c charges through R_i and R_g. Thus for direct current, C_e' and C_c are effectively in parallel. However, C_c obviously does not vibrate when C_e' does, and furthermore, *as far as a-c signals go,* C_c and C_g' act as a capacitance voltage divider, reducing the alternating voltage reaching the grid. These two factors decrease the conversion efficiency, which is equivalent to reducing the forward gain A of the over-all system.

As seen from the grid of the tube looking to the left, the total capacitance is C'_g shunted by the series combination of C_c and C'_e. This total capacitance is defined as

$$C_g = C'_g + \frac{C'_e C_c}{C'_e + C_c} \qquad (7\text{-}31)$$

Finally, we must define a factor that shows what fraction of the noise arising in the grid circuit appears to be associated with C'_e alone. This quantity is called K.

$$K = \frac{C_c}{C'_e + C_c} = \frac{C_c}{C_e} \qquad (7\text{-}32)$$

Note that K is always less than 1.

The derivation of the equivalent noise input is rather involved, but the end result is given as Eq. (7-33). The charge Q_o expressed there is the amount of charge in coulombs that *appears* to be at the input circuit as a result of the noise that is *actually* there.

$$Q_o = \left[kTC_e + \frac{K^2 C_e^2}{2C_g} (2kT + eI_g R_g) \right]^{1/2} \qquad (7\text{-}33)$$

Here k is Boltzmann's constant, 1.38×10^{-23}, T is temperature in degrees Kelvin, and I_g is the sum of the absolute values of all grid currents, both electron and positive ion. Note that 1 $\mu\mu$a of electron current and 1 $\mu\mu$a of positive ion current do not cancel; rather, I_g would be 2 $\mu\mu$a.

Frequently, the first term inside the bracket of Eq. (7-33) is large compared with the second, and it is a reasonable approximation to say

$$Q_o \cong (kTC_e)^{1/2} \qquad (7\text{-}34)$$

This approximation is not always very reliable, and should be checked for a given circuit. When it does hold, the value of Q_o may be expressed in terms of the number of *electronic charges* as

$$Q_o \cong 450 C_e^{1/2} \qquad (7\text{-}35)$$

for T equal to room temperature and C_e expressed directly in micromicro-farads. Thus if the approximations of Eq. (7-34) hold, and $C_e = 49$ $\mu\mu$f, for example, then $Q_o = 450 \times 7 = 3150$ electrons. This is the charge that would give the same effect at the input terminals of a *noiseless* circuit as noise causes in the physically extant circuit. Here Q_o is the theoretical lower limit of sensitivity of the dynamic capacitor electrometer. Charges less than Q_o are measured with ever-decreasing reliability as the input charge decreases relative to Q_o. Feedback will not reduce Q_o, since Q_o is *referred to the input*. Of course, feedback does help combat noise arising elsewhere than in the input stage.

(f) *Mechanical Details.* The main considerations in the mechanical assembly are ruggedness, simplicity, freedom from microphonics, and freedom from drift. The first amplifier stage should use a tube of good mechanical design with low grid current. The over-all amplifier circuit should pass as narrow a band of frequencies as possible, centered, of course, about f_e. Also, the frequency f_e should be well away from any mechanical resonant frequency of the tubes or other components in order to avoid microphonics.

The dynamic capacitor itself should be designed for maximum change in capacitance and minimum stray capacitance. The latter is especially important, as it limits the former. Also, great care must be taken to guard against changes in the contact potential between the capacitor plates. Even though these plates never touch each other physically, changes in the contact potentials of the surfaces are equivalent to placing an input charge in the system. The technique of construction described by Palevsky is to use ferromagnetic material for the plates in order that they may be moved by an electromagnet. This steel material is then gold-plated, first with several layers of 16 karat gold, and finally with 24 karat. The final plating is done by gold evaporation. During assembly, the plates are continually blown by nitrogen jets to keep them clean. The final assembly is hermetically sealed in argon, after having been filled with argon and evacuated several times in succession. This treatment results in capacitor plates that are clean to start with, and have very little chance of becoming contaminated later. Since changes in contact potentials can arise only from changes in the surfaces of the plates, there is good reason to expect excellent stability of contact potential over a long period of time. A drift of $\frac{1}{10}$ mv per 24 hr may reasonably be expected with a carefully made capacitor.

It was mentioned at the end of Section 7-4a that automatic nulling or self-balancing of the electrometer can be achieved by using the manual circuit of Fig. 7-7 with a servo motor to adjust the potentiometer. The easiest way to implement this idea in practice is to vibrate the capacitor at 60 cycles from the power lines, amplify the 60-cycle voltage generated in the capacitor, and apply it to one winding of a 60-cycle two-phase motor. The other winding of the motor is connected to the power line, through a phase shifting network if necessary. The direction and speed of rotation of the motor will depend on the a-c signal from the electrometer, and this depends in turn on the *polarity* and *magnitude* of the d-c charge on the capacitor. The motor drives the shaft of the potentiometer to provide automatic nulling. The potentiometer shaft may be geared to a pointer or recording pen if a permanent ink record is desired. It is perfectly feasible to replace the vibrating reed type chopper of

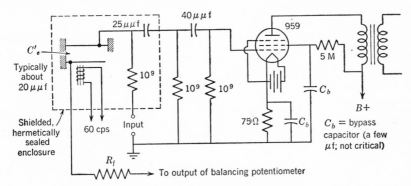

Fig. 7-10. Palevsky's preamplifier. The tube is selected for low grid current, I_g.

commercial recording d-c millivoltmeters with the dynamic capacitor assembly and a suitable preamplifier.

One such preamplifier is shown in Fig. 7-10. The tube, type 959, is an "acorn" pentode. It must be selected especially for low grid current, I_g. Essentially the same circuit configuration, but with different values of the components, could be used with standard electrometer tubes, such as the Victoreen VX series, or the General Electric GL5740/FP54.

REFERENCES

1. John A. Victoreen, "Electrometer Tubes for the Measurement of Small Current," *Proc. I.R.E.* (1949), vol. 37, p. 432.
2. General Electric Company, Data sheets for tube type GL5740/FP54. *Electronic Tube Manual, Industrial Types.*
3. H. Palevsky, R. K. Swank, and R. Grenchik, "Design of Dynamic Condenser Electrometers," *Rev. Sci. Instr.* (May 1947), vol. 18, p. 298.

Chapter 8

ELECTRONIC WATTMETERS

The problem of measuring power by electronic methods is one of the more difficult tasks in the area of electronic instrumentation. To the best of the author's knowledge, there is no good, simple electronic watt-meter circuit. The circuits that might by any stretch of the imagination be called "simple" usually place very demanding requirements upon their components. In particular, it is often necessary to postulate square law behavior in certain tubes. The crux of the problem is that power is a *product, EI* cos θ. The simplest way to multiply with tubes is to employ their nonlinearities, but this is a rather undependable process. Analog or digital computer techniques come to mind as a solution, but with them comes much circuit complexity. Accordingly, this chapter is more a report on the current state of the electronic watt-meter art than a treatise on how to measure power electronically.

8-1. Two phases of the power measurement problem

The foregoing pessimistic remarks apply to one type of power measurement only: that which involves attaching a wattmeter to a purely arbitrary load of any impedance and phase angle and finding the product *EI* cos θ. There is a second type of power measurement that is fairly straightforward. That is the determination of the power output from a source. If it appears at first that this is a semantic quibble, the author wishes to point out a very basic difference in the philosophy of measurement. The problem of finding the power flowing into an arbitrary load is a true wattmeter problem. On the other hand, if one wishes to measure the power that a source is capable of delivering, it is necessary only to provide a matched, resistive load. This is relatively easy anyplace in the frequency band, from direct current to microwave.

Accordingly, in this chapter we must deal with two different power-measuring problems, one quite easy and the other very difficult. We shall start with the simple case first.

8-2. Methods of determining output power

When the problem is simply one of determining the power a signal generator can supply to a resistive load, there are a number of simple, effective approaches. The first is shown in Fig. 8-1. This is a calorim-

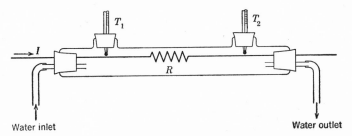

Fig. 8-1. The calorimeter.

eter, in which water cools a resistor. The power developed in this resistive load is obviously I^2R. Inlet water temperature is indicated by thermometer T_1 and outlet temperature by T_2. The power expended in heating the water is proportional to the rate of flow of the water times the temperature differential. Expressed in watts, this is

$$P = 4185(T_2 - T_1)V \qquad (8\text{-}1)$$

where T_2 and T_1 are, respectively, the outlet and inlet temperatures in degrees centigrade, V is the flow in liters per second, and P is power in watts.

This technique for determining power is extremely accurate. It is, of course, slow. Time must be allowed for the thermal steady-state to be reached by all pieces of the apparatus. The result is an "average" power measurement. Minor fluctuations in the load current lasting for a few seconds would never be detected. Radiation, conduction, and convection losses around the calorimeter will introduce small errors. The worst feature of the technique is that it is inherently troublesome. Water and electric equipment have a natural antipathy to each other, and laboratory glassware and sinks are not always readily available.

In spite of these objections, the calorimeter is a fairly useful and popular method when high power is involved. It may be used as shown over the frequency spectrum from direct current to the start of the microwave region, and is readily extended to higher frequencies by allowing the cooling water to flow over the end of a waveguide fitted with a suitable power-absorbing termination.

Figure 8-2 is another system useful chiefly at audio frequencies. Taps on the transformer secondary are changed until the voltmeter

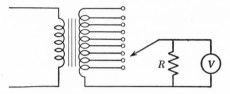

Fig. 8-2. Impedance-matching transformer.

reading is a maximum. This shows the optimum impedance match has been achieved. The input power, neglecting losses in the transformer, is then E^2/R, where E is the voltmeter reading. In practice, the voltmeter is usually calibrated to read watts directly, R being fixed at the time the circuit is designed. The range of the instrument may be extended by using different values of R, or by providing for various multiplier resistors to be placed in series with the voltmeter.

A system employing a photometer for substitution measurements is shown in Fig. 8-3. This method is used fairly often for measurements of radio frequency power. With sufficient care, it can be very accurate indeed. The switch is initially placed in position 1, and the grease spot

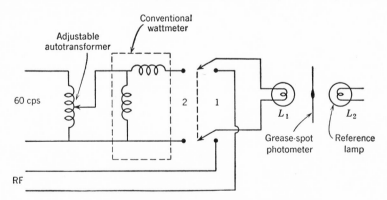

Fig. 8-3. Substitution measurement with photometer.

photometer is placed in such a position that it receives equal illumination from lamp 1 (the radio frequency load) and lamp 2. This condition is evident when the grease spot disappears. Then the switch is thrown to position 2, and the autotransformer is adjusted until the spot again disappears. When this happens, lamp 1 is receiving as much power from the 60-cycle line as it formerly did from the radio frequency source. The radio frequency power is therefore equal to the 60-cycle power shown by the wattmeter. The method is most commonly used for power from about ten to a few hundred watts, but without much trouble can be extended in either direction.

8-3. Impedance-matching attenuator pads

It is often necessary in measuring the output of high-power devices to reduce the power to a more convenient level for instrumentation. The functions of attenuation and impedance matching can usually be combined in a resistive T attenuator. This section presents the design equations for such a T pad, and defines the limits of their applicability. The derivation is rather lengthy, but consists of essentially routine algebra. Its inclusion in full does not seem justified.

The problem is to devise an attenuator that presents an input impedance R_g to the source, an output impedance R_L to the load, and has a power attenuation of A, where A is the ratio

$$A = \frac{\text{available power from source}}{\text{power delivered to load}} \qquad (8\text{-}2)$$

The attenuator and its components are shown in Fig. 8-4.

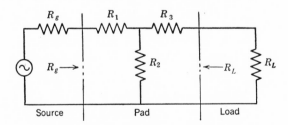

Fig. 8-4. The impedance-matching T pad.

Let a quantity α be defined as

$$\alpha = R_L/R_g \qquad (8\text{-}3)$$

Then
$$R_1 = \frac{R_g}{A - 1} (A + 1 - 2\sqrt{A\alpha}) \tag{8-4}$$

$$R_2 = \frac{R_g}{A - 1} (2\sqrt{A\alpha}) \tag{8-5}$$

$$R_3 = \frac{R_g}{A - 1} (A\alpha + \alpha - 2\sqrt{A\alpha}) \tag{8-6}$$

For certain combinations of A and α, negative values are obtained for one or more of the resistors R_1, R_2, and R_3. Figure 8-5 shows when

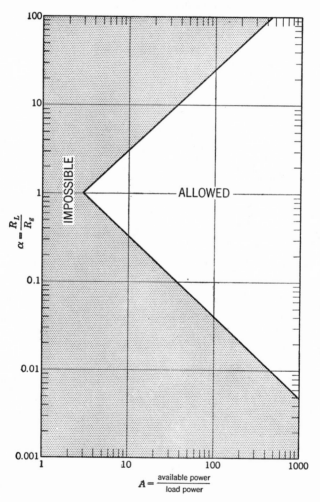

Fig. 8-5. Region of applicability of Eqs. (8-4) to (8-6).

this will occur. The boundaries are straight lines on log-log paper, and may be extrapolated indefinitely. Any proposed design should be checked for feasibility on this chart before spending time in the computation of resistor values. As long as the point defined by coordinates (A,α) falls within the *allowed* region, *both* the impedance match and the desired attenuation may be achieved.

8-4. Self-balancing power bridges

Section 6-5 described a voltmeter that measures true rms voltage by a feedback method. Power supplied from an external source to heat the filament of a diode is neutralized by reduction of a d-c heating current, and the *change* in this direct current is a measure of the input to the instrument. This voltmeter may be used for the type of power measurements we are discussing. It is necessary only to provide for coupling the power from the signal source into the filament of the diode. A resistive impedance-matching T pad of the type described in Section 8-3 is suitable for such an application.

There are other feedback circuits that may be used to measure power. Most of these employ bridges with a bolometer as a heat-sensing element $(1,2)$. A bolometer is a fine wire with a high temperature coefficient of resistivity. Historically, the first bolometers were instrument fuses, and the symbol for a bolometer is still the same as that for a fuse. A bolometer may be heated by microwave energy, infrared, or visible light, and requires no direct electric connections to deliver input power. For this reason, bolometer bridges are especially suited to microwave power measurements.

These bridges may be extraordinarily sensitive. As an example, the radiant energy of components in the luminous spectrum of a star may be measured by moving a bolometer across the pattern produced by a prism or diffraction grating. One of the author's colleagues reported a mysterious, erratic performance in a bolometer that eventually was traced to a lighted cigarette many feet away.

One form of a self-balancing bolometer bridge is shown in Fig. 8-6. Radiant energy falling on the bolometer unbalances the bridge, and causes a voltage to appear at the input of the amplifier. This amplified voltage drives one phase of a two-phase servomotor. The other motor winding is connected to the power line as a reference. In this way, the direction of the motor's rotation becomes a function of the direction of

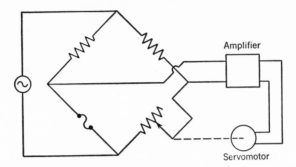

Fig. 8-6. One form of self-balancing bolometer bridge.

unbalance of the bridge. The motor drives the potentiometer in such a direction as to restore balance. Since the initial unbalance is a function of the power reaching the bolometer, this power is measured indirectly by the position of the potentiometer after the new balance is achieved.

A different principle is used in the bridge of Fig. 8-7, which is the heart of the Hewlett-Packard Model 430C Microwave Power Meter.

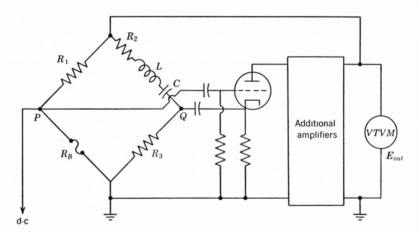

Fig. 8-7. A self-balancing bridge as the beta network of an oscillator.

In this system, the bolometer bridge is the feedback network of an oscillator, and a stable, linear amplifier of constant gain provides the forward gain K. As explained in Section 4-7, if the product of the forward gain and the feedback factor β is identically unity at zero phase angle, steady-state oscillation results. Now if K is a fixed quantity, and oscillation is to be achieved, β must also be fixed.

The feedback factor β is the ratio of the potential difference between points P and Q to E_{out}. That is,

$$\beta = \frac{E_{PQ}}{E_{out}} \tag{8-7}$$

It may be seen by inspection that E_{PQ} is

$$E_{PQ} = \left(\frac{R_B}{R_B + R_1} - \frac{R_3}{R_2 + R_3}\right) E_{out} \tag{8-8}$$

assuming that the resistors between grid and ground and cathode and ground are large enough to neglect, and assuming further that L and C are in series resonance so that R_2 is the only impedance in the LCR_2 portion of the bridge. Now if Eq. (8-8) is divided by E_{out} to obtain β and if R_1, R_2, and R_3 are constant, it is obvious that R_B must also be a constant if β is to have a fixed value. The only way this can happen, if R_B is temperature-sensitive and affected by incident microwave or radiant energy, is for the bridge-driving voltage E_{out} to decrease exactly enough to offset the added energy received through radiation.

An adjustable d-c source is provided for setting the initial temperature of the bolometer. This determines the initial output voltage from the bridge and amplifier combination, and serves as a zero set for the vacuum tube voltmeter. If radiant heating power is supplied to the bolometer from an external source, and R_B and β attempt to change, the output voltage will decrease exactly enough to let the bolometer cool to its original temperature and restore β to the value such that $\beta K \equiv 1$. The actual measurement of the input power to the bolometer is made indirectly through reading the vacuum tube voltmeter, which may be calibrated in watts for convenience.

Care must be taken to design the bridge so that a change in E_{out} will *restore initial conditions* rather than drive R_B further from its correct value. Otherwise, a cumulative, unsuccessful attempt at correction will be made by the circuit, causing it to "run away." By proper arrangement of the bridge, a thermistor may be used instead of a bolometer.

8-5. Some elementary wattmeters reading $EI \cos \theta$

We have just studied several methods for determining the output power from a source. The measurement of power delivered to a load presents somewhat more of a challenge. The problem arises quite often when loads of a practical nature are considered. For example, the ordinary direct-radiator cone loudspeaker presents a reactive load to its source at almost all frequencies. Since the power factor is not unity in general, the product EI is meaningless even though the voltage and current are both measured very easily. It is essential to take into account the phase angle between the voltage and current.

Several fairly simple direct-reading electronic wattmeters have been proposed, but none have come into general use. We shall discuss two types, primarily to point out their inherent difficulties.

(a) *The Square-Law Principle (3,4).* One type of electronic watt-meter, operating on a square-law principle, is shown in Fig. 8-8. Resis-

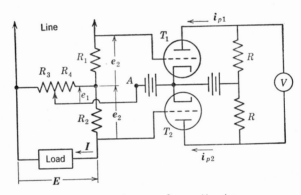

Fig. 8-8. A square-law wattmeter.

tors R_1 and R_2 are equal, and given different names simply for identification. The same is true of R_3 and R_4, which are the two halves of a potentiometer. A matched pair of precision resistors could be used as well; R_1 and R_2 are very small, of the order of a few ohms. Their purpose is to give a voltage proportional to the load current. Furthermore, it is necessary to assume that e_1 is one-half the load voltage E, which means that the IR drop in R_1 and R_2 must be much less than e_1.

Relative to point A, the alternating voltage applied to the grid of T_1 is $e_1 + e_2$; that on the grid of T_2 is $e_1 - e_2$. If *the tubes operate in a square-law region,* then the a-c components of their plate currents are

$$i_{p1} = k(e_1 + e_2)^2 = ke_1^2 + ke_2^2 + 2ke_1e_2 \qquad (8\text{-}9)$$

$$i_{p2} = k(e_1 - e_2)^2 = ke_1^2 + ke_2^2 - 2ke_1e_2 \qquad (8\text{-}10)$$

$$\text{meter voltage} = V = R(i_{p1} - i_{p2}) = 4ke_1e_2R \tag{8-11}$$

Suppose $e_1 = A \sin \omega t$ and $e_2 = B \sin (\omega t + \theta)$. Then

$$V = 4kRAB(\sin \omega t)[\sin (\omega t + \theta)] \tag{8-12}$$

Expanding the product of the sines in Eq. (8-12) leads to a more convenient expression,

$$V = 2kRAB \,[\cos \theta - \cos (2\omega t + \theta)] \tag{8-13}$$

If the meter is a D'Arsonval type, it will respond only to the first term of Eq. (8-13), giving as its indication

$$V_{dc} = 2kRAB \cos \theta \tag{8-14}$$

Since A is proportional to the load voltage and B to the load current, the voltage V_{dc} is a true measure of the power delivered to the load.

If more than one frequency component is present in the energy supplied to the load, the meter gives a direct voltage proportional to the sum of the powers delivered by each frequency. Thus, if

$$e_1 = A_1 \sin \omega_1 t + A_2 \sin \omega_2 t \tag{8-15}$$

and

$$e_2 = B_1 \sin (\omega_1 t + \theta_1) + B_2 \sin (\omega_2 t + \theta_2) \tag{8-16}$$

then

$$V_{dc} = 2kRA_1B_1 \cos \theta_1 + 2kRA_2B_2 \cos \theta_2 \tag{8-17}$$

It is reassuring that in spite of the square-law operation, there are no spurious terms in Eq. (8-17) involving the product of a voltage at one frequency and a current of a different frequency.

This appears to be an excellent wattmeter in principle, but it is limited in practice by the fact that the tubes *must* operate in a square-law region. Hence they can accommodate only a narrow range of signal amplitudes before entering a region of at least approximately linear operation. One can never be absolutely certain the signal levels are correct. Furthermore, small changes in the quiescent operating points of the tubes may lead to departures from square-law behavior. If the tubes are not matched, the proportionality factor k will be different in Eq. (8-10) from that in Eq. (8-9), and there will not be perfect cancellation of the terms involving e_1^2 and e_2^2. In this event, additional d-c terms will be introduced in the reading of the voltmeter. These terms are not a measure of power, but arise from squaring the sinusoidal functions e_1 and e_2 individually. All in all, square-law operation is a very shaky proposition. It is interesting in theory, but the practical difficulties are such that this type of wattmeter has not come into general use.

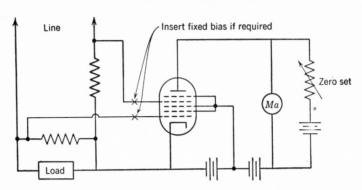

Fig. 8-9. The Pierce wattmeter.

(b) *The Linear Principle.* An electronic wattmeter operating on a linear principle has been proposed by Pierce (*5*). This circuit employs tubes with several grids, using one grid to sample voltage across the load, and a different grid to sample a voltage proportional to the load current. The arrangement is shown in Fig. 8-9.

The key to an understanding of the operation lies in the way currents are distributed among the various grids in the tube. An enlargement of the inside of the tube is shown in Fig. 8-10. At the cathode, a

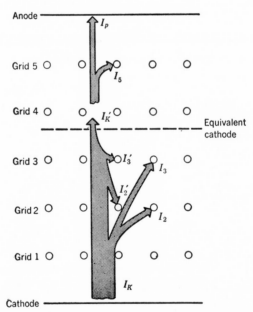

Fig. 8-10. Distribution of currents in tube of Fig. 8-9.

total current I_K is emitted. The magnitude of this current is determined for all practical purposes by the fixed potentials at grids 2 and 3, and the varying potential of grid 1. Grids 4, 5, and the anode are effectively shielded from the cathode by the other grids, and play essentially no part in determining the value of I_K. As I_K starts across the tube, part of it is bled away by grids 2 and 3, both on the initial upward path (I_2 and I_3) and in the form of electrons repelled back from the vicinity of grid 4 (I_2' and I_3'). The current that eventually crosses the dividing line between grids 3 and 4 is

$$I_K' = Ge_{g1} \qquad (8\text{-}18)$$

where G has the dimensions of conductance, but is *not* the ordinary mutual conductance, g_m, of the tube. As far as the anode and grids 4 and 5 are concerned, the plane between grid 3 and grid 4 is like a cathode, which "emits" electrons in accordance with the law expressed in Eq. (8-18).

Now we must postulate that

$$I_p = I_K' \alpha e_{g4} \qquad (8\text{-}19)$$

where α is a proportionality constant having the dimensions of reciprocal voltage. Combining Eqs. (8-18) and (8-19),

$$I_p = \alpha G e_{g1} e_{g4} \qquad (8\text{-}20)$$

If $e_{g1} = K_1 \sin \omega t$ and $e_{g4} = K_2 \sin (\omega t + \theta)$, Eq. (8-20) may be put in the form

$$I_p = \tfrac{1}{2}\alpha G K_1 K_2 [\cos \theta - \cos (2\omega t + \theta)] \qquad (8\text{-}21)$$

Only the first term of Eq. (8-21) will be indicated by a d-c meter movement. This indication gives the load power, since it is proportional to the product of the load voltage, load current, and the power-factor angle. The quiescent current is neutralized by the zero-set circuit, and does not enter into the discussion.

It is important to note that *linear* relationships are assumed between I_K' and e_{g1} and between I_p and e_{g4}. This is as serious a drawback as was the requirement for absolutely square-law operation in the previous circuit. The effects of nonlinearity may be reduced by using two pentagrid tubes in a push-pull configuration, as described in Pierce's paper.

8-6. The double-modulator wattmeter

A wattmeter employing a system of double modulation has been described by Garrett and Cole (*6*). The circuit is much more elaborate than those described previously in this chapter, and contains some interesting features that we shall describe in detail.

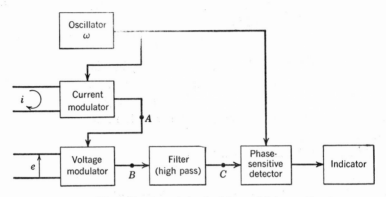

Fig. 8-11. Block diagram of the double-modulator wattmeter.

The system is shown in block diagram form in Fig. 8-11. The current i is the load current, and e is the load voltage. These are of the form

$$i = I_m \sin qt \tag{8-22}$$

$$e = E_m \sin (qt + \theta) \tag{8-23}$$

The current i flows through a small resistance, between 4 and 40 ohms, to obtain a voltage for use in the current modulator. After modulation of a much higher carrier frequency ω by this voltage, we are at point A in the block diagram, where the signal is of the form

$$e_A = K_1 i \cos \omega t = K_1 I_m \sin qt \cos \omega t \tag{8-24}$$

This voltage e_A in turn becomes a carrier, which is modulated by the load voltage e in the voltage modulator.

The voltage modulator is a balanced modulator, similar in principle to the simplified balanced modulator shown in Fig. 8-12 (*7*). The circuit details are quite different, since the voltage e_A is introduced through a capacitor coupling, and $K_2 e$ is introduced through direct-coupled phase inverters. However, the action is a little easier to visualize from the transformer-coupled configuration. As shown in Eq. (8-24), e_A is

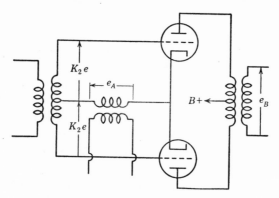

Fig. 8-12. Balanced modulator.

the output from the current modulator, and K_2e is some fraction of the load voltage.

The output from the balanced modulator is found at point B in Fig. 8-11. It is

$$e_B = K_3(\alpha_1 K_2 e + 2\alpha_2 K_2 e e_A)$$ (8-25)

where K_3 is a proportionality constant, and α_1 and α_2 are tube coefficients relating the plate current to the grid voltage:

$$i_p = \alpha_1 e_g + \alpha_2 e_g^2$$ (8-26)

The parameters α_1 and α_2 are presumed equal for both tubes. This is a shaky assumption, and indeed was the main difficulty in the square-law wattmeter of Section 8-4. However, Garrett and Cole report that satisfactory matching between tubes can be obtained by individual adjustments of their grid bias.

If we substitute Eqs. (8-23) and (8-24) into Eq. (8-25), it is found that

$$e_B = K_3[\alpha_1 K_2 E_m \sin(qt + \theta)$$
$$+ 2\alpha_2 K_2 E_m \sin(qt + \theta)K_1 I_m \sin qt \cos \omega t_p]$$ (8-27)

The filter removes the low-frequency term involving q alone. The remaining voltage appearing at point C is

$$e_C = [\alpha_2 K_1 K_2 I_m E_m \cos \theta - \alpha_2 K_1 K_2 I_m E_m \cos(2qt + \theta)] \cos \omega t]$$ (8-28)

The quantity in brackets is the amplitude of the carrier signal ω. When the signal of Eq. (8-28) is demodulated, two components are produced. One is a d-c component proportional to $I_m E_m \cos \theta$, and therefore indicates the average power taken by the load. The second term is a double-frequency function relative to q, and represents the *instantaneous* power taken by the load. The former may be read by a D'Arsonval meter; the latter may be observed on an oscilloscope. Since instantaneous power is negative during part of each cycle (except when θ is zero radians), a phase-sensitive detector must be employed to preserve the sense of this quantity.

A somewhat simplified phase-sensitive detector is illustrated in Fig. 8-13. Here e_R is a reference voltage at the frequency ω, while e_C is the voltage appearing at point C, and given in Eq. (8-28). The peak value of e_R, which we shall call $E_{R\,max}$, must be greater than the peak value of e_C for correct operation. The frequency q is assumed sufficiently smaller than ω so that over several cycles of ω, the bracketed coefficient of $\cos \omega t$ in Eq. (8-28) is constant. This is an "instantaneous peak," so to speak. It is not necessarily the largest value the coefficient may assume, but it *is* the peak value of Eq. (8-28) during a period of time lasting a few cycles of ω. We shall call this quantity $e_{C\,max}$. The main point to keep in mind about $e_{C\,max}$ is that it is constant over a short time (say a microsecond, for example), but does in fact vary with time at the angular frequency q.

In the phase-sensitive detector, capacitor C_1 charges to a voltage of

$$|e_{c1}| = E_{R\,max} + e_{C\,max} = E_M \qquad (8\text{-}29)$$

while C_2 acquires a voltage of

$$|e_{c2}| = E_{R\,max} - e_{C\,max} = -E_N \qquad (8\text{-}30)$$

$$e_{out} = \frac{E_M + E_N}{2} \qquad (8\text{-}31)$$

Substitution of Eqs. (8-29) and (8-30) in Eq. (8-31) shows

$$e_{out} = e_{C\,max} \qquad (8\text{-}32)$$

and therefore is a representation of the coefficient of Eq. (8-28) as a function of time. A d'Arsonval meter at the output terminals displays the first term in this coefficient, and therefore gives the average power. An oscilloscope connected to the output portrays the entire coefficient as a function of time, and hence the instantaneous power through a cycle of the frequency q may be examined.

Both Figs. 8-12 and 8-13 are considerably simplified from those in the Garrett and Cole wattmeter. The greatest difference is that the circuits given here employ input transformers as a matter of simplicity. This does not invalidate the analysis, except if $q \to 0$.

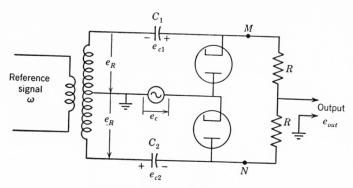

Fig. 8-13. Phase-sensitive detector.

In the foregoing treatment, the current modulator was passed by rather quickly. This was done in order to avoid a lengthy break in the general flow of discussion. The current modulator is a very interesting circuit, but a rather tricky one to analyze. The author feels it deserves some additional explanation.

An equivalent circuit of the current modulator is shown in Fig. 8-14. Here e_ω is the carrier voltage, represented by a lower-case letter since we are concerned with its instantaneous values during a given cycle, and E_q is shown as a direct voltage, since the frequency q is sufficiently small compared with ω that any voltage at frequency q is constant during one cycle of ω. The voltage E_q is equal to iR_1 where i is the load current, and R_1 is a small resistor through which i flows to obtain a voltage proportional to current. The resistor-current combination is equivalent to the battery in Fig. 8-14. The forward resistance of the diodes is represented by R_4; R_2 and R_3 are resistors of 15,000 ohms value.

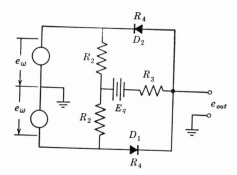

Fig. 8-14. Equivalent circuit of the current modulator.

Now the business at hand is to show that the amplitude of e_A as given by Eq. (8-24) is indeed proportional to i and the voltage E_q produced by i. To do this, we must examine the output waveform of the current modulator. This is essentially a truncated half sine wave, as

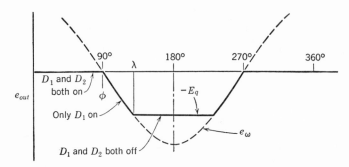

Fig. 8-15. Output of the current modulator (heavy solid line). Dotted line shows portion of one cycle of carrier frequency.

sketched in Fig. 8-15. For small values of E_q, it approaches a square wave.

The waveform of e_{out} consists of three portions: one when both diodes D_1 and D_2 conduct; a second when D_1 conducts alone; and a third when both diodes are off. Reversing the polarity of E_q will invert the drawing of Fig. 8-15, and cause D_2 rather than D_1 to conduct alone for part of the cycle. However, this does not affect the discussion in any material way.

We shall define the carrier as

$$e_\omega = E_{\omega\,max} \cos \omega t \tag{8-33}$$

The angle ϕ in electrical degrees at which diode 2 turns off is

$$\phi = \text{arc cos} \frac{\beta E_q}{E_{\omega\,max}} \tag{8-34}$$

where β is a constant for the circuit defined by

$$\beta = \frac{R_4}{R_2 + 2R_3 + R_4} \tag{8-35}$$

Within slide rule accuracy, ϕ is almost identically 90° for any practical values of circuit parameters. Diode 1 stops conducting at the angle λ defined by

$$\lambda = \text{arc cos} \frac{-E_q}{E_{\omega\,max}} \tag{8-36}$$

The output voltages during the several portions of the cycle are

Both diodes on:

$$e_{out} = \frac{-E_q R_4}{R_2 + 2R_3 + R_4} \tag{8-37}$$

D_1 conducting alone:

$$e_{out} = \frac{e_\omega(R_2 + 2R_3) - 2E_q R_4}{R_2 + 2R_3 + R_4} \tag{8-38}$$

Both diodes off:

$$e_{out} = -E_q \tag{8-39}$$

From Eqs. (8-34) through (8-39), the output waveform may be constructed, and a Fourier analysis is then performed to determine its harmonic content. In particular, we are interested in the relationship between the fundamental frequency amplitude (i.e., the amplitude of the component at an angular frequency ω) and the value of E_q. The waveform in Fig. 8-15 is obviously rich in harmonics, but all save the fundamental are removed by a tuned circuit at the output of the current modulator. Therefore the voltage e_A contains only a cos ωt term, as was stated in Eq. (8-24). The synthesis and Fourier analysis of e_{out} are straightforward but tedious, and only the results are presented. These are shown as Fig. 8-16, which gives the amplitude of the cos ωt

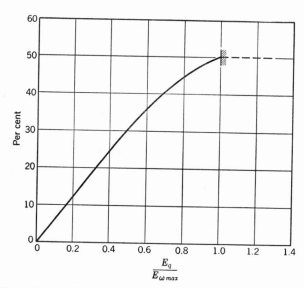

Fig. 8-16. Amplitude of carrier frequency component of e_{out} expressed as a percentage of $E_{\omega\,max}$.

component as a percentage of $E_{\omega\,max}$ for various values of the ratio $E_q/E_{\omega\,max}$. This percentage corresponds to the coefficient $K_1 i$ in Eq. (8-24). It is seen from the figure that the voltage e_A is indeed linearly proportional to the load current for values of E_q up to about $0.6E_{\omega\,max}$. The linearity degenerates rapidly beyond this point, and the curve comes to an abrupt end at $E_q = E_{\omega\,max}$. If E_q should exceed this value, the amplitude of e_A would remain at 50% of $E_{\omega\,max}$. It is therefore important not to overdrive the current modulator, or a serious error results in the power indication.

The Carrett and Cole instrument is complicated, but overcomes the defects of the simpler circuits discussed earlier in this chapter. The actual circuit (6) is direct coupled. Therefore it will operate down to zero frequency. As noted previously, it provides for display of the average power or the instantaneous power. This choice can be a very valuable feature, especially in dealing with pulse circuits and intermittent loads where the average power may be very small, but the peak power quite high. The current modulator circuit by itself offers interesting possibilities for applications requiring the production of a carrier frequency voltage linearly proportional to a d-c or low-frequency signal.

REFERENCES

1. Francis H. Becker, "A Self-Balancing Bolometer Bridge" (Master's Thesis, Purdue University, 1951).
2. "Power Measurements from 10 to 12,400 Megacycles," *Hewlett-Packard Journal*, vol. 2, no. 7-8, July-August 1951.
3. Eugene Peterson, "A Thermionic Meter," U.S. Patent 1,586,533, June 1, 1926.
4. H. M. Turner and F. T. McNamara, "An Electron Tube Wattmeter and Voltmeter and a Phase Shifting Bridge," *Proc. I.R.E.*, vol. 30, October 1930, p. 1743.
5. John R. Pierce, "A Proposed Wattmeter Using Multielectrode Tubes," *Proc. I.R.E.*, vol. 24, April 1936, p. 577.
6. Don E. Garrett and Frank G. Cole, "A General-Purpose Electronic Wattmeter," *Proc. I.R.E.*, vol. 40, February 1952, p. 165.
7. Cruft Laboratory, Harvard University, *Electronic Circuits and Tubes* (New York: McGraw-Hill Book Company, Inc., 1947), chap. 20, sect. 8.

Chapter 9

FREQUENCY MEASURING INSTRUMENTS

The problem of frequency measurement is in some ways more fundamental than those we have considered heretofore. This is because frequency is the reciprocal of time, and time is one of the basic dimensions. Also, frequency must often be measured to much greater precision than other quantities. A vacuum tube voltmeter, for example, is seldom better than 3 per cent accurate; the very best are of 1 per cent accuracy. But if frequency could be determined to no better than 1 per cent, radio and television, radar, sonar, and navigation systems such as loran and shoran, would all be impossible. A standard broadcast station operating on a nominal frequency of 1 megacycle could be found anywhere between 990 kc and 1010 kc if 1 per cent tolerance represented a good frequency measurement. A 1 per cent error in the 60-cycle frequency of a public utility's power would cause an error of nearly 15 min a day in the reading of electric clocks. The confusion in daily life would be hard to imagine if frequency could not be controlled to something like 1 part in 10^5 at the least. Therefore the emphasis in this chapter, more than any other in the book, will be on *accuracy* of the instrumentation. It is appropriate, therefore, to open with a discussion of frequency standards.

9-1. Frequency standards (1)

(a) WWV. Because of the *reciprocal time* nature of frequency, it follows that an accurate measure of time is also an accurate standard for calibrating frequency-measuring instruments. One of the best standards of time is the apparent motion of the heavenly bodies, and astronomical observations are in fact the primary standard of frequency all over the world. The Naval Observatory and the National Bureau of Standards are the keepers of standard time and frequency in the United States.

The Bureau of Standards Radio Station WWV located near Washington, D.C., and its companion WWVH in Hawaii, transmit standard frequency and time signals, which are obtained from banks of extremely precise crystal-controlled oscillators. These oscillators are used to synchronize low-frequency multivibrators, dividing down the frequency until it is low enough to operate an electric clock, which in turn is compared with Naval Observatory time. It is this comparison which makes WWV and WWVH *primary* standards of frequency. The same crystal oscillators, if not checked against astronomical time, would be merely secondary standards, albeit very good ones.

The broadcasting schedules of WWV and WWVH are revised from time to time, but consist basically of standard frequency transmissions on a number of carrier frequencies; standard audio frequency signals; time pulses; time announcements by voice; and time announcements and forecasts of radio propagation conditions in Morse code (*2*).

The carrier frequencies of WWV are 2.5, 5, 10, 15, 20, and 25 megacycles. These are accurate to better than 1 part in 10^8, and stable within better than 1 part in 10^9 at the transmitter. They may be considerably degraded at the location of the receiver, since motion of the Heaviside layer introduces a doppler frequency shift. This will average out over a period of time, and accuracy at the receiver is about one part in 10^8 over a 24-hour period. The audio frequencies are 600 cycles and 440 cycles. The former was selected because it has a large number of integral harmonics and subharmonics, and is convenient for checking the 60-cycle power frequency; the latter because it is the standard musical pitch (A above middle C). The audio frequencies are likewise accurate to one part in 10^8. The seconds pulses consist of 5-cycle bursts of a 1000-cycle tone. They are timed to an accuracy of one part in 10^8 plus or minus 1 μsec. Minute intervals are identified by omitting the pulse at the 59th second, and starting the new minute with two pulses spaced 0.1 sec apart.

The above summary gives an idea of the services available from WWV. Those of WWVH are similar, but slightly less comprehensive. Detailed program schedules are given in Reference *2*, or may be obtained from the Bureau of Standards.

(b) *Laboratory Standard Oscillators.* As a matter of convenience in the laboratory, some companies maintain their own secondary frequency standards such as crystal-controlled oscillators. The most commonly used frequency is 100 kc. This may be divided by a chain of frequency dividers or multiplied by tuned circuits in order to obtain a wide selection of standard frequencies from the same crystal-controlled source. One of the lower frequencies, usually 1 kc, may be used to drive a clock which is compared with Naval Observatory time, giving the equivalent of a primary standard in the laboratory.

It is important to realize that a primary standard of frequency need not be some *exact* value, but rather that it be a *known* value. A frequency of 99,999.99 cycles is just as good as 100,000.00 cycles for a standard, provided one knows *which* of these it is. If a clock driven by a standard oscillator always runs slow by x milliseconds per day compared with Naval Observatory time, the oscillator is a satisfactory standard of frequency. But if it runs x milliseconds slow one day and y the next, it is of little value.

Special clocks are available for comparing the frequency of laboratory standard oscillators with WWV. One example is the "Syncronometer" made by the General Radio Company. This clock produces a pulse once each second to be compared with the time pulses of WWV. A precision dial calibrated in hundredths of a second allows the phase of the clock pulses to be adjusted to coincide with WWV. There are exactly 8.64 million intervals of 1/100 second each day, so the accuracy of the crystal oscillator driving the clock may be determined to one part in 8.64 million—one part in ten million for all practical purposes.

Most standard crystal oscillators employ a circuit known as the "Meacham Bridge" (*3*). Because of its extraordinary stability and consequent importance in frequency measuring systems, we shall describe it in some detail. The analysis follows that of Meacham's paper except for slight changes in notation.

The equivalent circuit of Fig. 9-1 shows the arrangement of the Meacham bridge. It is seen to be very similar to the bolometer bridge of Fig. 8-7, and indeed has many of the same features including self-balancing. Here R_1 is a temperature-sensitive resistor; R_2 and R_3 are precision resistors with as low a temperature coefficient of resistance as possible; Z_4 is the crystal; R_5 is the input impedance to the amplifier; and R_6 is the output impedance. Both R_5 and R_6 are assumed to be purely resistive and are so shown in the circuit diagram.

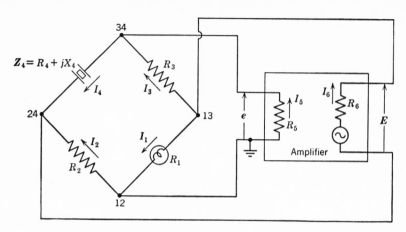

Fig. 9-1. The Meacham bridge oscillator.

The bridge is *very nearly* in balance during operation. If it were *exactly* balanced, no voltage e would be present, and oscillation would not be sustained. The loss in the bridge is defined as

$$\beta = |\beta|\angle\phi = e/E \qquad (9\text{-}1)$$

and the amplifier gain is

$$K = |K|\angle\theta = E/e \qquad (9\text{-}2)$$

For steady-state oscillation, the product $\beta K \equiv 1\angle 0°$. If any changes occur in the amplifier gain, tending to reduce K, the amplitude of oscillation will start to decrease. Then temperature-sensitive resistor R_1 becomes cooler, e increases, and the amplifier receives slightly more input signal. Thus the circuit tends to oscillate at constant amplitude, and also is self-compensating for changes in its forward gain.

The Meacham bridge produces an exceptionally clean waveform. Since the amplitude of oscillation is determined primarily by the linear circuit of the bridge, it does not have to be limited by nonlinearities in the amplifier. The amplifier may therefore operate in a linear Class A region. The resistance of R_1 cannot vary significantly during one cycle of the 100 kc sine wave, so it is not a source of harmonics either.

Since frequency stability is the main consideration in the Meacham bridge, the analysis of the circuit is directed to finding the factors that have the greatest influence on frequency. It is assumed the crystal operates almost exactly at series resonance, and that it may be represented as an RLC series circuit. The resistive component is called R_4;

the reactive component is

$$X_4 = \omega L - \frac{1}{\omega C} \tag{9-3}$$

If Eq. (9-3) is solved for ω,

$$\omega = \frac{X_4}{2\sqrt{LC}} \sqrt{\frac{C}{L}} + \frac{1}{\sqrt{LC}} \sqrt{1 + \left(\frac{X_4}{2}\sqrt{\frac{C}{L}}\right)^2} \tag{9-4}$$

The radical in the second term is of the form $(1 + y^2)^{1/2}$ and may be written as a series

$$(1 + y^2)^{1/2} = 1 + \frac{1}{2} y^2 - \frac{y^4}{2 \times 4} + \frac{y^6}{2 \times 4 \times 6} + \cdots \tag{9-5}$$

If the crystal is near series resonance,

$$y = \frac{X_4}{2}\sqrt{\frac{C}{L}} \ll 1 \tag{9-6}$$

so terms involving powers of y greater than one may be neglected in •Eq. (9-5). Then the second term of Eq. (9-4) may be called simply $1/\sqrt{LC}$, and

$$\omega = \frac{1}{\sqrt{LC}} \left(1 + \frac{X_4}{2}\sqrt{\frac{C}{L}}\right) \tag{9-7}$$

The angular frequency at resonance is

$$\omega_r = 1/\sqrt{LC} \tag{9-8}$$

and the *deviation* from the resonant frequency is

$$\omega - \omega_r = \frac{1}{\sqrt{LC}} \frac{X_4}{2} \sqrt{\frac{C}{L}} \tag{9-9}$$

Expressed as a decimal fraction, this becomes

$$\frac{\omega - \omega_r}{\omega_r} = \frac{X_4}{2} \sqrt{\frac{C}{L}} \tag{9-10}$$

The obvious question is how to minimize Eq. (9-10).

There are two aspects to this problem. One is the relationship between the Q of the crystal and the fractional deviation, and the other is how the amplifier and bridge network affect the deviation. First, we shall consider the crystal alone. The approach is to put Eq. (9-10) into a form involving Q.

$$\sqrt{C/L} = \sqrt{LC/L^2} = \sqrt{LC}/L = 1/\omega_r L \tag{9-11}$$

$$Q = \omega_r L/R_4 \tag{9-12}$$

$$1/\omega_r L = 1/QR_4 = \sqrt{C/L} \tag{9-13}$$

Substitute Eq. (9-13) into Eq. (9-10).

$$\frac{\omega - \omega_r}{\omega_r} = \frac{X_4}{2QR_4} \tag{9-14}$$

Equation (9-14) shows that for maximum frequency stability, Q should be as large as possible. This is not at all remarkable, but it is useful to have the concept expressed in quantitative form.

Next, let us determine the effect of the gain of the amplifier and the value of β.

$$\beta = \frac{e}{E} = \frac{I_5 R_5}{E} = \frac{AR_4 - jBX_4}{MR_4 + jNX_4} \tag{9-15}$$

where

$$A = R_5(R_2 R_3 - R_1 R_4) \tag{9-16}$$

$$B = R_1 R_4 R_5 \tag{9-17}$$

$$M = (R_1 + R_2)(R_3 R_4 + R_5 R_6) + (R_3 + R_4)(R_1 R_2 + R_5 R_6)$$
$$+ (R_5 + R_6)(R_1 R_4 + R_2 R_3) + R_5(R_1 R_3 + R_2 R_4)$$
$$+ R_6(R_1 R_2 + R_3 R_4) \tag{9-18}$$

and

$$N = R_4(R_1 + R_3 + R_5)(R_2 + R_6) + R_1 R_4(R_3 + R_5) \tag{9-19}$$

The requirement for oscillation is that $\beta K \equiv 1\angle 0°$. Suppose

$$K = K_{Re} + jK_{Im} \tag{9-20}$$

Then

$$(K_{Re} + jK_{Im})\left(\frac{AR_4 - jBX_4}{MR_4 + jNX_4}\right) = 1 \tag{9-21}$$

Equating real and imaginary parts of Eq. (9-21) gives

(reals)

$$K_{Re}AR_4 + K_{Im}BX_4 - MR_4 = 0 \tag{9-22}$$

(imaginaries)

$$K_{Im}AR_4 - (K_{Re}B + N)X_4 = 0 \tag{9-23}$$

If $\theta = 0°$, $K_{Im} = 0$. In this case, Eq. (9-22) leads to

$$K_{Re} = K = M/A \tag{9-24}$$

and $X_4 = 0$. When $X_4 = 0$, $(\omega - \omega_r)/\omega_r = 0$. Therefore the frequency of oscillation is independent of changes in any circuit parameter except the crystal. At $X_4 = 0$, the crystal is exactly in series resonance.

It is evident from the above paragraph that the ideal case is for the amplifier to have zero phase angle. However, even with the most careful design and adjustment, there may be some slight phase angle, so that $K_{Im} \neq 0$. However, if we assume K_{Im} is very small,

$$K_{Im}BX_4 \ll K_{Re}AR_4 \tag{9-25}$$

and

$$K_{Re} \cong M/A = |K| \tag{9-26}$$

$$A \cong M/K_{Re} \tag{9-27}$$

Substitute Eq. (9-27) into Eq. (9-23) and solve for X_4.

$$X_4 = \frac{MR_4}{K_{Re}B + N} \frac{K_{Im}}{K_{Re}} \tag{9-28}$$

$$K_{Im}/K_{Re} = \tan \theta \cong \theta \tag{9-29}$$

if θ is very small. Substitution of Eqs. (9-26) and (9-29) into Eq. (9-28) gives

$$X_4 = \frac{MR_4\theta}{B|K| + N} \tag{9-30}$$

This value of X_4 may be used in Eq. (9-14), leading to a final expression for frequency stability of

$$\frac{\omega - \omega_r}{\omega_r} = \frac{M\theta}{2Q(B|K| + N)} \tag{9-31}$$

Equation (9-31) shows that for the frequency to be as stable as possible, the amplifier phase angle should be small, M should be small, and Q, B, $|K|$, and N must be large.

In the design of a Meacham bridge circuit, the large values of B and N are achieved primarily by making R_5 large. Both B and N depend heavily on R_1, R_4, and R_5 for their values, but R_1 and R_4 are usually limited to something of the order of a few thousand ohms, since this is typical of the value of series resistance for a crystal or a small incandescent lamp which is often used for R_1. In a practical circuit, the bridge itself may serve as the grid leak for the first amplifier stage, and therefore the resistor R_5 need not be physically present at all. Thus, $R_5 \cong \infty$ in many cases.

The crystal used in a standard frequency oscillator is rather different in shape and mounting from those found in conventional crystal-controlled oscillators. Figure 9-2 illustrates the crystal and mount used by the General Radio Company. The crystal vibrates in the second-harmonic extensional mode, and is held in a harness placed around the bar at the position of the vibrational nodes. This type of mounting introduces the least possible damping, and is therefore least detrimental to the Q. The crystal is cut to have zero temperature coefficient of frequency in the vicinity of 60°C, the temperature at which it is held in its oven. After one year's aging, such a crystal will have a short-term stability of two parts in 10^9 per day, and a long-term stability of a few parts in 10^8 over a period of several months.

Fig. 9-2. A quartz bar in its mounting, as prepared for use in a standard frequency oscillator. (Photograph courtesy of General Radio Company.)

(c) *Atomic Frequency Standards.* There are a few quantities in nature that appear to be absolute. The best known of these is the velocity of light, but there are other phenomena of comparable dependability. Precise measurements in optics, for example, have standardized on the wavelength of the cadmium red line. If it were possible to design electronic oscillators to operate at the frequency of visible light, optical standards of wavelength could be converted to electronic standards of frequency.

However, just as excited atoms in a particular energy state can emit quanta of visible light at certain invariant frequencies, they are also capable of emitting much lower-frequency quanta when excited to some other energy level. Many of these lower frequencies fall in the microwave region, where they are at least theoretically available to us. Two atomic frequency sources appear especially adaptable for practical use. These are the ammonia molecule inversion line at 23,870 megacycles and the cesium atom line at 9192 megacycles.

Just as a vapor of each element exhibits characteristic absorption lines in a spectrograph, so the vapor of ammonia molecules (NH_3) absorbs energy at 23,870 megacycles. This fact is the basis of the ammonia absorption cell stabilizing system for a frequency standard shown in Fig. 9-3.

A crystal-controlled oscillator is provided with a trimmer capacitor that allows the frequency to be adjusted by a small amount, say ± 1

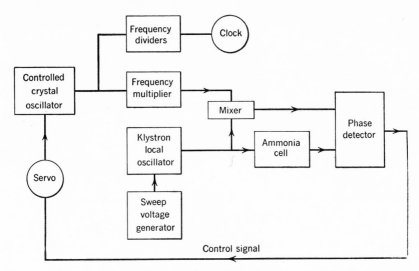

Fig. 9-3. Ammonia absorption cell for frequency stabilization.

cycle. The output of this oscillator is divided to a lower frequency, such as 1 kc, to drive a synchronous clock. A second portion of the output is multiplied by frequency multipliers to approximately 23,870 megacycles. The next step is to bring this approximate frequency to the exact value.

This is accomplished by the use of a klystron local oscillator with a varying repeller voltage that causes its frequency to be swept across a small range centered about 23,870 megacycles. This local oscillator frequency is applied to (1) a mixer, where it beats with the multiplied frequency from the crystal oscillator; and (2) to the ammonia absorption cell. At the moment in time when the frequency of the swept oscillator is equal to the multiplied crystal-controlled frequency, a zero beat is produced in the mixer, and this condition results in a brief interval of time when the output of the mixer is zero. We shall call this moment T_1 relative to the starting time of the klystron oscillator sweep. It is seen on an oscillograph as a somewhat rounded negative pulse. Likewise, at the moment when the klystron local oscillator frequency sweeps through exactly 23,870 megacycles, the ammonia cell absorbs virtually all the energy, and gives no output. We may call this moment T_2 and it is also recognized by the production of a pulse. The moments T_1 and T_2 both occur once during each period of the klystron sweep.

Now if T_1 and T_2 coincide, it follows that the multiplied frequency from the crystal oscillator is exactly the same as the frequency absorbed by the ammonia molecules, i.e., 23,870 megacycles. If T_1 and T_2 do not coincide, the phase detector senses which moment occurred first, and sends a control signal to a servo motor for adjusting the crystal oscillator trimmer capacitor. If T_1 comes before T_2, the crystal oscillator frequency must be increased; if T_2 comes first, the frequency is too high.

Inevitably, the standard frequency of the crystal oscillator will drift a bit, but as long as the phase detector does not miss by a full cycle (i.e., mistake the case of T_1 slightly before T_2 for the case of T_1 falling almost a full period after T_2), this frequency will be held captive by the ammonia absorption cell, and small variations will average out over a period of a few hours or days. Lewis (1) describes several other versions of the ammonia clock, as well as the cesium controlled type, which is discussed below.

The cesium frequency standard operates in somewhat the same manner as the system of Fig. 9-3 as far as circuitry is concerned. However, the frequency-sensing action of a cesium atomic-beam tube is quite different from that of the ammonia absorption cell. The principle involved may be explained with reference to Fig. 9-4.

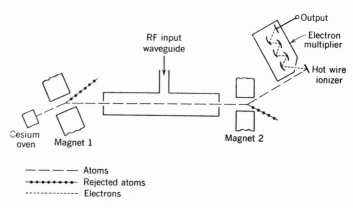

Fig. 9-4. Cesium cell for use in a frequency standard. (Courtesy, National Company, Inc.)

An atom of cesium exhibits a magnetic moment which may be in one of two states. One is when the spin vector of the valence electron is aligned with the magnetic moment of the nucleus; the other is when the spin vector is opposite to the nuclear magnetic moment. Now if a small quantity of cesium is heated, some of the atoms vaporize and drift away from the main mass of the material. These atoms are directed between the poles of a magnet (magnet 1 in Fig. 9-4). Atoms in one state are deflected in one direction by the magnetic field, while atoms in the other state are deflected oppositely and allowed to enter a resonant cavity into which energy at 9192 megacycles is injected through a waveguide. This energy is absorbed by the cesium atoms, the absorption process being associated with a change in the direction of the spin vector of the valence electron.

The atoms leaving the resonant cavity pass through a second magnet, so oriented that atoms which have undergone a change of state pass to a hot wire. Atoms that were unaffected drift away to the side. Upon contact with the hot wire, the cesium atoms absorb sufficient thermal energy to become ionized, and the electrons given off during ionization pass into an electron multiplier. The dynodes of this device are constructed of material having high secondary emission, so several electrons leave each dynode for each incident electron. After several such stages of secondary emission multiplication, a relatively large current appears at the anode. This is amplified further by external circuits, and used to control a feedback system that stabilizes the 9192 megacycle injected frequency.

The exact frequency desired in the resonant cavity is 9192.63+ megacycles. The closer the actual frequency comes to this value, the greater the number of cesium atoms that change their state, and the greater the output direct current. Therefore the magnitude of this direct current is a measure of how close the frequency is to the correct value. The action of the feedback system is to vary the frequency of the local oscillator feeding the cavity until the current is maximized.

A cesium frequency standard operating in essentially the manner described is manufactured by the National Company, Malden, Massachusetts, under the name "Atomichron." However, this device uses a frequency-sweeping technique so that the output from the electron multiplier is in the form of pulses rather than straight direct current. These pulses are fed into a detector and correcting system similar to that described in connection with Fig. 9-3. The "Atomichron" specifications (4) call for a short-term stability of 5 parts in 10^{10}, and a long-term accuracy of 1 part in 10^9.

The ammonia and cesium frequency standards are both examples of a general class of systems known as *MASER*s (*M*icrowave *A*mplifier by

*S*timulation of *E*mitted *R*adiation). It seems possible that with continued research, they may lead to frequency standards accurate to 1 part in 10^{12}.

(d) *Other Frequency Standards (5,6)*. In cases where the high precision and stability of standard frequency sources are not required, there are a number of good, inexpensive frequency references available. Ordinary crystal oscillators can be expected to keep frequency constant to around 10 to 100 parts per million. A good quality crystal in a temperature controlling oven should hold a frequency within one part in 10^6 or 10^7. Greater stability than one part in 10^7 calls for secondary standard quality, and significant increase in cost and complexity.

In some large metropolitan areas, the 60-cycle power frequency is held to sufficiently close tolerance to be a suitable frequency standard. Information on the accuracy and stability of the power frequency in a given area may be obtained from the engineering department of the public utility company.

Audio frequencies accurate to a fraction of 1 per cent may be obtained from tuning forks. It is only necessary to provide a means for keeping the fork in continuous oscillation. This may be done by the method shown in Fig. 9-5. The tuning fork in effect is an electromechanical

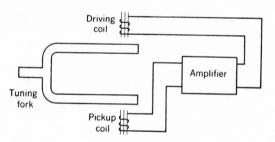

Fig. 9-5. A tuning fork oscillator.

feedback network in the closed loop system. It may be made of ferromagnetic material, or have ferromagnetic insets in its arms. A voltage induced in the pickup coil by the vibrating fork is amplified and passed on to the driving coil to provide continuous oscillation. Two other pickup methods include a capacitor plate placed near the bottom tine, with the fork itself serving as the other plate; and a carbon microphone button attached to the fork. This last method introduces some mechanical loading, and therefore reduces the Q of the vibrating member.

The energy removed from the system by coil or capacitor pickup methods will be negligible if the amplifier has a sufficiently high input impedance. A good quality fork standard with electromagnetic drive and pickup may have a Q as high as 20,000, comparable to many crystal oscillators. If the fork is mounted in a temperature-controlled oven, stability of the order of one part in 10^5 is possible. The amplified tuning fork signal may be used to drive a synchronous clock to provide a long-run determination of accuracy.

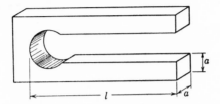

Fig. 9-6. Tuning fork consisting of square bars clamped at one end and free at the other.

The fundamental frequency of a tuning fork of the shape shown in Fig. 9-6 is (7)

$$f_1 = \frac{0.5596}{l^2} \sqrt{\frac{QK^2}{\rho}} \tag{9-32}$$

where Q is Young's modulus (not the same as the Q of the vibrating system discussed above), K is the radius of gyration, equal to $a/\sqrt{12}$, and ρ is the density of the material, grams per centimeter cube. The dimensions a and l are in centimeters. Some typical values of ρ and Q are given in Table 9-1.

TABLE 9-1. CONSTANTS OF MATERIALS USED IN
TUNING FORKS (8)

Material	ρ grams/cm³	Q dynes/cm²
Aluminum	2.7	7.3×10^{11}
Brass	8.4	9.5×10^{11}
Steel, 0.08% carbon	7.7	19.0×10^{11}
Steel, 0.38% carbon	7.7	20.0×10^{11}

9-2. Review of elementary frequency measuring techniques

The purpose of this section is to review briefly certain frequency-measuring techniques, namely, frequency-sensitive bridges and Lissajous figures. The former are not electronic by nature, or at least need not be, but they are useful devices and one type will be examined briefly. Conventional Lissajous figures are well known as a means of comparing an unknown frequency and a standard. We shall investigate two modifications of cathode ray oscillograph equipment for obtaining Lissajous figures of less common types.

One example of a frequency-sensitive bridge is shown in Fig. 9-7. Assume the detector has infinite input impedance. Then the only currents are I_1 and I_2. At balance, $E_a - E_b = 0$.

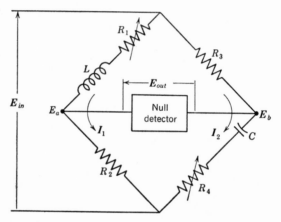

Fig. 9-7. One form of frequency-sensitive bridge. (By permission from *Theory and Applications of Electron Tubes* by Herbert J. Reich. Copyright, 1944. McGraw-Hill Book Co., Inc.)

The expression for $E_a - E_b$ may be written by inspection. It is

$$E_a - E_b = E_{out} = E\left(\frac{R_2}{R_1 + R_2 + j\omega L} - \frac{R_4 - j/\omega C}{R_3 + R_4 - j/\omega C}\right) \qquad (9\text{-}33)$$

To determine the balance conditions, Eq. (9-33) may be set equal to zero, and the real and imaginary terms equated independently to zero. This results in the following two expressions:

$$R_2 R_3 - R_1 R_4 - \frac{L}{C} = 0 \qquad (9\text{-}34)$$

$$-\frac{R_2}{\omega C} - R_4\omega L + \frac{R_1}{\omega C} + \frac{R_2}{\omega C} = 0 \qquad (9\text{-}35)$$

From Eq. (9-34), an expression is obtained for R_4:

$$R_4 = \frac{R_2 R_3 - L/C}{R_1} \qquad (9\text{-}36)$$

Substitute this into Eq. (9-35) and solve for ω. The result is

$$\omega = R_1 \sqrt{\frac{1}{LC(R_2 R_3 - L/C)}} \qquad (9\text{-}37)$$

Note that the frequency is directly proportional to R_1. This is a convenience in the calibration of the bridge, since a linear potentiometer with a linear dial may be used for R_1. It was because of this linear relationship between frequency and resistor R_1 that this particular bridge was chosen for discussion. The resistor R_4 must have a hyperbolic function for its winding (i.e., the resistance is proportional to the reciprocal of the shaft rotation), since Eq. (9-36) shows that the product of $R_1 R_4$ must be a constant. Resistors R_1 and R_4 may be ganged together so the bridge can be balanced with a single control knob.

This is just one example of frequency-sensitive bridges. Many other types are described in the literature (9).

Lissajous figures consist of patterns produced on an oscillograph by the application of signals of different frequencies to the X and Y axes. The conventional Lissajous figures are so well known that there seems little point in describing them here. However, certain other techniques

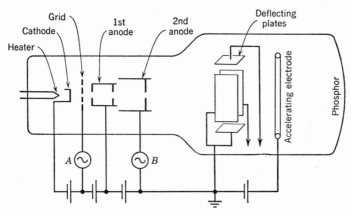

Fig. 9-8. Connections to obtain dotted line or gear-shaped Lissajous figures with a cathode ray tube.

may be employed for comparing two frequencies on an oscilloscope, especially when they differ by a rather large ratio. These methods require connections to *both* the deflecting plate and focusing systems of the cathode ray tube, as illustrated in Fig. 9-8.

The first Lissajous figure we shall consider is obtained by placing a signal source in position A, while the lower-frequency signal against which A is to be compared is placed on the deflecting plates as a circular trace. (The circular trace is obtained by the use of a 90° phase shifting network, such as a resistor and capacitor series circuit.) Intensity modulation takes place at the first grid in the electron gun assembly, and produces a pattern of alternate bright and dark spaces in the circular trace. The number of bright spots in the pattern is equal to the ratio

$$\frac{\text{frequency of signal at } A}{\text{frequency of circular trace}}$$

Many oscilloscopes have external terminals for injecting a signal into position A. Such terminals are usually designated "Z axis input." In some cases, the cathode rather than the deflecting plates is at ground potential. Oscilloscopes constructed in this fashion may have a cathode grounding strap accessible from the outside of the case. A signal may be injected here between cathode and ground, providing the same results as a signal at position A.

If a varying voltage is placed in series with the power supply of the second anode, the velocity acquired by the electron beam at the time it reaches the deflecting plate assembly will vary in response to this signal. The higher the beam velocity, the harder the beam is to deflect. Therefore an instantaneous voltage at point B of such phase as to *increase* the second anode voltage forces the beam to remain relatively close to the center of the tube, while a signal that reduces the second anode voltage causes the trace to move out toward the edge of the phosphor. Consequently, if a circular trace is produced by the deflecting plates in the absence of a signal at B, the pattern changes to a gear-shaped figure if a sinusoidal signal of higher frequency is applied. An example is given in Fig. 9-9(a). Figure 9-9(b) is a pattern obtained in a similar way, but with a linear sawtooth waveform applied at B. One disadvantage in this type of display is that the displacement obtained for a given deflecting plate voltage is proportional to the *reciprocal* of the second anode voltage (*10*).

Provided that the signal is small compared with the normal supply

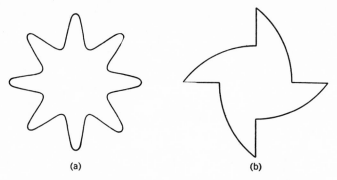

(a)   (b)

Fig. 9-9. Lissajous patterns produced by signal at point B in Fig. 9-8: (a) sine wave at B, 8:1 frequency ratio; (b) linear sawtooth at B, 4:1 ratio.

voltage, this nonlinearity is not serious, since

$$\frac{1}{V_{2a}(1 + \delta)} \cong \frac{1}{V_{2a}}(1 - \delta) \qquad (9\text{-}38)$$

where V_{2a} is the second anode voltage and δ is a quantity much less than one.

9-3. A direct-reading frequency meter

The frequency measuring instruments described so far in this chapter have been either standard frequency sources or devices that required some effort to use, such as balancing a bridge or interpreting the pattern on an oscilloscope. It would be a convenience to measure frequency directly by connecting the unknown to a pair of terminals and reading the frequency on a meter. Such a circuit has been described by Reich and Ungvary (*11*). Its functional arrangement is indicated in block diagram form in Fig. 9-10.

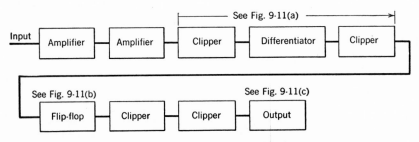

Fig. 9-10. Block diagram of a direct-reading frequency meter.

The instrument operates on the principle that if a square wave can be derived from the input signal, this square wave can be used to charge a capacitor. The capacitor discharges through a milliammeter during the negative half cycle of the square wave, and the average current through the meter is proportional to the number of square waves per second, and therefore to the frequency of the unknown signal.

The first three blocks are all high-gain amplifiers, even though the third block is labeled "clipper." If the amplitude of the input signal is at least 0.5 volt at 60 cycles, and 0.03 volt between 800 and 200,000 cycles, one or more of these first three stages will be driven into saturation in one direction and cutoff in the other, producing square waves. The first two amplifiers use 6SJ7 tubes; the third, a 6V6, is shown in detail in Fig. 9-11(a). The plate load of this tube includes a 100 μh peaking coil to improve the rise time of the square waves. It is followed by a differentiator consisting of the 50 $\mu\mu$f capacitor and a resistor adjustable between 1000 and 3500 ohms. A diode removes the positive pulses produced by the differentiator, leaving only negative pulses which are passed on to trigger a flip-flop.

The flip-flop is shown as part (b) of Fig. 9-11. It is a little out of the ordinary in that the switching action is initiated on the control grids, but the follow-through is achieved by coupling between the suppressor grids. This technique provides isolation between the flip-flop and the source of trigger pulses. Also it eliminates the need for the "steering" diodes placed in series with the control grids of conventional flip-flops to prevent interaction between these grids via the input bus. The flip-flop provides a complete and final isolation between the measuring circuit proper and the input signal. Even if the 6SJ7 and 6V6 stages produce only an *almost*-square wave from the original input signal, the flip-flop will deliver a perfectly square wave to the rest of the circuit, entirely independent of the shape of the input signal.

Following the flip-flop, there are two more stages of clippers. These are to insure that the amplitude of the square wave ultimately applied to the output assembly is absolutely constant.

The output system is shown in Fig. 9-11(c). The source of square waves is represented by a Thévenin equivalent with an internal impedance of R_1. Resistances R_2 and R_3 are the forward resistances of the two halves of the 6H6 rectifier, and R_4 is a shunt across the milliammeter. Capacitor C and resistor R_4 are ganged together, and act as the range-switching system for the instrument. For purposes of the follow-

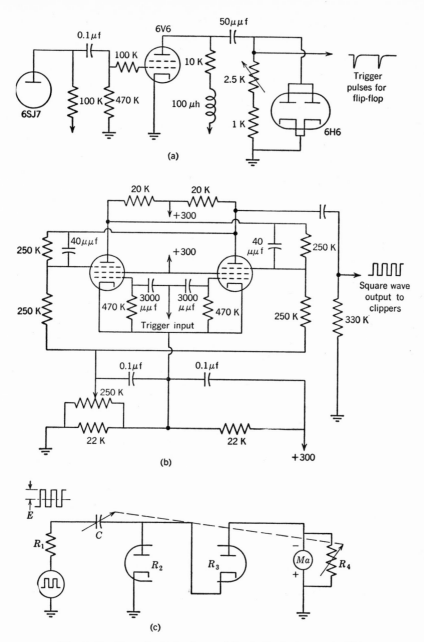

Fig. 9-11. The principal subassemblies in the instrument of Fig. 9-10: (a) clipper-differentiator-clipper; (b) flip-flop; (c) output.

ing discussion, R_4 will be defined as the value of the meter and shunt resistances in parallel.

If the time constants $(R_1 + R_2)C$ and $(R_1 + R_3 + R_4)C$ are both much shorter than half the period of the square wave, the capacitor will charge to approximately E volts during the positive half cycle of the square wave, and discharge *through the meter and shunt* to a voltage of approximately $-E$ during the negative half cycle. The charge per square wave cycle flowing through the meter and shunt will therefore be

$$Q = 2CE \tag{9-39}$$

The current is equal to the charge per second, and therefore is proportional to the frequency of the incoming signal.

The frequency indication is independent of the input waveform, provided the input signal does not cross its axis more than twice during its fundamental period. Each pair of axis crossings produces one trigger pulse at the flip-flop, so a wave with multiple crossings will result in too high a reading of the meter.

9-4. Heterodyne wave analyzers

In a great many applications, both electronic and acoustic, it is important to determine not only the fundamental frequency of a signal, but its harmonic components. The instruments used for this purpose are known as "wave analyzers," and usually operate on a heterodyne principle.

The system is illustrated in Fig. 9-12. After any necessary amplification or attenuation, the signal being analyzed is applied to a balanced modulator, together with a carrier frequency obtained from an ac-

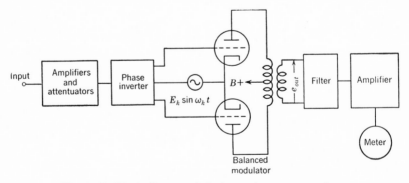

Fig. 9-12. Block diagram of the heterodyne wave analyzer.

curately calibrated oscillator. The output from the balanced modulator is a signal of the form

$$e_{out} = AE_m(1 + BE_k \sin \omega_k t) \sin \omega_m t \qquad (9\text{-}40)$$

where $E_m \sin \omega_m t$ is the modulating signal and $E_k \sin \omega_k t$ is the carrier. In general, the modulating waveform will contain a number of frequency components, but to simplify the explanation we assume only one is present. The quantities A and B in Eq. (9-40) are constants depending on the values of tube and circuit parameters.

Equation (9-40) may be broken up into three components: one at the radian frequency ω_m, one at $\omega_k + \omega_m$, and one at $\omega_k - \omega_m$. A highly selective crystal filter is employed, which eliminates the frequency ω_m and the lower side band as well. Consequently, the output of the filter consists of one term only, which is of the form $\alpha E_m E_k \cos (\omega_k + \omega_m)t$. Here α is an all-inclusive proportionality constant that includes the insertion loss of the filter as well as the effects of all gains and losses in prior components. The filter output is a function of both the carrier and input amplitudes. Therefore it is essential that the carrier amplitude be constant so that only the value of E_m will affect the final reading. The output is displayed on a voltmeter after suitable amplification.

The crystal filter is really the heart of this analyzer. It has a very narrow pass band, on the order of a few cycles per second each side of resonance. An output indication is obtained only when $\omega_k + \omega_m$ falls within this pass band. The carrier oscillator need cover only a range of frequencies such that the sum of the input and oscillator frequencies will equal the crystal center frequency. For example, an audio frequency harmonic analyzer might be designed to determine the presence of frequency components between zero and 20,000 cycles. Then the local oscillator would be designed to tune between 100,000 and 80,000 cycles if the crystal selects 100,000 cycles. This rather narrow range of local oscillator frequencies helps greatly with the problem of keeping E_k constant. The local oscillator dial is marked with the frequency which must be present at the input to fall within the filter pass-band. Thus, with a 100 kc filter, the dial would be marked "1 kc" when the oscillator frequency is 99 kc.

Frequently a rapid analysis of a signal is desired. This may be achieved by providing a motor drive for the local oscillator tuning system. The motor shaft is also coupled to a potentiometer that produces a voltage proportional to the angular displacement. This voltage may be used to deflect the X axis of an oscilloscope or paper chart recorder, while the output of the harmonic analyzer is applied to the Y axis. This arrangement allows a plot of amplitude as a function of frequency to be traced in a few seconds. It is a very useful technique in semipermanent test setups. For example, a public utility might require a transformer manufacturer to give a written report of lamination noise in transformers to be installed in residential areas. A chart drawn by a semiautomatic wave analyzer would make a very suitable inspection report, and could be obtained quickly and at low cost.

9-5. Swept heterodyne wave analyzers

When extremely rapid analysis with visual display is required, electronic frequency sweeping systems may be coupled with the basic wave analyzer. These permit the full frequency range to be covered many times per second. Obviously a meter or recording pen could not operate at such a speed, so the output is ordinarily displayed on a cathode ray oscilloscope. The Y axis is usually equipped with logarithmic amplifiers (see Chapter 6 for examples of logarithm-determining circuits) to provide a display in decibels. A logarithmic display is almost a necessity, for if a range of 100 or 1000 to 1 in voltage is encountered, the highest-amplitude components would drive linear amplifiers into saturation, and the smallest might be less than the width of the cathode ray beam. Most commercial swept wave analyzers do provide for substituting linear amplifiers once the general magnitude of input components has been found logarithmically and one is ready to make a detailed analysis of some particular part of the frequency spectrum.

Figure 9-13 shows a block diagram of the swept heterodyne wave

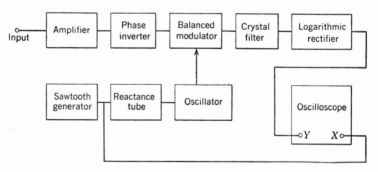

Fig. 9-13. Swept heterodyne wave analyzer.

analyzer. It is similar to Fig. 9-12, but has the additional blocks labeled "Sawtooth Generator" and "Reactance Tube." The reactance tube circuit has the property of presenting a variable input capacitance at its terminals. The variable capacitance may be shunted across an oscillator to vary the frequency of oscillation. The sawtooth generator causes the capacitance to sweep through a prescribed range many times per second. It simultaneously provides the X-axis deflection for the cathode ray oscilloscope, so that the horizontal axis position is proportional to the frequency of the input signal that can pass through the balanced modulator at any given instant.

The feature of principal interest in the swept wave analyzer is the reactance tube control. There are several forms of reactance tube

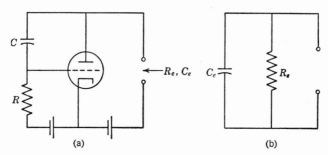

Fig. 9-14. (a) The reactance tube circuit. (b) The equivalent, consisting of resistance and capacitance in parallel.

circuits (*12*), the most common type being that shown in Fig. 9-14. This is equivalent to a parallel RC circuit, in which the resistance is

$$R_e = \frac{r_p(R^2\omega^2C^2 + 1)}{\omega^2R^2C^2(\mu + 1) + r_pR\omega^2C^2 + 1} \tag{9-41}$$

and

$$C_e = \frac{C}{\omega^2R^2C^2 + 1}\,(g_mR + 1) \tag{9-42}$$

Frequently, $g_mR \gg 1$, in which case Eq. (9-42) simplifies to

$$C_e \cong \frac{CRg_m}{\omega^2R^2C^2 + 1} \tag{9-43}$$

Equation (9-43) has a maximum value when $R = 1/\omega C$. This is

$$C_{e\,max} = g_m/2\omega \tag{9-44}$$

Equation (9-44) is a useful guide in picking tube types to give a certain value of C_e at a particular frequency. The value of R_e when C_e is at its maximum is equal to $2/g_m$.

In Fig. 9-15, we see one possible practical circuit employing the reactance tube as a frequency-controlling element with a tuned-plate oscillator. The tuned-plate oscillator was chosen for an example because it is easy to understand, and consequently will not obscure the explana-

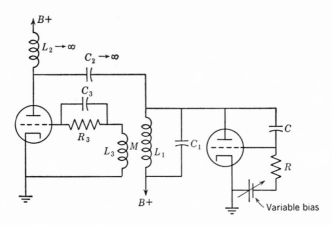

Fig. 9-15. Reactance tube controlled tuned-plate oscillator.

tion of the reactance tube. In a final design, a Hartley oscillator would be a better choice, since it has much less distortion than the tuned-plate type.

Neglecting a small correction factor associated with the r_p of a tuned-plate oscillator tube, the angular frequency of oscillation is

$$\omega = 1/\sqrt{L_1 C_T} \tag{9-45}$$

where L_1 is the tank circuit inductance in Fig. 9-15, and C_T is the total tank circuit capacitance, equal to $C_1 + C_e$. If we substitute Eq. (9-43) for C_e, Eq. (9-45) may be put into the form

$$\omega^2 = \frac{1}{L_1 C_1 + L_1 C R g_{mRT}/(\omega^2 R^2 C^2 + 1)} \tag{9-46}$$

The notation is as in Fig. 9-15, except the letters RT have been added as a subscript to g_m to emphasize that it is the g_m of the *reactance tube* that is of importance. Equation (9-46) may be solved for ω^2. The result is shown as Eq. (9-47). It is rather cumbersome, because C_e is a function of ω.

$$\omega^2 = \frac{-(L_1 C_1 + L_1 C R g_{mRT} - R^2 C^2) + \sqrt{(L_1 C_1 + L_1 C R g_{mRT} - R^2 C^2)^2 + 4 L_1 C_1 R^2 C^2}}{2 L_1 C_1 R^2 C^2}$$

$$\tag{9-47}$$

In a given circuit, all parameters will be constant except g_{mRT}, so Eq. (9-47) is not difficult to apply in practice.

It should be noted that oscillation may cease due to the loading of R_e across the tank circuit. Therefore it is well to check a proposed design to be sure that oscillation is possible. Every oscillator circuit has a minimum value of g_m that must be equaled or exceeded for oscillation to occur. In the case of the tuned-plate oscillator used in this example, it is necessary that

$$g_{m\,osc} \geqq \frac{L_1}{M}\left(\frac{1}{R_e} + \frac{1}{r_p} + \frac{1}{R_{sh}}\right) \qquad (9\text{-}48)$$

where $g_{m\,osc}$ is the g_m of the *oscillator* tube, r_p is the plate resistance of this same tube, and R_{sh} is the equivalent shunt impedance of L_1 (equal to $Q^2 R_{ser}$ where R_{ser} is the series resistance of L_1, and Q is the customary figure of merit of an inductor, both measured at the intended frequency of oscillation).

Example: Suppose in the circuit of Fig. 9-15, $L_1 = 10$ millihenries, $C_1 = 500$ $\mu\mu$f, $R = 20,000$ ohms, $C = 2430$ $\mu\mu$f, $M = 8$ millihenries, and g_{mRT} varies with grid voltage as in Fig. 9-16. A fixed bias of -8.5 volts

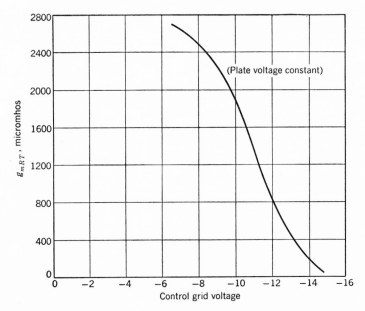

Fig. 9-16. Reactance tube transconductance as a function of control grid voltage.

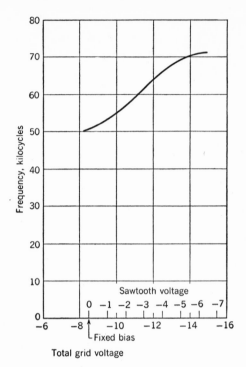

Fig. 9-17. Frequency of reactance tube controlled tuned-plate oscillator as a function of sawtooth sweep voltage.

is applied to the control grid, and in series with this, a sawtooth waveform of 7 volts amplitude. By the use of Eq. (9-47), a curve of frequency vs sawtooth voltage can be constructed, and is shown in Fig. 9-17. The frequency varies from about 50 to 70 kc, and is at least approximately linear over a fair part of the curve. Checking with Eq. (9-48) shows that oscillation is possible.

Sweeping oscillators are by no means limited to wave analyzers. They are of great convenience in both laboratory and production testing, especially in applications involving the adjustment of networks to specified frequency responses. When used as the local oscillators in superheterodyne radio receivers, they permit a rapid examination of the spectrum to determine at what frequencies various transmitters are broadcasting.

In addition to wave analyzers employing crystal filters, there is a wider-band type commonly employed in acoustical work. In situations involving the study of noise, such as machine shops, heavy traffic, or offices with many typewriters and business machines, the acoustician may find it more useful to break the noise into a general pattern rather than pinpoint it to discrete frequencies. Therefore sound analyzers are often designed to accept bandwidths one octave wide rather than two or three cycles. This type of instrument will be studied in more detail in the chapter on sound.

9-6. Frequency counters

Probably the most elegant frequency-measuring instruments are those designed to count the number of cycles that occur during a given time. The majority employ vacuum tubes, but there is a decided trend toward transistors and magnetic registers for counting. The electronic computer field, which deals in similar but more complicated circuitry, has given great impetus to the design of tubeless systems.

All frequency counters operate along the lines of the block diagram shown in Fig. 9-18. A crystal-controlled oscillator, operating in most

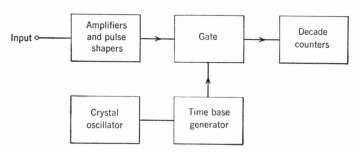

Fig. 9-18. Block diagram of frequency counter.

cases at 100 kc, drives a time-base generator. This generator consists of a chain of decade frequency dividers, providing frequencies between 0.1 and 1000 cycles in decade steps. The input signal, after amplification and shaping into pulses, is applied to the input of a gate. The gate is opened when one cycle of the time base starts, and closed at the start of the following cycle. Thus pulses at the unknown frequency are sent to the counters for one period of the time base.

When relatively low-frequency signals are counted, the percentage accuracy may be rather low. Obviously, there is no such thing as a fractional count in the digital counters. The first or last pulse in a sequence may or may not squeak through the gate, so there is an inherent possibility of plus or minus one count error. A frequency of 100 cycles might therefore be counted as 99, 100, or 101 cycles, a possible error of 1 per cent either way. Consequently, when low frequencies are to be determined with accuracy, the input signal is connected to control the gate, and the crystal-controlled clock frequency is gated into the counters. Thus the *period* rather than the frequency of the unknown is measured. For example, if a 1-megacycle clock frequency is employed (obtained as the tenth harmonic of the 100-kc crystal frequency), and the gate held open for one period of a 100-cycle signal, either 9999, 10,000, or 10,001 counts may be registered. The accuracy is then 0.01 per cent instead of the 1 per cent that would result from counting the 100-cycle frequency directly.

Most commercial counters are designed for great versatility. The time-base sections include a number of decade frequency dividers, giving choices of gate time ranging in most cases from 10 sec down to 1 millisec in decade steps. When connected for period measurements as described above, the gates may be adjusted to remain open for more than one period in order to increase the time available for counting. This permits a higher accuracy. Likewise, the clock frequency fed through the gate to the counters may be varied in decade steps, by selecting harmonics or subharmonics of 100 kc. If an extremely accurate measure of period is desired, the counter could be set to hold open the gate for ten periods, and during this time count 10-megacycle clock pulses. If 1-megacycle pulses are counted for one period, the number displayed on the counters is equal to the period in microseconds; a clock frequency of 1000 cycles and a gate duration of one period will give the answer in milliseconds.

Many commercial counters provide for opening the gate with a signal from one source and closing it with a different signal. During the open time of the gate, any one of the various clock frequencies may be fed into the counters. The count displayed after the gate has closed is the time between the starting and stopping signals: microseconds if a 1-megacycle clock frequency was used; milliseconds if a 1-kc frequency was counted; etc. When used in this manner, the counter is referred to as a *time interval meter*.

The *ratio* between two frequencies is found by letting the lower frequency control the gate and feeding the higher one into the counters. For example, suppose a signal of 50 cycles is used to control the gate, and 2 kc is fed to the counters. Then in one period of the lower-frequency signal, 40 cycles of the 2 kc will be counted. The displayed count, 40, is the ratio of one frequency to the other.

The crystals employed in counters must be of secondary standard quality, properly aged, and mounted in temperature-controlled ovens. Usually the crystal oscillator signal is brought to external binding posts through a buffer amplifier so that the counter may be employed as a laboratory frequency standard. Frequently there are also binding posts for injecting a 100-kc signal to replace that from the crystal oscillator. Laboratories maintaining a primary frequency standard compared against WWV might find it advantageous to use their own reference frequency. The vast majority of users find the self-contained crystal oscillator perfectly satisfactory.

Counters on the market differ in many details, even though all operate in the same general way. The main differences are in the maximum counting rate, the number of digits displayed, the choices of clock frequencies and timing bases, and the auxiliary functions available, such as measuring period, time interval, ratio, etc. Some counters employ the 60-cycle power line frequency as a standard; some have output connections for transferring the reading stored in the counters to a printed tape for permanent records; some use plug-in units for different functions.

Any quantity that may be expressed in terms of frequency may be measured with a counter. The most obvious examples are tachometry and the determination of frequencies of vibration in mechanical and acoustical equipment.

A typical counter will include the following basic subassemblies:

1. High-speed registers
2. Medium-speed registers
3. Low-speed registers
4. Gating system
5. Time-base system
6. Power supplies

Of the six in this list, only one will be discussed in detail. This is the gating system. The various decade counters used as registers for storing and displaying the output are considered in Chapter 12, as they are common to many digital systems, and by no means restricted to frequency-measuring apparatus. The time-base system consists of the crystal oscillator and decade multipliers and dividers. Naturally it must be properly engineered and built with care and skill. But the principles are fairly self-evident and the author feels there is not a great deal of instructional value in discussing it in detail.

Gating assemblies are similar in most commercial instruments. The one discussed here is based on the Hewlett-Packard 524B counter, and includes many features designed to enhance the over-all versatility of the instrument. A designer planning to incorporate a counter in a specific piece of equipment rather than an all-purpose instrument should look for possible simplifications. In particular, in many cases it might be possible to omit either the automatic or the manual recycling features.

Figure 9-19 shows the gating system arranged for counting an unknown frequency. The action can best be explained by following through

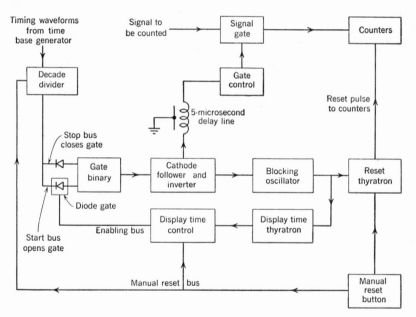

Fig. 9-19. Block diagram of the gating system of the 524B Frequency Counter. (Courtesy, Hewlett-Packard Co.)

a full sequence of the gating operation. Assume that the signal gate is closed and a count is displayed in the decade registers of the counters. Eventually a pulse from the display time-control circuit enables the diode at the start bus preceding the gate binary. The next pulse from the decade divider passes through this diode and changes the state of the gate binary. This binary, or flip-flop, produces an output pulse that passes through the cathode follower and inverter. This pulse is of such polarity as to fire the blocking oscillator, which in turn triggers the reset thyratron and the display time thyratron. The reset thyratron resets the counters to zero, while the display time thyratron initiates a relatively long time delay. This delay is adjustable by a front panel control, and can be set between 0.1 and 10 sec.

In the meantime, the pulse from the cathode follower and inverter travels up the 5-μsec delay line. This 5-μsec delay permits the counters to be reset before the signal gate opens. As soon as the signal gate is opened by the gate control circuit, the signal to be counted flows through to the counters.

The next pulse from the decade divider enters the gate binary, which reverses its state again and delivers an output pulse that will not trigger the blocking oscillator, but will close the signal gate via the delay line and gate control. The counting stops, and the counters display the accumulated result. The start bus at the gate binary is disabled by the display time-control circuit until the selected display time runs out. After this interval has elapsed, the display time control again enables the start bus, and the next pulse from the decade counter produces resetting and starts a new count, as we have already explained.

If manual control of the counting cycle is desired, the display time control is turned to the "infinity" position. In this setting, a switch disconnects the display time thyratron from its timing circuit, while permitting it to fire from the blocking oscillator. When the manual reset button is pressed, it sends a pulse into the reset thyratron to return the count to zero; triggers the display time control circuit to enable the diode gate in the start bus; and sets the decade divider to a count of eight, so at worst not more than 2 sec must elapse before a new count starts. When the pulse from the decade divider reaches the start bus, the gate binary triggers the cathode follower and inverter, blocking oscillator, display time thyratron, and display time control. Five microseconds later the signal gate opens and counting begins.

The display time control disables the start bus at the gate binary just as in automatic operation. The difference is that this bus remains disabled until the manual reset button is pushed again, because in manual operation the timing components are disconnected from the display time thyratron circuit. Thus, after the counting interval, the decade divider pulses the stop bus, and the count is displayed permanently because the display time thyratron and display time control assembly will not re-enable the start bus.

While most of the building blocks in the gating circuit contain devices of rather conventional nature, such as flip-flops, blocking oscillators, and gates, they must meet rather difficult performance specifications. If the signal gate is to be controlled with sufficient speed to keep the error down to plus or minus one count, it follows that the circuits in the gating system must operate at a speed equivalent to the fastest of the decade registers. This means that a given switching action must be accomplished in 0.1 μsec (except for the reset function, which has 5 μsec to be completed).

We shall take a closer look at some of the high-speed circuitry, in particular the signal gate. The gate binary also deserves further study, but this is deferred to Chapter 12 which deals with the general problem of digital display. The gate binary is essentially the same as one binary stage of the high-speed decade scalers discussed in this later chapter. Another circuit of interest is the so-called Schmitt trigger. This is used in a number of places where a square step with very fast rise time is required. For example, the display time control circuit is a Schmitt trigger, and the input to the signal gate and the decade divider are both obtained from Schmitt triggers.

The signal gate is shown in Fig. 9-20. This circuit employs a special

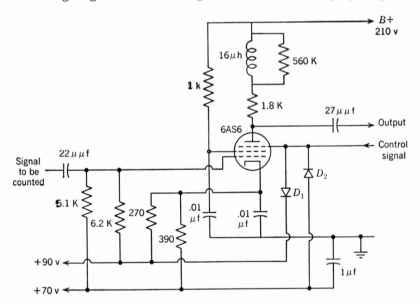

Fig. 9-20. Signal gate of 524B Frequency Counter. (Courtesy, Hewlett-Packard Co.)

gating tube, the type 6AS6. The suppressor grid in this tube functions as a second control grid, allowing the tube to be biased on or off with a relatively small change in voltage. The direct potential at the grid of the 6AS6 is +79 volts; and at the cathode is +83. The suppressor grid potential is raised or lowered by the control signal: if the control signal tends to become more positive than +90 volts, diode D_1 clamps the suppressor at 90. This biases the tube into the conducting state, and signals appearing at the control grid are amplified and passed on to the plate, where they are delivered to the decade scalers via the output bus. When the control signal tends to bias the suppressor grid less positive than +70 volts, diode D_2 clamps the suppressor at 70. In this case, the suppressor is 13 volts negative with respect to the cathode. This represents a cutoff condition, and no signal at the control grid can reach the plate.

The circuits of Schmitt triggers (13) vary a great deal in specific detail depending upon the rise time required, the available driving voltages, d-c supply voltages, etc. A Schmitt trigger is shown in Fig.

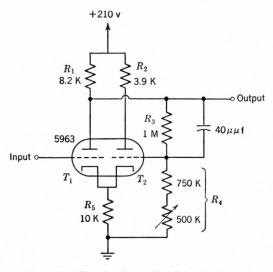

Fig. 9-21. Circuit of a typical Schmitt trigger.

9-21. While it does not correspond exactly to any of the Schmitt triggers in the counter we are discussing, it is fairly typical of circuits of its type. The operation of the device is as follows:

Assume the left-hand side (T_1) is conducting. The input voltage is then decreased by a signal, causing the anode potential to rise. This rise appears at the grid of T_2 scaled down in magnitude by the ratio of the resistors between ground and the plate of T_1. From the viewpoint of T_2, the common cathode resistor causes this tube to act as a cathode follower, so the cathode potential of both tubes increases as the plate voltage of T_1 increases. The result is that while the grid of T_1 goes down a small amount in voltage, the cathode potential of T_1 rises a great deal. This action is equivalent to driving T_1 with a very large input signal, and causes a very rapid and positive cutoff of T_1. After T_1 stops conducting, the grid potential of T_2 will be relatively high, since the top of the 1-megohm resistor is at $+210$ volts for all practical purposes (the IR drop through the 8200-ohm resistor will be negligible). Therefore T_2 begins to conduct heavily, and the voltage developed across the cathode resistor by the current from T_2 will hold T_1 in the cutoff condition.

If the input voltage at the grid of T_1 is subsequently raised, the process operates in reverse, causing a rapid switching of conduction from T_2 back to T_1. However, there is a small hysteresis effect. That is, the value of input voltage at which conduction transfers from T_1 to T_2 is not the same as that at which it transfers in the opposite direction.

An illustration of this fact may be found in the trigger circuit shown in Fig. 9-21. We shall assume $R_4 = 806,000$ ohms for this example. Determination of the d-c operating point is largely a matter of trial and error, but reference to the characteristic curves of Fig. 9-22 for the

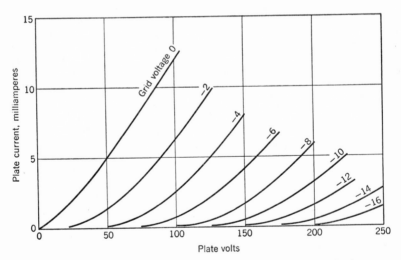

Fig. 9-22. Characteristics of the type 5963 tube (each section). (Courtesy, Radio Corporation of America.)

type 5963 tube shows that the following conditions will apply when T_1 is conducting: anode potential of $T_1 = 148$ volts; cathode potential = 76 volts; cathode current = 7.6 ma; potential between plate and cathode = $148 - 76 = 72$ volts. The curves of Fig. 9-22 show that these conditions are met when the control grid is about one-half volt negative with respect to the cathode. Therefore the direct potential at the grid of T_1 must be at least 75.5 volts. At tube 2, the voltages are: cathode, 76 volts; anode, 210 volts; grid, $148(0.806/1.806) = 66$ volts. This leaves the grid at -10 volts relative to the cathode, and the cathode-to-plate potential is $210 - 76 = 134$. Figure 9-22 shows that T_2 will be cut off, although just on the verge of conducting. Thus, with T_1 already on and T_2 off, a potential of 75.5 volts at the input will hold the *status quo*. Any decrease in this voltage will initiate the switching action.

Now suppose that switching has taken place, and T_2 is conducting. Examination of the characteristic curves and circuit parameters shows that the following conditions now prevail: Tube 2 has an anode current of 9 ma, cathode voltage of 90 volts, grid voltage (presumably) $210(0.806/1.806) = 94$ volts. This would leave the grid positive by 4 volts relative to the cathode, so a small grid current, about 4 μa, flows to clamp the grid at cathode potential, making the actual grid voltage in tube 2 come to 90 volts. Tube 1 is presumed to be cut off. Its potentials are: plate, 210 volts, cathode, 90 volts, grid, 80 volts, since Fig. 9-22 shows that the grid must be 10 volts negative relative to the cathode to prevent conduction with a cathode-to-plate voltage of 134 volts. Therefore, to hold T_1 in the cutoff state, the input voltage must be not more than 80 volts.

Summarizing, if T_1 is conducting, switching starts when the input voltage drops below 75.5 volts. Operation does not switch back to T_1 until the input voltage rises to 80 volts. Hence, there is a 4.5-volt "hysteresis" in the triggering cycle. The actual voltage levels may be adjusted by varying R_4, but there will still be a hysteresis effect.

Whether this is serious or not depends upon the application. Hysteresis may not matter if (1) the input to the trigger is either a pulse or a square wave of large amplitude and fast rise time, and (2) subsequent circuits respond to only one polarity of output from the trigger, so that the trigger is always going through the same part of its cycle when it initiates an action elsewhere in the system.

Schmitt triggers are good square wave generators in spite of the hysteresis effect, provided they are used properly. If a sinusoid is to be converted into a square wave with a Schmitt trigger, the wave should be of large amplitude, and be superimposed on an adjustable d-c bias. By proper setting of this bias, the trigger may be made to operate the same number of electrical degrees after the sine wave crosses the axis going negative as it did after the positive axis-crossing. If asymmetrical square waves are desired, they are easily obtained by changing the bias. A large negative bias would cause the triggering action to go one way as the sine wave nears its positive peak, and reverse shortly after the sine wave starts down again.

The design of a Schmitt trigger is largely a matter of trial and error. It is based on determining from the characteristic curves where the d-c operating points fall with T_1 conducting and with T_2 conducting.

The field of frequency measurements is one of the largest in instrumentation, since it is applicable to a great many fields. Acoustics and mechanics in particular often involve frequency determinations. In the second half of the book we shall find a number of situations where the frequency-measuring techniques discussed in this chapter are brought into play in assorted scientific disciplines.

REFERENCES

1. F. D. Lewis, "Frequency and Time Standards," *Proc. I.R.E.*, vol. 43, September 1955, p. 1046.
2. At the time of writing, the most up-to-date summary of WWV and WWVH services appeared in *Proc. I.R.E.*, vol. 44, October 1956, p. 1470. The latest schedules may be obtained from the National Bureau of Standards, Boulder Laboratory, Boulder, Colorado.
3. L. A. Meacham, "The Bridge-Stabilized Oscillator," *Proc. I.R.E.*, vol. 26, October 1938, p. 1278. See also J. K. Clapp, "A Bridge-Controlled Oscillator," *Gen. Radio Exptr.*, vol. 18, April 1944, p. 1; "An Analysis of the Bridge-Controlled Oscillator," *Gen. Radio Exptr.*, vol. 18, May 1944, p. 6; and "Notes on the Design of Temperature Control Units," *Gen. Radio Exptr.*, vol. 19, August 1944, p. 1.
4. *The National Atomichron* (Malden, Mass.: The National Company, 1956).

5. F. E. Terman, *Radio Engineers Handbook* (New York: McGraw-Hill Book Company, Inc., 1943), pp. 488-498.

6. L. L. Beranek, *Acoustic Measurements* (New York: John Wiley & Sons, Inc., 1949), sections 6-1, 6-2.

7. Harry F. Olson, *Acoustical Engineering* (Princeton: D. Van Nostrand Company, Inc., 1957), p. 58.

8. Harry F. Olson, *op. cit.*, p. 7.

9. Herbert J. Reich, *Theory and Applications of Electron Tubes* (New York: McGraw-Hill Book Company, Inc., 1944), section 15-16.

10. Karl R. Spangenberg, *Vacuum Tubes* (New York: McGraw-Hill Book Company, Inc., 1948), section 15-3.

11. Herbert J. Reich and Robert L. Ungvary, "A Direct-Reading Frequency Meter for the Audio and Supersonic Ranges," *Rev. Sci. Instr.*, vol. 19, January 1948, p. 43.

12. Herbert J. Reich, "The Use of Vacuum Tubes as Variable Impedance Elements," *Proc. I.R.E.*, vol. 30, June 1942, p. 288.

13. Otto H. Schmitt, "A Thermionic Trigger," *J. Sci. Instr.*, vol. 15, January 1938, p. 24.

Chapter 10

ELECTRONIC PHASEMETERS

The determination of the phase angle between two signals is one of the less difficult tasks in electronic measurements. There are several methods by which this may be accomplished, and all are relatively simple *in principle*. Such circuit complexity as is encountered is often simply in the design of interstage networks to avoid introducing phase errors within the instrument itself.

There is another problem related to phase angle measurement, which consists of determining the *phase distortion coefficient* in a system. This name is a trifle misleading, since the phase distortion coefficient is in reality a measure of the difference in propagation time of signals of various frequencies. We shall consider this problem in addition to basic phase measurements.

10-1. Lissajous figures for phase angle determination

One of the oldest, and still a very satisfactory method for finding the phase angle between two signals is through the use of Lissajous figures. Let us assume one signal is of the form

$$e_1 = E_1 \sin \omega t \tag{10-1}$$

while the other is $\qquad e_2 = E_2 \sin (\omega t + \phi) \tag{10-2}$

Suppose e_1 is placed on the X axis of a cathode ray oscilloscope, and e_2 on the Y axis. The resulting display is a figure similar to Fig. 10-1. This is an ellipse, or one of its degenerate forms, the circle or straight line. Now consider the parametric equations in time given as Eqs. (10-1) and (10-2). At the moment when $e_1 = 0$, $\omega t = 0$ or π. Suppose as a matter of convenience that $\omega t = 0$. Then at this same moment, $e_2 = E_2 \sin \phi$. This corresponds to height B in Fig. 10-1. Height A is

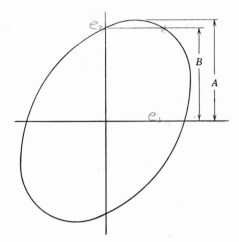

Fig. 10-1. Ellipse displayed on oscilloscope by two sine waves of the same frequency and different phase.

obviously the maximum amplitude of e_2; thus $A = E_2$. If we take the ratio of B/A,

$$\frac{B}{A} = \frac{E_2 \sin \phi}{E_2} = \sin \phi \qquad (10\text{-}3)$$

Then, completing the phase angle determination,

$$\phi = \text{arc sin } (B/A) \qquad (10\text{-}4)$$

Equation (10-4) is a little unusual in that it includes both the theoretical justification for the method of phase measurement, and complete instructions on how the measurement is to be made.

It is only necessary to be sure the ellipse is properly centered on the face of the cathode ray tube. Contrary to an impression often held, especially by undergraduates, it is absolutely not necessary that the amplitudes E_1 and E_2 be equal.

10-2. The phase-sensitive detector as a phasemeter (1)

The circuit of the phase-sensitive detector, shown as Fig. 10-2, may be used as a phasemeter. The operation of the circuit is perhaps most readily understood directly from the mathematical analysis

Suppose that the voltage e_1 is

$$e_1 = E \sin \omega t \qquad (10\text{-}5)$$

and e_2 is

$$e_2 = E \sin (\omega t + \phi) \qquad (10\text{-}6)$$

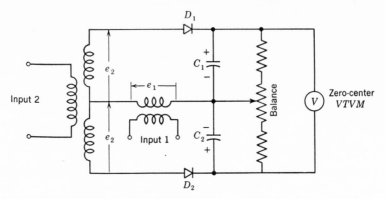

Fig. 10-2. The phase-sensitive detector for phase metering. (By permission from *Theory and Application of Industrial Electronics* by John M. Cage. Copyright, 1951. McGraw-Hill Book Co., Inc.)

Note that the *amplitudes are equal.* The voltage applied to diode D_1 is

$$e_1 + e_2 = E[\sin \omega t + \sin (\omega t + \phi)]$$
$$= 2E \sin \tfrac{1}{2}(2\omega t + \phi) \cos \tfrac{1}{2}(-\phi) \tag{10-7}$$

while D_2 has a voltage at its anode of

$$e_1 - e_2 = E[\sin \omega t - \sin (\omega t + \phi)]$$
$$= 2E \cos \tfrac{1}{2}(2\omega t + \phi) \sin \tfrac{1}{2}(-\phi) \tag{10-8}$$

The amplitudes of the direct voltages developed across capacitors C_1 and C_2 are equal, respectively, to the amplitudes of Eqs. (10-7) and (10-8), assuming that the resistors and the meter input impedance are high enough that the capacitors charge to the peak of the applied voltage. (Section 2-2 deals with the fine points of this assumption.) Thus

$$E_{C1} = 2E \left|\cos \tfrac{1}{2}(-\phi)\right| \tag{10-9}$$

$$E_{C2} = 2E \left|\sin \tfrac{1}{2}(-\phi)\right| \tag{10-10}$$

The voltmeter indication is proportional to the difference between E_{C1} and E_{C2}.

$$V = K[\left|\cos \tfrac{1}{2}(-\phi)\right| - \left|\sin \tfrac{1}{2}(-\phi)\right|] \tag{10-11}$$

where K is a proportionality constant. Equation (10-11) is plotted in Fig. 10-3, assuming $K = 1$ for convenience.

It will be noted that the indication is ambiguous, for any meter reading except $+1$ or -1 can correspond to two phase angles. However, enough is usually known about the circuit under test to tell which of the two possibilities is correct.

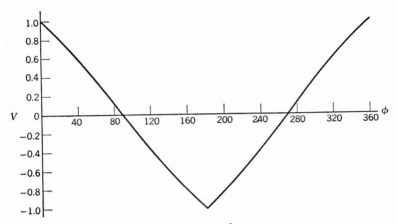

Fig. 10-3. Indication of the meter of Fig. 10-2 as a function of ϕ. K in Eq. (10-11) equals unity.

The value of V is a function of the amplitude of both e_1 and e_2. In the analysis above, it was assumed the amplitudes are equal. This is convenient for mathematical purposes, but not necessary for the operation of the circuit. However, the calibration definitely depends upon both amplitudes. Any desired values of e_1 and e_2 might be chosen, but once the instrument is calibrated for these values, they should be used consistently. This is a rather pronounced drawback. It might be minimized in practice by the use of automatic gain control circuits in the amplifiers that deliver e_1 and e_2 to the phase-sensitive rectifier. These AGC circuits would have to be designed to hold the voltages as constant as possible at specified values.

10-3. The bistable multivibrator as a phasemeter

Possibly the best of the schemes for obtaining direct readings of the phase difference between two signals is that shown in Fig. 10-4. Suppose T_1 is initially conducting, and the arrival of a pulse from Channel 1 switches conduction to T_2. Then T_2 will conduct until a pulse arrives from Channel 2, at which time T_1 comes on again, and T_2 goes into the cutoff state. The greater the phase lag of Channel 2 relative to Channel 1, the larger the fraction of a cycle T_2 conducts, and therefore the higher the reading of the milliammeter in series with its anode.

This circuit offers several very definite advantages. It is not necessary that the two signals being compared be of the same amplitude, or

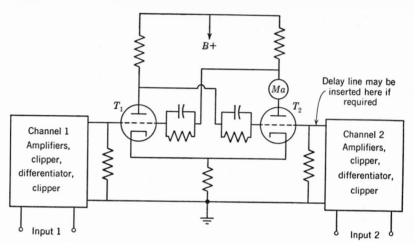

Fig. 10-4. The flip-flop as a phase-measuring system.

even the same waveshape. The only requirement is that they have the same fundamental frequency. The calibration is absolutely linear, provided that the switching times of the flip-flop are fast enough to eliminate error due to poor rise-time. By careful design, a flip-flop can be made to trigger in less than 0.1 μsec, so this is not ordinarily a serious problem. The flip-flop of Fig. 10-4 is the most basic type to illustrate the principle involved, and would not be suitable for extremely high-speed operation in the form shown.

Several ranges of readings can be accommodated by providing shunts across the milliammeter. Another possibility is to obtain great accuracy on differential phase shift (i.e., a small change $\Delta\phi$ from a phase angle ϕ initially prevailing between the two input signals) by employing a suppressed-zero meter of high sensitivity. The zero suppression amounts to forcing a "bucking" current through the meter in opposition to the direction of current flow through tube 2, as was shown in Fig. 3-2(a), for example.

The only real difficulty with this phasemeter occurs with phase angles very close to zero degrees. In this case, the flip-flop may or may not be able to resolve the two triggering pulses arriving very close together. The probability is that it will trigger about half the time, giving a half-scale reading on the milliammeter. This could be mistaken for a reading of 180 degrees. The better the flip-flop, the less likely this is to happen. When the trouble does occur, usually one can tell from the circuit being studied whether the correct value should be zero or 180 degrees. Another method for resolving the ambiguity is to place a delay line in series with Channel 2. This delay line could be inserted by a pushbutton switch so that it is normally not in the circuit. When a suspected ambiguity does occur, inserting the delay line will postpone briefly (say a half-microsecond, for example) the triggering of T_2. Then if the phase angle is actually zero, T_2 will fire almost instantly after T_1, and the meter reading will fall back to approximately zero. If the angle is 180 degrees, the small additional delay in Channel 2 will make substantially no difference, and the meter will continue to indicate half scale. It is only necessary that the delay line introduce a time lag slightly greater than the recovery time of the flip-flop.

One very obvious precaution in the design of this type of phasemeter is to make both channels as nearly identical in their phase shift properties as possible. The interstage coupling networks will inevitably introduce some phase shift as a function of frequency. This is immaterial, as long as the shift is *the same* in both channels.

10-4. Instruments for phase distortion measurement $(2,3)$

In any complete communications system, it is desirable that all the frequency components of a signal arrive at the output at the same time. That is, there must be a constant propagation time through the system. Failure to meet this goal results in *phase distortion*.

In practice, some phase distortion is inevitable, and can be tolerated. Audio frequency signals, such as telephone conversations, can withstand quite a bit (several hundred microseconds difference in propagation time for various frequencies in the voice band is permissible) since the ear is not especially sensitive to phase distortion. Other types of signals require very low phase distortion. Television must hold a tight tolerance on this factor, since the eye notes phase distortion readily. Pulses, such as teletype signals, should also be transmitted with relatively low phase distortion, since the shape of a pulse is seriously degraded by distortion of this type.

In elementary electronics texts, this concept of constant propagation time is often stated as the rule that phase shift must be proportional to frequency. Thus

$$\phi = K\omega \qquad (10\text{-}12)$$

where K is a constant with the dimensions of time, ϕ is phase shift in radians, and ω is frequency in radians per second. If Eq. (10-12) is differentiated on both sides, and $d\phi$ divided by $d\omega$, we obtain

$$\frac{d\phi}{d\omega} = K \qquad (10\text{-}13)$$

This derivative has the dimensions of *time*. If it is measured at several frequencies in the pass band of the system, and plotted as a function of ω, curves like those of Fig. 10-5 will result. These curves are constructed by measuring the phase shift between input and output signals of vari-

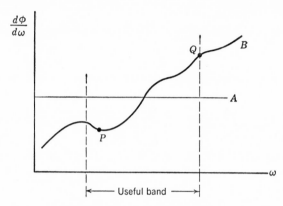

Fig. 10-5. Typical plots of $d\phi/d\omega$.

ous frequencies, and plotting the phase shift as a function of frequency. The *slope* $(d\phi/d\omega)$ of this plot is determined, and replotted as Fig. 10-5. Curve A is the theoretically perfect case, while curve B is more likely what one finds in practice.

A certain portion of the curve has been indicated as covering the useful band. For example, the useful band in a telephone system would be from about 300 to 3000 cycles, as virtually all the intelligence-carrying portion of speech is contained in this rather narrow portion of the spectrum. Within the useful band, two points, P and Q, are marked on curve B. Point P is the frequency that propagates through the system with the shortest time delay, while point Q requires the longest time of any frequency in the useful band. Now the *actual* time of propagation is usually not important. The question is whether all frequencies take the *same* time. Therefore the measure of the quality of the system from the phase distortion point of view is the *difference* between the propagation times represented by points P and Q. This difference is the phase distortion coefficient (PDC), usually expressed in microseconds. In terms of Fig. 10-5,

$$PDC = \frac{d\phi}{d\omega}\bigg|_Q - \frac{d\phi}{d\omega}\bigg|_P \qquad (10\text{-}14)$$

Determining phase shift as a function of frequency, plotting the results, finding the slope of the curve, plotting that, and reading the maximum and minimum values is a perfectly satisfactory method of determining the *PDC*, but represents a lot of work, and gives a great many opportunities for error. There is an easier method, which provides a most useful and interesting application for the electronic measurement of phase.

The basic approach is illustrated in Fig. 10-6. It consists of applying an amplitude-modulated signal to the input of the system, and

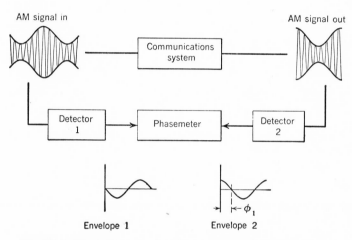

Fig. 10-6. Block diagram of method for measuring phase-distortion coefficient.

comparing the phase of the envelope of this input signal to that of the phase of the output envelope. The carrier frequency is the frequency at which the system time delay is to be determined. The modulating frequency is any convenient value, but it must be small compared to the carrier. For example, if the time delay at 300 cycles must be measured, the 300-cycle carrier might be modulated with a frequency of the order of 10 to 20 cycles. The phase shift between the two envelopes is a measure of the time delay. We shall attempt to prove this.

Suppose the input AM wave is represented mathematically by

$$e_{in} = E_m(1 + M \sin \omega_1 t) \sin \omega_2 t$$
$$= E_m \sin \omega_2 t$$
$$+ \tfrac{1}{2} M E_m \cos (\omega_2 t - \omega_1 t) - \tfrac{1}{2} M E_m \cos (\omega_2 t + \omega_1 t) \qquad (10\text{-}15)$$

The output is delayed by an amount of time Δt. Since ω_1 is much less than ω_2, the sidebands will be at essentially the same frequency as the carrier, so all three frequencies will be delayed the same amount. Note this delay is characteristic of the *carrier*, ω_2, and not the modulating frequency. The output signal is

$$e_{out} = E_m \sin (\omega_2 t - \omega_2 \Delta t)$$
$$+ \tfrac{1}{2} M E_m \cos (\omega_2 t - \omega_2 \Delta t - \omega_1 t + \omega_1 \Delta t)$$
$$- \tfrac{1}{2} M E_m \cos (\omega_2 t - \omega_2 \Delta t + \omega_1 t - \omega_1 \Delta t) \qquad (10\text{-}16)$$

Define $\omega_1 \Delta t$ as the angle ϕ_1 and $\omega_2 \Delta t$ as ϕ_2. Then Eq. (10-16) may be put in the form

$$e_{out} = E_m[1 + M \sin (\omega_1 t - \phi_1)] \sin (\omega_2 t - \phi_2) \qquad (10\text{-}17)$$

After the output signal is detected, an envelope is recovered that has a phase angle ϕ_1 relative to the phase angle of the input envelope. This phase angle may be measured by the phasemeter of Fig. 10-6. The modulating frequency ω_1 is known, and ϕ_1 is obtained during the measurement, so the time delay is easily computed. This is

$$\Delta t = \frac{\phi_1}{\omega_1} \qquad (10\text{-}18)$$

where ϕ_1 is expressed in radians and ω_1 in radians per second.

Now the possibilities of constructing a complete instrument to measure phase distortion coefficients should become obvious. The required component parts are two oscillators (one for the carrier, and one for ω_1), a modulator, two detectors, and a phasemeter. If the value of ω_1 is kept constant so that Δt is a function only of ϕ_1, the dial of the phasemeter may be calibrated directly in units of time rather than in radians or degrees. The phase distortion coefficient is then found by tuning the ω_2 oscillator through the useful frequency band, plotting the values of Δt directly from the phasemeter dial, and noting the difference between the largest and smallest of these values.

The ultimate in convenience where many phase distortion coefficient measurements are to be made is to provide for fully automatic operation. This might be done in several ways. One is suggested below.

Modify the phasemeter of Fig. 10-4 by placing a buffer amplifier between the anode of T_2 and a low-pass filter. The cutoff frequency of this filter must be low enough to remove the frequency ω_1, leaving only a d-c component. This direct voltage is applied to the Y axis of an oscilloscope. Thus the vertical deflection is a measure of ϕ_1 or Δt. For the ω_2 (carrier) oscillator, employ a sweeping oscillator of the type discussed in Chapter 9. The sweep rate should be slow compared with the frequency ω_1. A mechanically driven sweep is indicated for voice-frequency testing. The sweeping oscillator is coupled in some manner to the X axis of the oscilloscope so that as ω_2 increases, the X deflection increases toward the right of the cathode-ray tube. In an electronically swept oscillator, the sawtooth sweeping voltage may be fed to the X axis directly, while a mechanical sweeping type can employ a potentiometer ganged to the oscillator tuning system so that a voltage proportional to the shaft position can be fed to the X axis. In any case, the horizontal displacement on the oscilloscope is a measure of the frequency, while the vertical position measures the time delay. Thus the time delay as a function of frequency is displayed directly. Rapid, accurate testing can be performed by relatively unskilled personnel using this method.

The approach discussed here is by no means limited to phase distortion coefficient measurements in the voice spectrum. The same technique may be used for testing carrier systems, television channels, and radio and microwave links.

REFERENCES

1. John M. Cage, *Theory and Application of Industrial Electronics* (New York: McGraw-Hill Book Company, Inc., 1951), sect. 12-2.
2. W. D. Cannon, "An Envelope Delay-Measuring Instrument in the Audio-Frequency Range," *Transactions of the AIEE, Part I, Communications and Electronics*, no. 22 (January 1956), p. 710.
3. W. D. Cannon, "Delay Distortion Correction," *Transactions of the AIEE, Part I, Communications and Electronics*, no. 23 (March 1956), p. 55.

Chapter 11

INSTRUMENTS FOR
COMPONENT TESTING

One problem that faces every circuit designer at times is determining the values of components. This may be a relatively simple measurement, such as finding the value of a resistor with a Wheatstone bridge. Or it may be a rather elaborate type of measurement, such as determining the input impedance or transfer impedance of a complete network as a function of frequency. As in the rest of this text, emphasis is placed in so far as possible on *electronic* instruments for testing components.

11-1. Instruments for determining active parameters

In the majority of electronic circuits, there will be some *active* components—tubes or transistors, for example. The parameters of these components play just as important a part in the over-all circuit behavior as do the passive resistors, capacitors, and inductors. There are a great many types of parameter testing equipment, and we shall make no effort to cover the field. However, at least one method will be shown for measuring the important tube and transistor parameters.

(a) *Vacuum Tube Bridges.* A vacuum tube bridge is an instrument for determining the values of μ, r_p, and g_m under operating conditions. The actual circuit configuration is different for each measurement, but when one speaks of a "vacuum tube bridge," it is generally understood to mean an instrument with switches or other convenient means for arranging to measure any one of these three parameters. To simplify the explanation of the instrument, each arrangement will be shown independently. We shall start with the problem of finding μ, using the bridge of Fig. 11-1.

The bridge is balanced by adjusting R_2 and C. As in any a-c bridge, two balancing controls are necessary. Capacitor C balances out the effects of interelectrode capacitance.

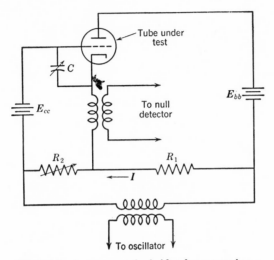

Fig. 11-1. A vacuum tube bridge for measuring μ.

When the bridge is in balance, no alternating component of plate current flows, and consequently there is no drop across the r_p of the tube. This means that the plate alternating voltage is equal to μE_g, where E_g is the input alternating voltage to the grid. Now to satisfy the requirement that no current flow in the tube, there must be an equal and opposite voltage applied to the plate. This voltage, E_p, is produced by the current I flowing in resistor R_1. Since $\mu E_g = E_p$, and E_g and E_p are IR_2 and IR_1, respectively, it follows by inspection that

$$\mu = \frac{IR_1}{IR_2} = \frac{R_1}{R_2} \qquad (11\text{-}1)$$

In the basic bridge of Fig. 11-1, R_2 would be made the variable resistor instead of R_1, since changing R_1 will change the plate direct current of the tube, and vary the operating point. A more elegant bridge of the same general nature could eliminate this problem by replacing R_1 and R_2 with the secondaries of transformers, which offer negligible impedance to the flow of the direct currents. The voltages E_g and E_p are fed into the circuit through these transformers. Variable attenuators placed in the primary windings permit balancing the bridge by adjusting the relative values of E_g and E_p until $E_p = \mu E_g$. The value of μ is then found as the ratio of the attenuator settings.

A simple bridge for measuring g_m is illustrated in Fig. 11-2. The

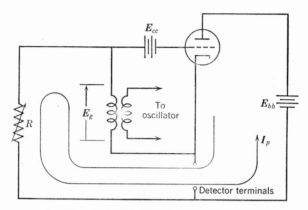

Fig. 11-2. A bridge for measuring g_m.

voltage across the high-impedance detector terminals is

$$E_D = E_g - I_p R \tag{11-2}$$

If R is much less than the r_p of the tube, the current I_p is

$$I_p = g_m E_g \tag{11-3}$$

Substitute Eq. (11-3) into (11-2), and set the result equal to zero, since E_D is zero at balance. This gives

$$g_m = 1/R \tag{11-4}$$

If the detector has a low impedance rather than a high impedance (for example, the voice coil of a loudspeaker might be connected to the detector terminals), it is no longer necessary to assume R is much less than r_p. There will be two current components in the low-impedance detector: one equal to E_g/R, and one equal to $g_m E_g$. These currents flow in opposite directions, so when they are equal, there will be no net current. Thus the condition for balance with a low-impedance detector is

$$E_g/R = g_m E_g \tag{11-5}$$

and

$$g_m = 1/R \tag{11-6}$$

as before.

It is necessary in this case that the detector impedance be negligible compared to the r_p of the tube, but this condition is relatively easy to fulfill.

Another transconductance-measuring circuit is given in Fig. 11-3. In terms of the equivalent circuit of Fig. 11-3(b), it is seen that the voltage developed across a high-impedance detector is

$$E_D = E_p - I_pR = -\mu E_g + I_pr_p \tag{11-7}$$

In the null condition, Eq. (11-7) is equal to zero, so

$$E_p - I_pR = 0 \tag{11-8a}$$

$$\mu E_g - I_pr_p = 0 \tag{11-8b}$$

Find the expression for I_p from each portion of Eq. (11-8):

$$I_p = E_p/R \tag{11-9a}$$

$$I_p = \mu E_g/r_p = g_mE_g \tag{11-9b}$$

Now equate the right-hand terms of the two parts of Eq. (11-9):

$$E_p/R = g_mE_g \tag{11-10}$$

from which we see by inspection that

$$g_m = \frac{E_p}{E_g}(1/R) \tag{11-11}$$

The value of R is known in any particular measurement, and the ratio E_p/E_g is easily obtained from the attenuator readings.

In the circuits of Figs. 11-2 and 11-3, it may be necessary to neutralize the signal fed directly from grid to plate through interelectrode

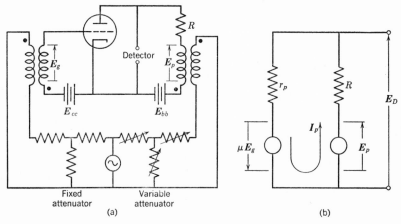

Fig. 11-3. A second type of mutual-conductance bridge. Part (b) is the equivalent circuit.

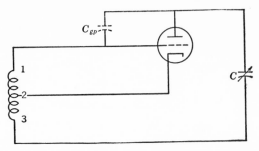

Fig. 11-4. A method of neutralizing interelectrode capacitance effects in the circuits of Figs. 11-2 and 11-3.

capacitance. This may be done by returning the cathode connection of the tube in Fig. 11-2 or the negative grid bias supply terminal in Fig. 11-3 to a tap on the secondary of the grid transformer. The free end of the winding is then connected to the plate through a small variable capacitor, as shown in Fig. 11-4. Terminal 3 of the transformer is of the opposite polarity from terminal 1, so current flowing through capacitor C neutralizes that flowing to the anode through C_{gp}.

The dynamic plate resistance r_p can be found with the bridge of Fig. 11-5. The equivalent of the tube is shown connected into the bridge with dotted lines. As with any bridge, balance exists when the products of the impedances in opposite arms are equal. Thus, if we let C_t represent the tube capacitances $C_{pk} + C_{gp}$ for convenience, the conditions for balance may be expressed as

$$R_2\left(r_p + \frac{1}{j\omega C_t}\right) = R_1\left(R_3 + \frac{1}{j\omega C}\right) \qquad (11\text{-}12)$$

From the real terms of Eq. (11-12), it is easily found that

$$r_p = R_1 R_3 / R_2 \qquad (11\text{-}13)$$

and from the imaginaries,

$$C_t = C R_2 / R_1 \qquad (11\text{-}14)$$

Many other systems for measuring vacuum tube parameters are described in the literature (*1*). Those shown above are typical, and rather widely employed in practice. All vacuum tube bridges require a fair amount of auxiliary equipment, such as power supplies for establishing the d-c operating point of the tube, an oscillator to furnish a-c driving signals, and a null detector.

These bridges are not to be confused with "tube testers," which generally give only an indication of cathode emission on a meter marked "bad-good."

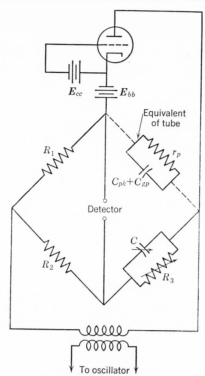

Fig. 11-5. A bridge for determining the plate resistance r_p of a tube.

(b) *Transistor Testing (2).* Since the announcement of the transistor in the late 1940's, a number of equivalent circuits have been proposed for use in the small-signal analysis of this device. The problem is somewhat more complicated than in the case of tubes, since transistors have a certain amount of transmission from the output back to the input. Therefore four parameters are necessary to represent a transistor, whereas two will serve in the case of a tube (r_p together with either μ or g_m).

In the present state of the transistor art, it appears that the so-called "hybrid" parameters will be the most popular in future work. Accordingly, our discussion will deal with the measurement of these quantities.

Figure 11-6 defines the hybrid parameters in terms of the small-signal a-c output and input voltages and currents. Figure 11-7 shows

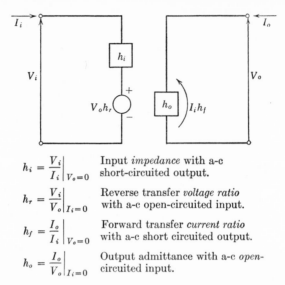

$$h_i = \frac{V_i}{I_i}\bigg|_{V_o=0}$$ Input *impedance* with a-c short-circuited output.

$$h_r = \frac{V_i}{V_o}\bigg|_{I_i=0}$$ Reverse transfer *voltage ratio* with a-c open-circuited input.

$$h_f = \frac{I_o}{I_i}\bigg|_{V_o=0}$$ Forward transfer *current ratio* with a-c short circuited output.

$$h_o = \frac{I_o}{V_o}\bigg|_{I_i=0}$$ Output admittance with a-c *open*-circuited input.

Fig. 11-6. Defining relationships for the transistor hybrid parameters. (From *IRE Standards on Methods of Testing Transistors*. Courtesy, Institute of Radio Engineers.)

configurations for measuring each of the four parameters in the grounded-emitter connection.

The batteries V_{cc} and V_{ee}, and resistor R fix the d-c operating point. The emitter current is equal for all practical purposes to V_{ee}/R, especially if V_{ee} is large enough to permit R to be several thousand ohms. The collector current is less than the emitter current by reason of the base current. Usually the collector direct current will be about 90 to 95 per cent of the emitter current.

Capacitor C should be large enough to present only an ohm or two of reactance at the testing frequency. Otherwise negative feedback is developed at the emitter lead, and the measurements give over-all circuit characteristics rather than transistor parameters alone.

It is necessary to provide low resistance between base and ground so that the base direct current, though small, will not develop any significant voltage. For this reason, chokes are placed in this path when the input must be open-circuited for a-c components. Since the base current will usually be of the order of a few microamperes to a milliampere, there is not much danger of d-c saturation in the choke. It is perfectly feasible to use fifty or a hundred henries, and still have an inductor of small physical size.

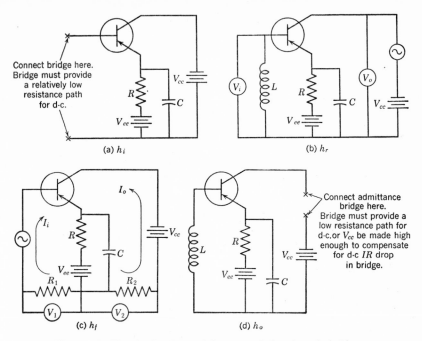

Fig. 11-7. Circuits for determining grounded emitter hybrid parameters. Supply voltages drawn for p-n-p transistors.

Part (a) of Fig. 11-7 shows the method of determining the input impedance h_i. Any bridge suited for a-c measurement of resistance may be used provided it places no more than a few thousand ohms resistance between base and ground.

The value of h_r is determined with the circuit of Fig. 11-7(b). A vacuum tube voltmeter is used for measuring V_i and V_o, the value of h_r being found as the ratio V_i/V_o.

The forward transfer current ratio h_f is obtained from the circuit of Fig. 11-7(c). The currents I_i and I_o flow through small resistors (typically a few hundred ohms at most), where they develop the voltages V_1 and V_2, respectively. These are measured with vacuum tube voltmeters, and h_f computed as

$$h_f = \frac{V_2 R_1}{V_1 R_2} \tag{11-15}$$

It is essential that R_2 be very small compared with the output impedance; i.e., $R_2 \ll 1/h_o$.

Finally, the output admittance is found from the circuit in Fig. 11-7(d). This is very similar to that used for finding h_i. Usually it is more accurate to use an admittance bridge than an impedance bridge, but either method is possible. If an admittance bridge is used, the value of h_o is read directly; an impedance bridge gives the reciprocal of h_o.

There are a great many additional important measurements that may be required in transistorized circuits. The cutoff frequency of the transistor and its output capacitance are two examples. However, the author feels that pursuing the topic much further would represent a major digression from our study of electronic instruments. The problem is basically one of measurement technique rather than instrumentation, and so lies outside the scope of this text.

11-2. The Q meter

While various types of impedance bridges are extremely useful in all fields of electrical measurements, they are not ordinarily "electronic" in the sense one uses the term. The reader seeking information on these bridges is referred to any of the standard texts on electrical measurements. However, there are several impedance-measuring instruments that are basically electronic in nature. One example is the Q meter.

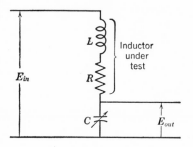

This device is used to measure the inductance and Q of coils by measuring the voltage developed across a capacitor in series resonance with the coil.

Fig. 11-8. An RLC series circuit.

Before undertaking a study of the circuitry, it might be worth while to review the relationship between Q and the voltage developed across the elements of a series resonant circuit.

Consider the RLC series circuit of Fig. 11-8. The ratio E_{out}/E_{in} is seen by inspection to be

$$\frac{E_{out}}{E_{in}} = \frac{-j/\omega C}{R + j(\omega L - 1/\omega C)} \tag{11-16}$$

With some manipulation, it may be shown that

$$\left|\frac{E_{out}}{E_{in}}\right| = \frac{\sqrt{(1/\omega_r^2 C^2 - L/C)^2 + L^2/Q^2 C^2}}{\omega_r^2 L^2/Q^2 + \omega_r^2 L^2 - 2L/C + 1/\omega_r^2 C^2} \tag{11-17}$$

where ω_r is the frequency at which resonance will occur when C is correctly tuned, and Q is defined in the usual way as $\omega_r L/R$.

It is convenient to define C in terms of the value it must have to create series resonance. Thus we shall let

$$C = KC_r \qquad (11\text{-}18)$$

where K is a proportionality factor and C_r is the value of C at which resonance occurs.

$$C_r = 1/L\omega_r^2 \qquad (11\text{-}19)$$

Substituting Eq. (11-18) into Eq. (11-17) leads to a surprisingly compact result:

$$\left|\frac{E_{out}}{E_{in}}\right| = \frac{1/K}{\sqrt{1/Q^2 + (1 - 1/K)^2}} \qquad (11\text{-}20)$$

When $K \equiv 1$, the resonant condition is achieved, and

$$E_{out}/E_{in} = Q \qquad (11\text{-}21)$$

Two examples of tuning characteristics are shown in Fig. 11-9. Important points to note are that for high values of Q, the tuning curve is

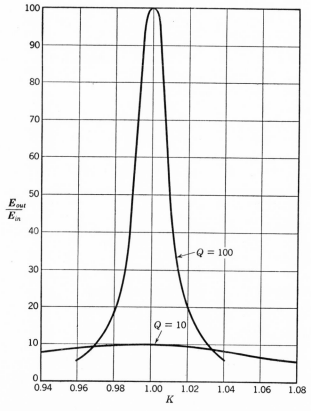

Fig. 11-9. Tuning characteristic of the series resonant circuit of Fig. 11-8.

very sharp, and careful tuning is necessary; also, for low values of Q, the curve is relatively broad and of low amplitude so that it is difficult to tell exactly when resonance occurs.

The principle of operation of the Q meter is contained entirely in Eq. (11-20). It should be observed that E_{out} increases linearly with E_{in}. Also, at the resonant frequency where $K \equiv 1$, $E_{out} = QE_{in}$. A given value of E_{out} might therefore be caused by *either* a particular value of Q or a particular value of E_{in}. For this reason, the complete instrument includes a voltmeter to monitor the value of E_{in}. This meter is calibrated to indicate the relative contribution to E_{out} made by E_{in}, and for this reason is labeled "Multiply Q by" rather than reading volts directly. The reading of the meter showing E_{out} is likewise marked not in volts but in values of Q, and these are multiplied by the factor shown on the scale of the monitoring meter to obtain the correct value of Q.

The circuit consists of an RF oscillator to supply a signal to the coil under test, and meters to measure E_{in} and E_{out} (marked "Multiply Q

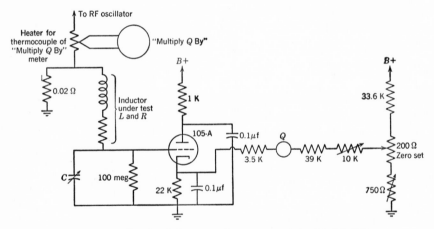

Fig. 11-10. Circuit of the measuring system of the Model 260A Q Meter, as connected for measuring Q in the range of 40 to 250. (Courtesy, Boonton Radio Corporation.)

by" and "Q" as noted above). The oscillator is of the tuned grid type, and because it is fairly conventional, we shall omit it from the discussion and consider the measuring circuit proper. This is illustrated in Fig. 11-10.

The value of E_{in} is monitored by a thermocouple meter. The voltage E_{out} is applied to the grid of a type 105A tube, which is self-biased nearly to cutoff. This is the high-bias plate detection system discussed in Chapter 5. Plate current flows as the result of an a-c signal at the grid and a direct voltage appears across the Q voltmeter in proportion to the voltage E_{out}. For very small values of E_{out} (of the order of 1 volt or less) the type 105A tube operates in a square law region, causing some compression at the low end of the Q scale. For values of Q greater than about 50, the scale is essentially linear.

Capacitor C is a precision air capacitor which varies from 30 $\mu\mu$f to 460 $\mu\mu$f. External terminals are provided for connecting additional capacitance in parallel with C to extend the tuning range, or to make measurements on the external capacitor itself. There is a trimmer capacitor, not shown in Fig. 11-10, in parallel with C for vernier adjustment. As may be seen from Fig. 11-9, precise tuning is essential when Q is high, and it is difficult to tune to exact resonance with C alone.

We shall not go into the numerous methods of making measurements with the Q meter, since this is a matter of laboratory practice and has little bearing on the basic circuit principles. However, by various techniques of using calibrated coils and capacitors in conjunction with the unknown component being tested, a wide variety of measurements may be made over a frequency range from 50 kc to 50 megacycles.

11-3. The Z-Angle meter

Another primarily electronic impedance measuring device is the Acton Laboratories, Inc., Z-Angle meter. The circuit by which the measurement of impedance and phase angle is accomplished is shown in Fig. 11-11.

Switch S_3 is first placed in the "Cal" position. The circuit then becomes equivalent to Fig. 11-12. The load includes the 100,000-ohm plate load resistor shunted by the 6H6 rectifier assembly. The "calibrate" control in Fig. 11-11 is adjusted until the VTVM gives a specified deflection, which is marked on its scale with a red line. The purpose of this step is to standardize the voltage at point A, for reasons that will become apparent as we study the phase-measuring operation.

Consider next the balancing of the instrument to find the magnitude of the unknown impedance, Z. During this operation, switch S_3 is in the "Bal" position. The two tubes have symmetrical plate loads, and

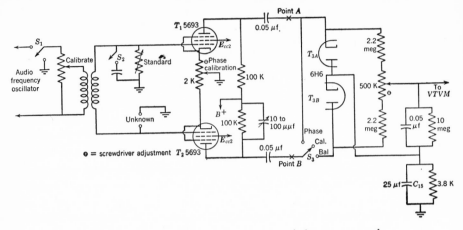

Fig. 11-11. Circuit of the Z-Angle meter, omitting power supply, oscillator, and VTVM. (Courtesy, Acton Laboratories, Inc.)

we will assume identical gains, K. At point A, the potential is E_A; at point B, it is E_B.

Assume the unknown impedance consists of a resistive component R and a reactive component jX. The standard resistor is adjustable.

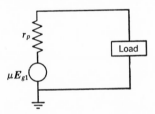

Fig. 11-12. Equivalent circuit with switch S_3 in "Cal" position.

We shall indicate its value at any particular setting by R_s. The portion of the circuit associated with the control grids is shown in Fig. 11-13, with components labeled as noted above. It is seen by inspection that

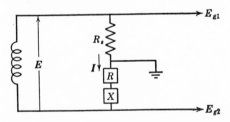

Fig. 11-13. The grid portion of the Z-Angle meter circuit.

the two grid voltages are

$$E_{g1} = E\,\frac{R_s}{R_s + R + jX} \tag{11-22}$$

$$E_{g2} = -E\,\frac{R + jX}{R_s + R + jX} \tag{11-23}$$

and therefore
$$E_A = KE\,\frac{R_s}{R_s + R + jX} \tag{11-24}$$

$$E_B = -KE\,\frac{R + jX}{R_s + R + jX} \tag{11-25}$$

Now we must determine the direct voltage across capacitor C_{15}. Tube 1 develops a negative charge on this capacitor, and tube 2 develops a positive charge. These charges are proportional to the magnitudes of E_A and E_B. From Eqs. (11-24) and (11-25),

$$\frac{E_A}{E_B} = \frac{R_s}{R + jX} \tag{11-26}$$

When E_A and E_B are of the same magnitude, the numerical value of Eq. (11-26) is unity, and there is no net charge on C_{15}. The VTVM will indicate a null, and from Eq. (11-26) it follows that

$$R_s = |R + jX| \tag{11-27}$$

R_s is adjusted by a calibrated dial, from which the magnitude of the unknown impedance is read.

When switch S_3 is shifted to the "Phase" position, the circuit takes the form shown in Fig. 11-14. The load R_L consists entirely of the 6H6 and its associated components, in shunt with both of the 100,000-ohm

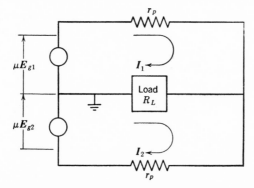

Fig. 11-14. Equivalent circuit with S_3 in "Phase" position. R_L is the equivalent load seen looking toward the right from point A in Fig. 11-11, in shunt with both 100,000-ohm resistors.

resistors. The voltmeter indication will be proportional to

$$E_{load} = (\mu E_{g1} - \mu E_{g2}) \frac{R_L}{r_p + 2R_L} \tag{11-28}$$

Now suppose the unknown impedance has a phase angle such that $E_{g1} = E \sin \omega t$ and $E_{g2} = E \sin (\omega t + \phi)$. The amplitudes are the same because the instrument was *left in balance* after finding the magnitude of the unknown. Then the voltage developed at point A in Fig. 11-11 (i.e., the voltage across R_L in Fig. 11-14) is

$$E_A = \mu E \frac{R_L}{r_p + 2R_L} [\sin \omega t - \sin (\omega t + \phi)] \tag{11-29}$$

Equation (11-29) may be written

$$E_A = 2\mu E \frac{R_L}{r_p + 2R_L} \sin (-\phi/2) \cos (\omega t + \phi/2) \tag{11-30}$$

The indication of the VTVM is proportional to the *amplitude* of Eq. (11-30), and therefore to the phase angle of the unknown. If the quantity E is held constant, ϕ is the only variable, and the VTVM can be calibrated to read degrees directly. We now see the purpose of the calibration step. This adjusts E to a specified value so that the phase angle indication will be a function only of ϕ.

There may be some question whether the angle of the unknown represents capacitive or inductive reactance. To identify which is which, a pushbutton switch S_2 is provided to shunt a small amount of capacitance across the standard resistor after the phase angle has been read. The direction the VTVM pointer moves after pushing the button shows whether the unknown includes inductance or capacitance.

11-4. The display of network impedances (3,4,5)

There are few tasks as tedious as determining point-by-point the impedance of a network over a very wide band of frequencies. Usually one is looking for a half-power frequency, a point of resonance, or something of the sort. It is very time consuming to make repeated measurements over a wide band until the desired point is located. An instrument that displays the real and reactive parts of the input impedance of a network would be most useful in such testing. This section describes such an instrument.

The basic system is shown in combined block diagram and schematic diagram in Fig. 11-15. The operation is as follows: A fixed

oscillator frequency is beaten in a mixer with a swept oscillator frequency, and the difference is applied to the network under test through
a large resistor R. This resistor should be of the order of 100 times the
highest impedance expected in the unknown network. Thus it effec-

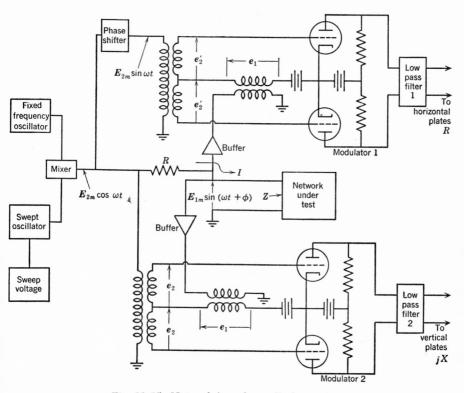

Fig. 11-15. Network impedance display system.

tively converts the output of the mixer to a variable-frequency, constant-current source.

The impedance of the network is $Z = E_1/I$, where E_1 is the rms
voltage across the terminals and I is the constant current. Now since
I *is* constant, it follows that Z is directly proportional to E_1, so if E_1
may be measured and broken into its real and reactive components,
the real and reactive components of Z are also determined.

This is accomplished by applying the voltage E_1 to each of two balanced modulators. The driving voltage is applied unchanged to one
modulator, and goes to the other modulator after being shifted 90° in

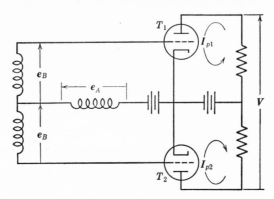

Fig.` 11-16. Detail of the balanced modulator.

phase. To see why the balanced modulators give the desired results, refer to the modulator circuit alone drawn in Fig. 11-16.

Consider two arbitrary voltages, e_A and e_B applied in the positions indicated. The two tubes will be assumed balanced, and linear and square-law terms are assumed in their plate currents. These currents are

$$I_{p1} = A_1(e_A + e_B) + A_2(e_A + e_B)^2 \qquad (11\text{-}31)$$

$$I_{p2} = A_1(e_A - e_B) + A_2(e_A - e_B)^2 \qquad (11\text{-}32)$$

where A_1 and A_2 are proportionality constants. The voltage V is proportional to $(I_{p2} - I_{p1})$. If Eqs. (11-31) and (11-32) are expanded, and the indicated subtraction performed, it is found that

$$V = A_3(-2A_1e_B - 4A_2e_Ae_B) \qquad (11\text{-}33)$$

Now we may apply Eq. (11-33) to the problem at hand. Consider first modulator 1 in Fig. 11-15. Here e_A is

$$e_A = e_1 = E_{1m} \sin (\omega t + \phi) \qquad (11\text{-}34)$$

and $\qquad\qquad e_B = e_2' = E_{2m} \sin \omega t \qquad (11\text{-}35)$

For convenience, it is assumed that the buffer amplifiers and transformers have unity gain. Now substitute Eqs. (11-34) and (11-35) into Eq. (11-33). This gives

$$V_1 = A_3[-2A_1E_{2m} \sin \omega t - 2A_2E_{1m}E_{2m} \cos \phi \\ + 2A_2E_{1m}E_{2m} \cos (2\omega t + \phi)] \qquad (11\text{-}36)$$

Likewise, it may be shown that the output of modulator 2 is

$$V_2 = A_3[-2A_1E_{2m} \cos \omega t - 2A_2E_{1m}E_{2m} \sin \phi \\ + 2A_2E_{1m}E_{2m} \sin (2\omega t + \phi)] \qquad (11\text{-}37)$$

After passing these voltages through the low-pass filters, the only terms remaining are those involving cos ϕ and sin ϕ. Thus the deflection voltage applied to the horizontal axis is of the form

$$V_x = A_4 E_{1m} \cos \phi \qquad (11\text{-}38)$$

and the vertical deflection is given by

$$V_y = A_4 E_{1m} \sin \phi \qquad (11\text{-}39)$$

The constant A_4 includes all constants used previously, and also the voltage E_{2m}, *which must be kept constant*. This restriction on E_{2m} is an important design consideration for the oscillators and mixer.

Since it was shown that the magnitude of E_1 is proportional to Z, it follows that Eq. (11-38) represents the real component of Z, while Eq. (11-39) is the reactive component, jX.

As the system is arranged in Fig. 11-15, the result would be a polar plot of the impedance. It is not always easy to identify the various frequencies in a polar plot, and the utility of the system is greatly increased by providing frequency markers. This is most conveniently done by intensity modulation of the display through the Z axis input of the oscilloscope. One possible method is shown in Fig. 11-17.

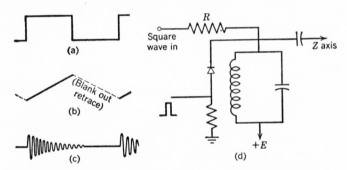

Fig. 11-17. (a) One-cycle square wave. (b) Integral of (a). (c) Ringing waveform to produce frequency markers. (d) Ringing circuit to generate waveform of (c).

Suppose the sweep of the variable oscillator is controlled by a triangular wave which is obtained in turn by integrating a low-frequency square wave (typical sweep speeds are of the order of 1 cycle in this equipment). When the square wave goes up, it is applied to a ringing circuit as in Fig. 11-17(d). If R is large, and the tank circuit Q is high, a train of damped sine waves is produced. If it is known that the sweep frequency changes at a certain rate, say 10 megacycles per second, and the damped sine wave is also at a known frequency, for example 10 cycles, then the brightening of the trace at the peaks of the damped wave train will produce useful frequency markers. For the numerical values used as an example, every sinusoidal peak represents 1/10 sec, and therefore a change of 10 megacycles ÷ 10 = 1 megacycle.

The diode in Fig. 11-17(c) is to damp out the wave train abruptly to prepare the ringing circuit for the next cycle. Sometime during the retrace time, a large positive pulse from a *low-impedance* source is applied to the anode of the diode, which ordinarily is at ground potential. This causes the normally-off diode to conduct, and applies a temporary short-circuit to the ringing circuit, reducing its Q and killing the oscillation. The ringing is then ready to resume in proper synchronization with the next square wave.

One can easily plot R and jX directly as functions of frequency by applying the output of either low-pass filter in Fig. 11-15 to the vertical plates of an oscilloscope, and sweeping the scope with the wave of Fig. 11-17(b).

The method just described for displaying the input impedance can also be used to plot the transfer gain of any network, including an active one. Sonnenfeldt (3) treats this application especially and includes numerous detailed circuit diagrams. Salzberg and Marini (5) deal primarily with the problem of finding input impedances. Both techniques are similar.

REFERENCES

1. Frederick E. Terman, *Radio Engineers Handbook* (New York: McGraw-Hill Book Company, Inc., 1943), pp. 960-964.
2. "I.R.E. Standards on Solid-State Devices: Methods of Testing Transistors, 1956," *Proc. I.R.E.*, November 1956, vol. 44, p. 1542.
3. Richard W. Sonnenfeldt, "A New Sweep for Displaying the True Parameters of a Network," *Proc. Natl. Electronics Conf.* (1954), vol. 10, p. 375.
4. M. S. Corrington, T. Murakami, and R. W. Sonnenfeldt, "The Complete Specification of a Network by a Single Parameter," *R.C.A. Rev.*, September 1954, vol. 15, p. 389.
5. B. Salzberg and J. W. Marini, "Rapid Measurement of Impedance and Admittance," *Transactions of the AIEE, Part I, Communications and Electronics*, May 1955, no. 18, p. 180.

Chapter 12

DIGITAL DISPLAY

There is a decided trend in instrument design to provide digital display of the measured quantity. That is, the value is indicated by a sequence of numbers rather than the position of a pointer on a dial. These numbers may be displayed in several ways. The most common are by mechanical dials ("cyclometers," similar to an automobile speedometer), images of digits projected from inside the instrument onto a ground glass screen on the front panel (so-called "in-line" display), and by banks of neon lights arranged in vertical columns of ten lamps, representing the digits zero through nine.

Digital display is convenient for the user of an instrument, although the author is inclined to question the wisdom of displaying with several significant figures a reading that might be accurate to only 5 per cent. One of the really significant advantages in digital readout is that the information is encoded in a form readily placed on punched cards or magnetic tape for use in data-processing machines and computers. Another is the great reduction of human error in repetitive readings by unskilled personnel, as in production-line testing.

There are three steps that must be carried out in arriving at a digital display. The first we shall call "sampling," and the second "encoding." Step three is the actual display of the result. One or more of these steps may sometimes be accomplished simultaneously.

12-1. The elements of digital display

In introducing this chapter, several terms—*sampling, encoding,* and *display*—were used. Before discussing circuits to accomplish these functions, let us explain what they mean.

211

Sampling is the process of determining the value of a variable at some particular moment of time. In pulse time multiplex communication systems, the sample must be taken frequently enough to permit reconstructing a waveform substantially like that of the spoken words transmitted. In instruments it is usually necessary to sample only a few times per second, since we do not seek to duplicate the signal, but merely to determine some of its properties. For example, if an alternating voltage is to be measured, we may convert it to direct current by rectifying and filtering, and the resulting d-c amplitude need be measured only once in a while to determine if the original alternating voltage has changed. If the time between samples is short compared with the time constant of the filter system, and this time constant in turn is long compared with the period of the a-c waveform being measured, then sample after sample will give the same voltage until the incoming signal assumes a new peak value. The sampling system in most electronic instruments operates at a rather low frequency, say around ten or twenty times per second.

Encoding is the process of converting the sample into a pattern of digits. The sample is basically an *analog* measurement, which is converted to a numerical or *digital* measurement by the encoding process.

Display consists of taking the digital code generated within the instrument and using it to light neon lamps, or move mechanical registers or pointers to specific numbers corresponding to the code.

There is one very obvious disadvantage in every digital system: the output must be indicated in discrete steps. There is no such thing as a fractional digit. If the amplitude of a sample is 12.7 volts, for example, it may be encoded and displayed as either 12 or 13. Obviously, the difficulty may be reduced by providing more digital registers and more precise encoding; but it is equally obvious that no matter how many registers are used, there will be samples that fail to coincide exactly with one of the digits in the last register. The fact that only discrete values may be indicated means that the last figure in a display will almost always be in error by plus or minus one.

Because display and encoding are frequently carried forth simultaneously by digital counters, circuits for accomplishing the functions outlined above will be described in this sequence: display, encoding, and sampling.

12-2. Methods of display

A number of methods may be employed for the display of a digital quantity. Several are shown in Fig. 12-1. The meter consists of a D'Arsonval movement with the digits zero through nine printed on the

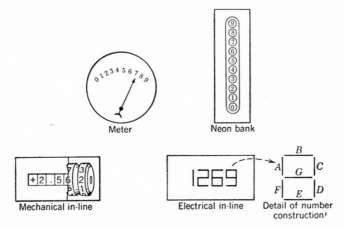

Fig. 12-1. Various forms of digital displays.

scale. The readout circuitry is so designed that currents corresponding to only these positions of the pointer can flow in the meter movement. Thus the pointer always falls on a particular position and gives an unambiguous reading. As many meters are required as the number of digits one wishes to display.

The neon bank indicator is similar to the meter in that several such banks must be included if one is to display several digits. The neon bank system is particularly well suited to combined encoding and display operations, for the flip-flop circuits that do the counting simultaneously turn the lamps on and off. More will be said of this shortly.

The various types of in-line registers have two advantages: first, the entire result can be read from left to right, as one would read a number printed on a sheet of paper. The eye does not have to wander up and down columns to look for a particular illuminated digit, or have to scan meters to see where the pointers came to rest. The second advantage is that there *appears* to be one readout assembly for the entire display, instead of a separate one for each digit. This is purely a convenience for the user. The designer must do just as much electrical work for an in-line readout as for any other type; the mechanical product design is usually more difficult.

Two types of in-line displays are shown in Fig. 12-1. The first is a cyclometer, similar to those on automobile dashboards. It is a purely mechanical device, usually actuated by a shaft coupled to a balancing potentiometer (*cf.* the discussion on self-balancing potentiometer techniques in Chapter 7). The sketch shows part of the front panel broken away to reveal the numbered wheels inside. Positions may also be included on the wheels for plus and minus signs, and decimal points. The electrical in-line readout of Fig. 12-1 is accomplished by the use of seven long, narrow slits cut in an opaque mask. Each slit is illuminated by a separate lamp, and several slits are lighted simultaneously to form a given number. For example, the number 4 is formed by lighting slits $AGCD$, or the number 9 by lighting every slit except F. This makes a very satisfactory display, but requires quite a bit of effort in mechanical product design.

Several optical techniques (not shown in Fig. 12-1) are possible for in-line readout. Basically, they consist of projecting an image of each digit onto a ground-glass screen in the front panel. For example, meters might be used for the individual registers, with disks having transparent numbers rotated by the meter movement instead of the usual pointer. Whatever number comes to rest in front of a lamp will have its image projected onto the screen.

12-3. Binary and decimal counting (*1*)

(a) *Binary Stages.* The various types of readout systems just illustrated all depend (with the possible exception of the cyclometer) on converting stored electrical information into a pattern of lights or mechanical positions. This stored information is almost invariably held in the form of binary numbers, which are identified by the two possible states of vacuum tube or transistor flip-flops, or by the state of magnetization of ferromagnetic cores. As a matter of convenience for the user, these binary numbers are ordinarily *translated* into decimal digits before being displayed. The translation is done automatically by the counters themselves.

The counters are usually used in a manner that combines encoding and display. Thus they count a number of pulses proportional to the

signal being measured, which is an *encoding* process; and simultaneously
show the accumulated count with neon lamps, which is *display*.

Figure 12-2 shows the basic circuit of a binary counter, bistable
multivibrator, Eccles-Jordan trigger circuit, or flip-flop as it is variously
called. We have encountered circuits of this type in several earlier
chapters, but they were more or less taken for granted as subassemblies

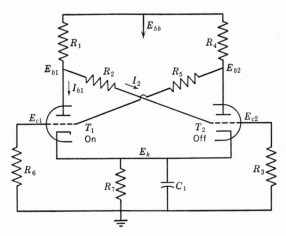

Fig. 12-2. The basic form of a flip-flop circuit. Note: All voltages
are referred to *ground*, not cathode.

in an over-all instrument. Since they are really the heart of many
digital readout systems, a more detailed explanation of their operation
and design is in order at this point.

Suppose that T_1 is conducting, and T_2 is off. Let a negative pulse be
applied to the control grid of T_1. This causes T_1 to stop conducting, and
the plate potential E_{b1} rises.* This causes the potential E_{c2} to rise, although a lesser amount because of the voltage divider action of R_2
and R_3. However, if E_{c2} rises enough to start conduction in T_2, the
potential E_{b2} drops and carries E_{c1} down with it. This keeps T_1 off,
and T_2 remains conducting because its grid potential is relatively high
as long as T_1 is off. If a negative pulse is subsequently applied to the
grid of T_2, the process reverses, and T_1 turns on.

Now suppose we consider the problem of flip-flop design. Figure 12-2
will be used as a prototype, and the design will be based on the charac-

* Voltages in Fig. 12-2 and related discussion are *referred to ground* rather than
cathode unless otherwise indicated.

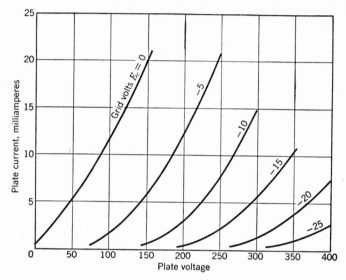

Fig. 12-3. Characteristics of the type 12AU7 tube. (Courtesy, Radio Corporation of America.)

teristic curves for the 12AU7 tube shown in Fig. 12-3. Nine steps are involved, as follows:

1. Arbitrarily assume T_1 is on and T_2 is off. Pick E_k, E_{bb}, E_{c1}, and I_{b1}. Suppose we choose $E_k = 100$ volts, $E_{bb} = 300$ volts, $E_{c1} = 95$ volts, and $I_{b1} = 3$ ma. E_k must be rather large so that the grid of T_2 can be positive with respect to ground, and still be very much negative with respect to the cathode. A value of E_k between one-quarter and one-half E_{bb} will usually lead to a satisfactory design, and E_{c1} should be fairly close to E_k so that the grid of the "on" tube will be just slightly negative. Also, I_{b1} must be large enough so that when it stops flowing at the start of the switching operation, a really noticeable potential difference will appear across R_1.

2. Find R_7.

$$R_7 = E_k/I_{b1} \tag{12-1}$$

In our example, $R_7 = 100/0.003 = 33{,}000$ ohms.

3. Pick I_2. This current should be appreciably less than I_{b1}. Suppose we let $I_2 = 1$ ma.

4. Refer to the tube characteristics to find the value of cathode-to-plate voltage corresponding to the chosen values of plate current and

grid bias. Here the bias is -5 volts, and the current 3 ma. This requires a cathode-to-plate voltage of 120 volts. The anode voltage relative to ground is

$$E_{b1} = E_k + E_{kp} \qquad (12\text{-}2)$$

5. Find R_1. This will be the same as R_4, since the two sides of a flip-flop are symmetrical.

$$R_1 = \frac{E_{bb} - E_{b1}}{I_{b1} + I_2} \qquad (12\text{-}3)$$

Substituting numerical values, $R_1 = (300 - 220)/(0.003 + 0.001) = 20,000$ ohms.

6. Relate the grid potential of T_1 to the supply voltage, in terms of the potential divider comprising R_4, R_5, and R_6.

$$\frac{E_{c1}}{E_{bb}} = \frac{R_6}{R_4 + R_5 + R_6} \qquad (12\text{-}4)$$

7. By inspection of Fig. 12-2, it is seen that

$$E_{b1} = I_2(R_2 + R_3) \qquad (12\text{-}5)$$

Because of the symmetry of the circuit, $R_2 \equiv R_5$ and $R_3 \equiv R_6$. Substitute R_5 and R_6 for R_2 and R_3 in Eq. (12-4).

$$E_{b1} = I_2(R_5 + R_6) \qquad (12\text{-}6)$$

Now R_5 and R_6 are still unknown, but may be determined by the simultaneous solution of Eqs. (12-4) and (12-6).

In the example we are working, this leads to $R_5 = R_2 = 144,000$ ohms, and $R_6 = R_3 = 76,000$ ohms. This completes the design.

8. CHECK to be sure T_2 is really off.

$$E_{c2} = I_2 R_3 \qquad (12\text{-}7)$$

For the numerical values involved here, $E_{c2} = 1$ ma $\times$ 76,000 ohms $= 76$ volts and E_k is 100 volts, so the grid of T_2 is 24 volts negative with respect to the cathode.

$$E_{b2} = E_{bb} \frac{R_5 + R_6}{R_4 + R_5 + R_6} \qquad (12\text{-}8)$$

Substituting numerical values, we find $E_{b2} = 275$ volts. Then the cathode-to-plate potential is $E_{b2} - E_k = 175$ volts. Reference to the curves of Fig. 12-3 shows that -24 volts bias is more than enough to cut off the tube with 175 volts from plate to cathode.

9. CHECK to be sure the gain is sufficient to cause triggering. In the most general sense, a flip-flop is an oscillator, and must have a loop

gain greater than unity during the moment of switching. Otherwise, it will act merely as an amplifier with positive feedback and not as a switch.

During the moment of switching, when one tube has started coming on and the other is not fully off, the value of g_m for the 12AU7 with the operating points involved here will be around 2000 micromhos. The load for tube 1 is $r_p||R_1||(R_2 + R_3)$, which is about 5000 ohms. The load is the same for tube 2. Then the gain for each tube is 2000 μmhos $\times$ 5000 ohms $= 10$. The loop gain is $10 \times 10 = 100$.

Step 8 makes or breaks the design. It often happens that after all the component values are determined, the grid voltage on tube 2 proves insufficient to insure cutoff. In this case, the currents and voltages assumed in Step 1 and Step 3 must be changed. This is largely a matter of trial and error, but becomes easier with practice and experience. The importance of Step 9 cannot be overemphasized either. Many a flip-flop that looks as though it should work proves on closer inspection to have a loop gain less than unity. It is also important to use a large enough trigger pulse to turn tube 1 thoroughly off. If its plate potential rises just a trifle, the grid of T_2 may not be lifted above cutoff. Triggering will fail to take place, even though the loop gain would have been greater than unity if the grid voltage of T_2 had risen just a bit higher.

The flip-flop just discussed differs from those used in binary counters in a few minor ways. In order to restrict attention to the design problem of establishing two independent steady-state conditions, a few components necessary for switching rapidly and reliably have been omitted. This omission is corrected in Fig. 12-4, which shows a complete flip-flop as it would be used for binary counting. The added components are the resistors R_8 and R_9 in conjunction with C_4 and diodes D_1 and D_2; the capacitors C_2 and C_3; the RC assembly $R_{10}C_5$; and switch S_1.

The resistor-diode assembly is for "steering" triggering pulses to the grids at the moment of switching. The grid of the "on" tube, let us say, is at $+95$ volts, and that of the "off" tube is at $+76$ volts. The potential at the junction of R_8, R_9, and C_4 might be 100 volts. Then both diodes are nonconducting except when a negative pulse is applied through C_4. Hence they effectively isolate the two grid assemblies from one another and from the input circuit. This is essential to prevent unwanted interaction. Silicon diodes are especially suited for this application because of their very high back resistance; vacuum diodes are equally good, but have the disadvantage of involving an extra tube.

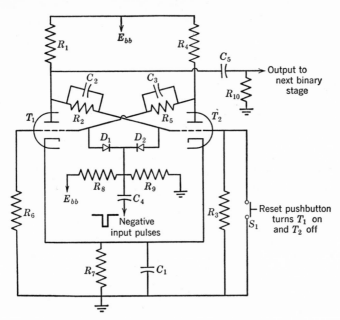

Fig. 12-4. A complete binary counter stage.

Capacitors C_2 and C_3 are called *speed-up* or *commutating* capacitors. Since the voltage across a capacitor cannot change instantaneously, the sudden change in the plate potential of a tube at the moment of switching is transmitted full-strength through these capacitors to the opposite grid. Thus, at the moment of switching, the voltage divider action between R_2 and R_3 or between R_5 and R_6 is eliminated. If the speed-up capacitors are small enough to create a very short time constant with R_2 and R_5, they will not postpone unduly the establishment of a new steady-state after switching. Typical values of speed-up capacitors are from 10 to 100 $\mu\mu f$.

Switch S_1 is a normally open pushbutton. When this is pressed, it grounds the grid of T_2, cutting that tube off and causing T_1 to conduct. This action is known as "resetting." In many systems, the grid of T_2 in every binary stage is connected through a steering diode to a common reset bus. A large negative pulse on this bus resets every binary counter simultaneously. The bus itself might be energized by a pushbutton, or electronically through a pulse generator.

Finally, if a number larger than zero or one is to be stored, more than one counter must be present. A second counter may be cascaded with the first through the C_5R_{10} network. This is connected to the input terminal of the following binary stage. The time constant C_5R_{10} should be short enough to differentiate the square step developed at the plate of T_1 at the moment of switching. When T_1 is turned off, the step goes positive, and the derivative is a positive pulse. This will not affect the next stage because the steering diodes at its input pass only negative pulses. When the plate of T_1 goes down in potential, a negative pulse is produced and the next binary triggers. Note that it takes two input pulses in a given binary stage to get one *negative* output pulse. *This is why the binary stage counts.* If a second binary is cascaded with it, it takes four input pulses to the first stage to get one negative output from the second. Thus counting by four is achieved. An assembly of n cascaded binary stages counts by 2^n.

(b) *Conversion to Decade Counting.* Binary counting is ideal for data-handling systems. Unfortunately, in a digital display system the number base ten is almost essential for the operator's convenience. People are used to thinking of the number fifty, for example, as 50 and not the binary number 110010. Therefore binary counters designed for digital display are constructed to operate to the base 16, with feedback circuits that insert extra pulses to make the 4 binary stages go through a full cycle with only ten input pulses. The way this is done is shown in Figs. 12-5 and 12-6.

Figure 12-5 illustrates four binary counters in block diagram form, with a feedback path from the fourth stage (D) to stages B and C. Disregard this path for the moment and refer to Fig. 12-6(a), which shows the waveforms that would appear at the plate of the left-hand tubes in binaries A, B, C, and D if evenly spaced input pulses were counted. With no feedback, the set of four counters recycles for sixteen input pulses. Note in particular that after pulse number eight, stages A, B, and C are "down" and D is "up" for the first time. After fourteen inputs, all stages are "up" except A.

Conditions after eight and fourteen pulses are the clue to decade

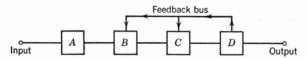

Fig. 12-5. A four-stage (scale-of-16) binary scaler converted to decade scaling by feedback.

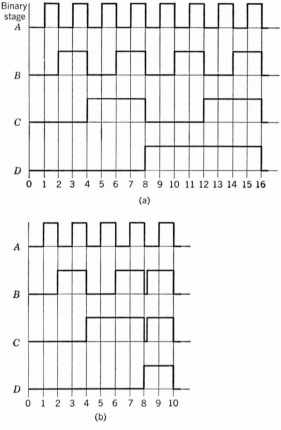

Fig. 12-6. Waveforms in cascaded binary counters. (a) Scale-of-16; (b) decade counting derived from scale-of-16.

counting, shown in Fig. 12-6(b). After the eighth input pulse, stage D switches and a pulse derived from this action is fed back to stages B and C, triggering them into the "up" condition again. Therefore the four binary stages automatically register a count of fourteen within a microsecond or thereabouts after they have received the eighth input pulse. The ninth input sets the binaries to a state equivalent to fifteen, and the tenth recycles all stages, resulting in a true decade count.

Figure 12-7 illustrates a complete decade scaler assembly. The stored count is displayed by neon lamps; for any configuration of conducting tubes, one and only one lamp is lighted. A number of lamps have appreciable potential difference between their terminals, but in only one of the ten is it higher than the ignition potential required to ionize the

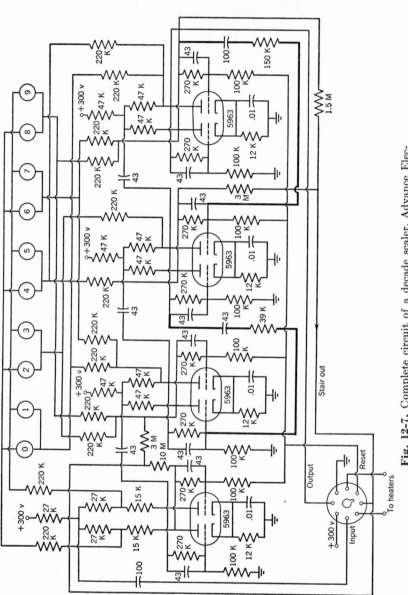

Fig. 12-7. Complete circuit of a decade scaler, Advance Electronics Lab., Inc., Type 100B. (Courtesy, Advance Electronics Lab., Inc.)

neon gas and light the lamp. It should also be noted that the feedback is accomplished in a slightly different manner from that sketched in Fig. 12-5. In the block diagram, a single feedback bus is shown going from binary D to B and C simultaneously. This converts the count of eight to a count of fourteen, as already explained. The system in Fig. 12-7 operates in two steps to convert to decade counting, and illustrates another method by which this objective may be achieved. After a count of four, stage C triggers stage B back to the "up" position (cf. Fig. 12-6), setting up a pattern equivalent to a count of six. Two more pulses enter the counter, giving an actual count of six, but an apparent count of eight, and firing stage D. This stage sends a feedback pulse to stage C, returning it to the "up" position, and giving an apparent count of 12. Thus the first six input pulses enter a stored count of 12, and input pulses 7, 8, 9, and 10 correspond respectively to 13, 14, 15, and 16, with reset after 10 actual or 16 apparent.

The two feedback buses are shown in Fig. 12-7 as extra heavy lines. Another novel feature is the "stair out" bus. This wire carries a voltage that changes in discrete steps, increasing one step for each count from zero to nine. Thus the voltage appearing here is an analog of the digital count. Auxiliary equipment is available to sense these voltage levels and control the position of printing bars, making it possible to print on tape the digits stored in the decade register.

(c) *High-Speed Binary Stages.* The binary stage of Fig. 12-4 is inherently a low-speed device. The exact counting rate will depend on the values of circuit components and on the amount of stray capacitance associated with the anodes of the tubes. However, it would probably not be greater than 100 kc, and might be around only 40 to 50 kc. There are several factors that act to slow down the speed of operation. The two worst ones are the rise time of a pulse at the anode of a tube and the time required for the speed-up capacitors to recharge to their new steady-state voltages.

Figure 12-8 shows several waveforms at various points in a flip-flop during the moment of switching. Tube 1 is being turned off and tube 2 is coming on. It will be noted that their potentials do not rise and fall as absolutely square steps, but rather follow exponential laws with time constants of

$$\tau_p = R_{eq} C_{sh} \tag{12-9}$$

where R_{eq} is the equivalent plate load resistance and C_{sh} is the shunt

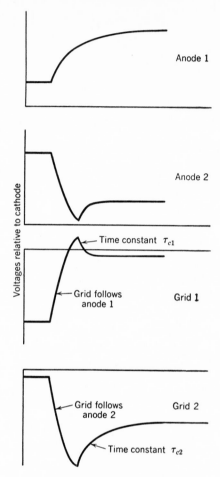

Fig. 12-8. Waveforms in a flip-flop at the moment of triggering.

capacitance between anode and ground. In the circuit of Fig. 12-4, it can be seen that τ_p might be reduced by decreasing the values of R_1 and R_4 to obtain a smaller R_{eq}. The value of C_{sh} can be made smaller by using pentodes instead of triodes. This reduces greatly the input capacitance of the opposite tube, which in the case of triodes is usually the largest portion of C_{sh}. After these modifications R_{eq} might be of the order of 5000 ohms and C_{sh} about 15×10^{-12} farads, giving a τ_p of 0.075 μsec. The rise time of a pulse measured from 10% to 90% is equal to 2.2 times this time constant. Hence the rise time of the pulses would be 0.165 μsec.

Much longer time constants are associated with the commutating capacitors. Consider the simple circuit of Fig. 12-9, in which a step of voltage is suddenly applied to an RC assembly as shown. The time

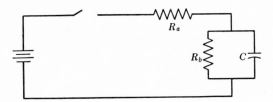

Fig. 12-9. A simple RC circuit analogous to the one involving the commutating capacitors.

constant for changing a voltage on the capacitor C is

$$\tau_C = C(R_a \| R_b) \tag{12-10}$$

Now let us relate the generalized resistors R_a and R_b to the actual resistors in the flip-flop of Fig. 12-4. For the configuration involving C_2, R_a corresponds to R_1 and R_b to R_2. The grid of T_2 is effectively clamped at cathode potential because it is driven momentarily positive by the surge of voltage transferred to it from the anode of T_1 via the speed-up capacitor C_2. Therefore resistor R_3 has no bearing on the time constant for capacitor C_2. If $C_2 = 30$ $\mu\mu$f, $R_1 = 20{,}000$ ohms, and $R_2 = 144{,}000$ ohms, then $\tau_{c2} = 0.53$ μsec.

The situation involving C_1 is a bit more complicated, since R_4 is shunted by the r_p of tube 2; and the grid of tube 1 is not clamped, so R_6 comes into the picture. Specifically, R_a corresponds to $(R_4 \| r_p) + R_6$ and R_b is equivalent to R_5. If we assume the r_p of the tube is 7000 ohms, $R_4 = 20{,}000$ ohms, $R_5 = 144{,}000$ ohms, and $R_6 = 76{,}000$ ohms, the time constant for C_1 is $\tau_{c1} = 1.56$ μsec. This time constant is determined mostly by R_5 and R_6. Even if the plate load were reduced to zero, τ_{c1} would still be 1.49 μsec.

Now the reason for concern over these time constants is that the voltages in the flip-flop must come almost to their new steady-state values before another switching action can be successfully initiated. Reducing the anode time constants by the use of smaller load resistors helps a little. This process cannot be carried too far, lest the loop gain drop below unity at the time of switching. Also, the time constants involving the commutating capacitors are so much greater that they almost swamp out the anode time constants. The real remedy for long switching times lies not so much in reducing the time constants as in making it unnecessary for the grids to recover from large voltage excursions.

The method by which this is accomplished is shown in Fig. 12-10.

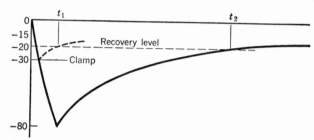

Fig. 12-10. The action of clamping in reducing recovery time.

Suppose that under normal conditions, the grid of the off-going tube is driven to -80 volts relative to its cathode, and a new switching cannot occur until it rises to -20 volts. The ultimate steady-state value is -15. It is seen that -20 volts is reached at time t_2. Now suppose that a diode is placed between the grid and a -30-volt potential source to

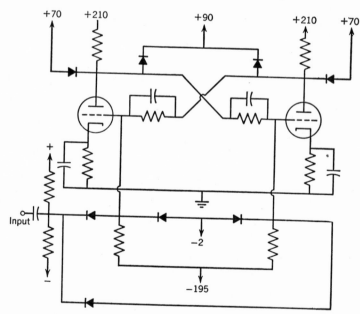

Fig. 12-11. Ten megacycle binary stage, slightly simplified. Note extensive use of clamping. (Courtesy of Hewlett-Packard Co.)

act as a clamp. The grid then starts its recovery from -30 volts rather than -80, and follows the dashed line in Fig. 12-10. Recovery takes place at time t_1. The dashed and solid lines have *exactly the same time constants*. The striking improvement is due wholly to clamping. If the time constants for C_1 and C_2 are shortened as well, there is a still greater reduction in recovery time. Clamps at the anodes are also useful when the ultimate in switching speed is required. A binary counter using clamps at all plates and grids is shown in Fig. 12-11. The tubes are type 6AH6 pentodes, but drawn as triodes in the figure to avoid the added complexity of screen-grid wiring. This is one stage of a decade scaler designed to operate at 10 megacycles in the Hewlett-Packard 524B frequency counter. The decade arrangement is similar to that of Fig. 12-5, except that to achieve maximum speed, the time spent in the feedback operation must be reduced. This is done by providing a system of gating that allows the eighth pulse to pass to stage D without having to trigger B and C first.

12-4. Counters as combined display and encoding elements

As we have seen in the previous section, decade counters equipped with neon lamp indicators make very satisfactory devices for storing a digital number and simultaneously indicating what that stored number is. The next question is how to make the stored number represent the quantity that is measured.

One solution to this problem is shown in Fig. 12-12. The unknown voltage is applied to one input of a circuit known as a "comparator," which determines when the sawtooth wave becomes equal to the unknown. At that moment, the comparator sends out a signal to close the gate and stop counting.

Suppose we follow a complete cycle of the encoding and display operation. The square wave generator operates at a low frequency, say 20 cycles. As the square wave goes from negative to positive at the start of a cycle, it first of all resets the counters. This might be done by applying to the reset bus a pulse obtained by differentiating the square wave. Simultaneously a delay circuit is triggered.

This delay assembly might consist of a one-shot multivibrator with a relatively long time constant, say 50 or 100 μsec, allowing ample time for the counters to reset. The pulse produced when the one-shot returns to its original state could fire a flip-flop, so that at the output of this

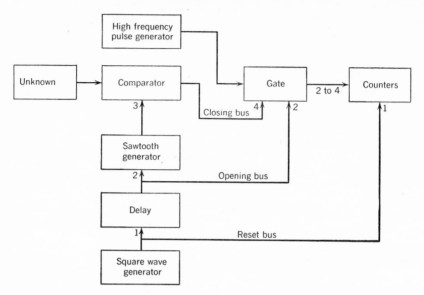

Fig. 12-12. Combined encoding and readout system based on decade counters. Numbers beside arrows show relative sequence of operations.

flip-flop we obtain a square wave synchronized with the original square wave, but delayed 50 to 100 μsec. The initial triggering of this flip-flop opens the gate, and allows pulses from the high-frequency (100 kc, for example) pulse generator to flow to the counters. The sawtooth generator integrates the flip-flop output, producing a triangular wave with a known, controlled rate of rise. This might be of the order of 10 volts per millisecond. When the amplitude of the triangular wave reaches the value of the unknown, the comparator sends out a pulse to close the gate, and the counting stops. For example, if the unknown is 125 volts, and the sawtooth rises at 10 volts per millisecond, it will be 12.5 milliseconds after the counting gate opens and the sawtooth starts until the gate closes again. During this length of time, 1250 pulses from the high-frequency pulse generator will pass through the gate and be stored in the counters. The decimal point will be located either from the operating instructions, or in many cases by small incandescent lamps placed between the banks of decade scalers on the front panel.

The count will be displayed until the next reset pulse comes along. In the present case, since the square wave generator is assumed to run at 20 cycles, there is a span of 50 millisec allowed for each cycle of counting and display. Since 12.5 millisec were used for counting, the display will remain for 37.5 millisec. This may seem like an impossibly short time for anyone to read the results, but remember that the process repeats twenty times a second, and persistence of vision will make the final count perfectly readable.

There are some drawbacks in the system just described that can be eliminated at the expense of circuit complexity. One problem is that if the unknown is too large, the comparator will never give an output, and counting will continue right up to the time of reset. This is analogous to driving the pointer of a D'Arsonval meter off scale. Some instruments with digital readout include circuits that sense the absence of a gate-closing pulse, and automatically switch to the next higher range when this happens.

Another trouble is that if counting continues for all but a few milliseconds of the allotted cycling time, even persistence of vision will not give a readable result. This is fairly easy to remedy by providing for manual operation so resetting of the counters will not occur until one has ample time to read the results. A one-shot multivibrator triggered by a pushbutton on the front panel could replace the square wave generator in this situation.

It is essential that the sawtooth generator produce a linear increase in voltage with time. This process cannot continue indefinitely, as eventually some sort of saturation must occur. In automatic recycling, this trouble would be identified by the absence of a gate-closing pulse, and the counters would count and reset with no display, as described above. In manual operation, the result would be that counting continues indefinitely. This would again indicate that the range switch must be changed to a less sensitive scale so that the unknown voltage will fall within the range of the comparator.

One type of comparator circuit is shown in Fig. 12-13. The action is understood most easily by thinking of the left-hand tube as a cathode follower and the right-hand one as an amplifier. A direct voltage proportional to the quantity being measured is applied to the "unknown input" terminal. Most of this voltage appears as a positive bias across resistor R_k. The sawtooth will be of a low enough amplitude from time t_0 to time t_1 that the amplifier is biased below cutoff, and no output is present. At time t_1, the amplifier is driven above cutoff, and the plate voltage begins to drop. The sudden break in plate voltage from a constant to a steadily decreasing quantity could be differentiated to provide a negative-going square step for closing the gate; or a Schmitt trigger

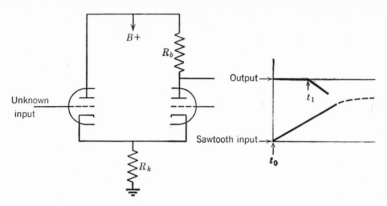

Fig. 12-13. One form of comparator.

might be driven by the decreasing plate voltage to provide a more rapid and positive action.

Another comparator is sketched in Fig. 12-14. The unknown is applied to a pair of resistors, R_1 and R_2, while the sawtooth is applied to the junction between them via a diode. As soon as the sawtooth voltage

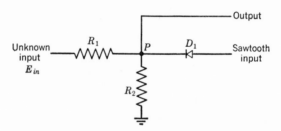

Fig. 12-14. Another type of comparator.

exceeds the potential at point P, the diode becomes conducting, and the voltage at P rises following the sawtooth. Resistors R_1 and R_2 should be large and/or the sawtooth voltage should be delivered by a low-impedance source lest it be clamped at or near the value of E_{in}.

12-5. Some other encoders (*2*)

Three other types of encoders are singled out for mention in this section, although these by no means exhaust the number of possibilities. The first is shown in Fig. 12-15.

This consists of a special cathode-ray tube, known as the *Sears en-*

coding tube. This tube contains a metal mask into which is cut a pattern of holes representing a binary code. The vertical displacement of the beam selects which line of the mask is to be scanned, while the horizontal deflecting plates provide a conventional linear sweep. Therefore

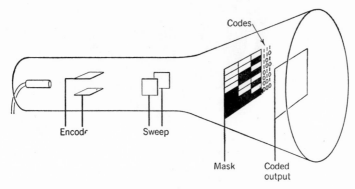

Fig. 12-15. The Sears encoding tube.

a binary code is generated as a function of *time*. The time relationship could be eliminated by arranging a set of gates to open and close in synchronism with the sweep. Thus, when the first digit is being scanned, gate 1 would pass the output pulse, if any, into a storage register. At the time when the second digit is about to be scanned, gate 1 would close and gate 2 would open, so if a pulse is present in the second position, it will enter a second binary storage unit, etc. These storage units could give a decimal readout through a system of neon lamps, as shown earlier.

The Sears encoding tube is extremely rapid in operation. It was actually designed for pulse-code-modulated telephone systems, and is too elaborate for applications in routine digital instrumentation. However, it is included as an example of a very elegant encoder.

Figure 12-16 is a mechanical encoder designed to give a binary pattern dependent upon the angular position of a shaft. Only a three-bit (*bit* for binary dig*it*) code is shown on the disk in the sketch. In practice, a much larger code is required for any accuracy. Eight or 9 bits would be necessary to give a resolution of about one degree of arc. This coder might be used on the shaft of a self-balancing potentiometer to provide digital display of a measured quantity. Another possible use would be in the feedback loop of a fire control system, so that the gun heading could be encoded for use in a digital computer. A strobe lamp is mounted

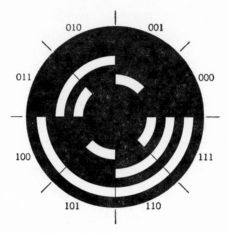

Fig. 12-16. Aperture disk for shaft position encoding.

on one side of the disk and a set of photocells on the other, one cell at the position of each circular band. The actual encoding occurs when the strobe light flashes, letting a pulse of light reach every photocell that is in front of a "one" position. The pulses from the photocells may be stored or displayed by binary registers or converted to decimal readout.

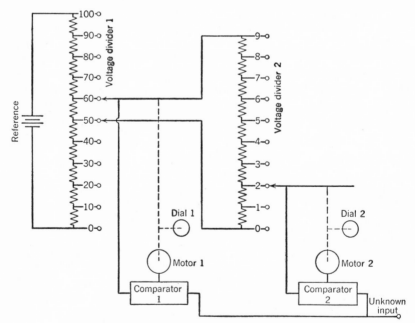

Fig. 12-17. A self-balancing potentiometer encoder.

A rather widely used encoder (which displays simultaneously) is shown in Fig. 12-17. This operates on the principle of comparing a given fraction of a reference voltage with an unknown. The action can be most easily explained by considering an example.

Suppose the unknown voltage is 51.3 volts, and the reference is 100 volts, divided into ten portions by voltage divider 1. Comparator 1 compares the voltage at the upper of the two ganged taps with the input, and drives the taps upward with a small motor until the upper tap voltage exceeds the input. The same shaft drives the first of two cyclometer dials, and so indicates the first significant figure. For the 51.3 volt input, the upper tap of voltage divider 1 will be driven to 60 volts, and cyclometer dial 1 will read 5.

When comparator 1 is satisfied, comparator 2 is switched into operation. This comparator drives the tap on voltage divider 2 upwards until the tap voltage exceeds the input, and simultaneously drives dial 2. For the input of this example the second voltage divider will be driven to position 2, at which point the input voltage is exceeded and the comparator stops motor 2. The dial displays 2 as the second significant digit. Note there is an error of 0.7 volt.

There are many variations of this basic scheme. A simpler system from the standpoint of comparators and servomotors would be a single continuously variable potentiometer driven by one servomotor and controlled by one comparator. To get several digits in the displayed answer it would be necessary to provide a gear train so that the cyclometer dials would be driven in ratios of 10 or 100 relative to the potentiometer shaft. Thus 0.513 revolution of the potentiometer shaft would produce 51 shifts in the least significant figure dial and 5 shifts in the first significant figure. In this case, the answer is in error on the low side rather than the high.

The system of Fig. 12-17 is given in about the simplest possible form. The voltage dividers would have to be reset to zero at the start of each new encoding operation, and the whole encoding process tends to be rather slow. By going to more elaborate comparators that sense whether the voltages on the taps are too high *or* too low, the coding process may be made a continuous one, with the dials constantly following any changes in the input voltage. It is well, however, not to provide too rapid a response or there will be an annoying jitter in the least significant digit as the encoder tries to follow every minor fluctuation of the input.

It is important that voltage divider 2 not shunt a given section of divider 1 enough to cause appreciable error. The total resistance of divider 2 should therefore be something like ten or twenty times as high as the resistance of one section of divider 1. An even better plan would be to eliminate the shunting problem altogether by designing the switch on voltage divider 1 so that divider 2 is connected *in place of* a particular section rather than in shunt. The comparators likewise must have high input impedances in order to avoid heavy shunting of the voltage dividers.

12-6. Samplers

The problem of sampling is quite different, and usually much easier, in instruments from that of sampling in communications systems. In many cases, sampling as the term is ordinarily used is not necessary at all. Most quantities one might wish to measure may somehow be converted to a direct voltage, and this voltage is encoded directly without sampling, since it is constant over a time of at least a few seconds. The encoding process should nevertheless be repeated from time to time, at rates from once every few seconds in a mechanical system such as Fig. 12-17, to ten or twenty times per second in the more rapid electronic systems. Then if the direct voltage does change, the encoder will sense the new value soon after.

Because of the relatively minor importance of sampling in the systems of this book, only one sampler will be shown. The circuit is given in Fig. 12-18, and is known as a *four-diode* sampler. Voltages of $-E$ and $+E$ are applied to resistors R_1 and R_2 respectively, holding the four diodes in the nonconducting state most of the time. However, at certain moments of time, indicated as t_0 through t_8, very short pulses (typically a few microseconds wide) of amplitude much greater than E are applied to points B and D in the polarity shown. These pulses cause the four diodes to conduct, and they act for the duration of the pulse like closed switches. The unknown voltage being sampled then flows through the two parallel paths ABC and ADC, and charges capacitor C to the value the unknown has at that moment. It is assumed that the unknown is changing at a slow enough rate that it will have an essentially constant value during the sampling time, and that the source of the unknown is a low impedance so that capacitor C may acquire its full new charge in just a few microseconds. The unknown voltage is ordinarily supplied

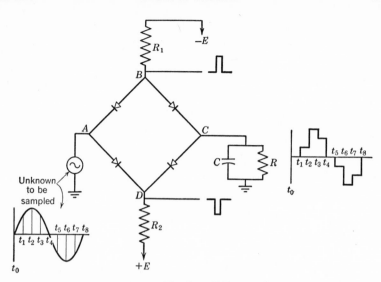

Fig. 12-18. The four-diode sampler.

from a cathode follower or similar low-impedance circuit. Resistor R represents whatever components may be connected across C. It will ordinarily be the input resistance to the encoder assembly. The time constant RC must be long compared with the time between samples. Otherwise, if a code of many digits is to be produced, the value of the sample will change before the encoding process can be completed. The voltage developed across C (assuming no sag due to the shunt resistance) is sketched at the right of the circuit. This type of waveform is often called "boxcars," since when viewed on an oscilloscope, the pattern suggests a string of freight cars.

12-7. Conclusion

The subject of digital circuitry in general is much larger and much more important than the treatment in this text can show. It has not come fully into its own in electronic instruments, and possibly never will. Adding a digital display system to any conventional electronic instrument represents a considerable increase in cost and complexity. However, almost any instrument will be more valuable with digital features where data processing is done by electronic computers. Equipments are commercially available for translating the voltages in binary counters directly onto punched cards for feeding the computer. Instruments designed with this possibility in mind would almost surely be based on the system of Fig. 12-12.

The system of Fig. 12-17 or one of its variations is very satisfactory for routine instrumentation. It is rugged and accurate, but much slower in operation than an all-electronic instrument.

REFERENCES

1. Jacob Millman and Herbert Taub, *Pulse and Digital Circuits* (New York: McGraw-Hill Book Company, Inc., 1956), sects. 5-5 and 5-6.
2. Harry E. Burke, Jr., "A Survey of Analog-to-Digital Converters," *Proc. I.R.E.*, October 1953, vol. 41, p. 1455.
3. R. W. Sears, "Electron Beam Deflection Tube for Pulse Code Modulation," *Bell System Tech. J.*, January 1948, vol. 27, p. 44.

Chapter 13

TRANSDUCERS FOR BASIC MECHANICAL
MEASUREMENTS

This chapter and the remaining ones deal with various problems in the electronic instrumentation of nonelectric systems. The first twelve chapters have considered circuits by which electrical quantities can be measured electronically. If we put the case that somehow *any* quantity can be converted to an electric signal, it follows that one of the techniques already described can be used to analyze this quantity. Accordingly, we shall be concerned in large measure with the means for performing the conversion.

Devices that convert one form of energy to another are known as *transducers*. We shall be dealing specifically with transducers that give an electric output. The input requirements depend entirely on the type of nonelectric system to be studied. Displacement, acceleration, velocity, time, sound, temperature, light, pressure, radioactivity, mass and weight, pH, salinity—almost anything one might care to name can be coupled to an electronic instrument by a suitable transducer. The rest of the book is a study of transducers, their uses, and their associated circuitry.

13-1. The SR4 strain gage (1)

Figure 13-1 shows a transducer known as an SR4 strain gage. This consists of a length of wire laid back and forth in hairpin fashion to form several approximately parallel lines of wire. The principle of operation is that if the wire is slightly stretched, its resistance increases; compressing the wire causes a reduction in resistance. If the strain gage is made one leg of a bridge, the output of the bridge is a function of the elongation or compression of the wire. The most obvious uses are in studying the forces in structural members, and many thousands of SR4 strain gages are used for this purpose by civil engineers, metallurgists, and others concerned with the mechanical properties of materials. Installa-

Fig. 13-1. A typical SR4 strain gage. (Courtesy, Baldwin-Lima-Hamilton Corp.)

tion consists merely of cementing the gage to the member to be tested. This is easily accomplished, as the resistance wire is itself cemented into a packet of tough, parchment-like paper which transmits the motion of the member to the wires.

The sensitivity of the strain gage to mechanical motion is expressed by a quantity known as the "gage factor." This is defined as

$$S = \frac{dR/R}{dL/L} \qquad (13\text{-}1)$$

where R is the nominal resistance and L is the length of the wire. Values of S normally run slight over 2; R is typically about 120 ohms.

Since the strain gage is connected in a bridge, the balance is changed by anything that changes R. Thus temperature variations may give an indication comparable to the motion being studied. To prevent this error, a second gage may be used as a temperature reference in another arm of the bridge. This gage should be cemented to the member under test by *one corner only* so that it will be at the same ambient temperature as the "active" gage, but not subject to mechanical stress. The other resistors in the bridge should be of high-quality, low temperature coefficient design.

Another possibility for temperature compensation is offered by special self-compensating strain gages which employ a wire with positive temperature coefficient for part of their total length, and one of negative temperature coefficient for the rest. These gages command a premium price, but only one is required. Either the self-compensating gage or the dummy gage for temperature compensation is perfectly satisfactory, and the author does not recommend strongly one way or the other. Circuit diagrams in this chapter will show only one gage for simplicity, the other three arms being resistors. By implication, the one gage must be a self-compensating type, but this is not to be taken as a specific recommendation.

Figure 13-2 illustrates an a-c operated Wheatstone bridge used with a strain gage. In practice, it will usually be necessary to add some compensating capacitors, especially if the gage is mounted on a metal

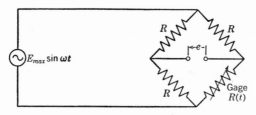

Fig. 13-2. The basic a-c strain gage bridge.

structural member with resulting high capacitance to ground. The first place to try such a capacitor is in shunt with one of the resistors in a leg adjacent to the gage. However, a certain amount of trial and error is sometimes required. One of the resistors R must also be variable to obtain the initial bridge balance. However, for simplicity, we shall assume that all three resistors R are equal to the unstressed resistance of the gage, and that there is no stray capacitance to be neutralized.

Let us assume that the gage is fixed to a member subject to simple harmonic motion. Such a situation arises frequently: for example, in columns supporting or adjacent to rotating machinery. The gage resistance will then vary with time according to the expression

$$R(t) = R_0 + r \sin \omega_0 t \qquad (13\text{-}2)$$

where R_0 is the nominal resistance (possibly 120 ohms), r is the maximum change of resistance, and ω_0 is the angular frequency of the vibration.

Now imagine for the moment that the driving voltage is a direct voltage E rather than alternating, so that we may consider the effect of the strain gage without the added complication of a carrier frequency.

It is seen by inspection of Fig. 13-2 that

$$e = \frac{E}{2} - \frac{ER(t)}{R + R(t)} = \frac{E}{2} - \frac{E(R_0 + r \sin \omega_0 t)}{R + R_0 + r \sin \omega_0 t} \tag{13-3}$$

Let $R = R_0$ so that the bridge is in balance whenever no strain is present. Then

$$e = E \left(\frac{1}{2} - \frac{R_0 + r \sin \omega_0 t}{2R_0 + r \sin \omega_0 t} \right) \tag{13-4}$$

The denominator of the second term within the parentheses is of the form $(1 + x)K$ where $x = (r/2R_0) \sin \omega_0 t$ and $K = 2R_0$. Now if $x \ll 1$, $(1 + x)^{-1} \cong (1 - x)$. If we take advantage of this fact, Eq. (13-4) may be put in the form

$$e \cong E \left(\frac{-\dfrac{r}{2} \sin \omega_0 t + \dfrac{r^2}{2R_0} \sin^2 \omega_0 t}{2R_0} \right) \tag{13-5}$$

The term involving r^2 is almost always negligible, usually less than the distortion encountered in a good amplifier. If we neglect it, Eq. (13-5) becomes

$$e = E \frac{-r \sin \omega_0 t}{4R_0} \tag{13-6}$$

Now let us introduce the added complication of an a-c rather than a d-c supply for the bridge. We must substitute for E the quantity $E_{max} \sin \omega t$, where ω is a carrier frequency, of the order of at least 10 times ω_0. Making this substitution gives

$$e = -\frac{E_{max} r}{4R_0} \sin \omega t \sin \omega_0 t \tag{13-7}$$

$$e = \frac{E_{max} r}{8R_0} [\cos (\omega + \omega_0)t - \cos (\omega - \omega_0)t] \tag{13-8}$$

Equation (13-8) is the final result of the analysis, and the expression to be reckoned with in designing the instrumentation for recovering the information from the bridge. It is seen to be a double-sideband suppressed-carrier signal. Therefore the output of the bridge must be detected with a phase-sensitive detector which supplies the missing carrier. Once this is accomplished, the recovered signal at the frequency ω_0 may be displayed on a cathode ray oscilloscope or more probably plotted with a paper chart recorder. The signal might also be measured with a vacuum tube voltmeter if the amplitude only is of interest, or the frequency determined by any of the frequency-measuring instruments already discussed.

While the suppressed carrier is a slight nuisance, a-c operation is extremely widespread in strain gage bridges. The voltage given by Eq. (13-6) is invariably quite small. If a-c drive is not used, a direct-coupled amplifier will be required, if one wishes to retain the constant unbalance voltage that occurs if there is a static strain. The d-c amplifier is generally far more difficult to design than a good phase-sensitive detector because of the problem of drift. Static strains in an a-c oper-ated system result in a direct voltage at the output of the phase-sensitive detector, and represent no difficulty in measurement or interpretation.

The SR4 strain gage is an extremely rugged little device and very easy to install and use. It is capable of measuring vibrations at very high frequencies indeed—something around 100 kc or more. The limita-tion is generally in the frequency response of the carrier or recorder equipment rather than in the gage. A number of manufacturers offer strain gage bridge assemblies, with driving oscillators, detectors, and recorders as a complete package.

All strain gages, magnetic, SR4, and mechanical, are capable of indicating any quantity which is *proportional* to strain. For example,

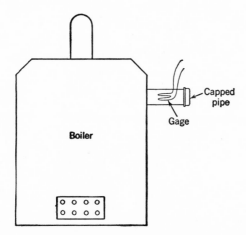

Fig. 13-3. An SR4 strain gage used in pressure measurement.

Fig. 13-3 shows an SR4 gage used to determine the pressure in a boiler. A piece of closed pipe is attached to the boiler, and as the pressure varies, the pipe expands and contracts. As long as the elasticity of the pipe is not exceeded, the strain is directly proportional to the pressure. The output of the strain gage bridge could be calibrated directly in psi. These SR4 gages are even used in such surprising fields as physiology.

The gage may be cemented to the skin or even placed inside the body to study the motion of muscles.

13-2. The magnetic strain gage

Another type of strain gage operates on a magnetic principle, based on the fact that if the magnetomotive force in a magnetic path is kept constant and the reluctance of the path varies, there will be a change in flux. This change of flux produces a voltage according to the well-known law:

$$e = N \, d\Phi/dt \tag{13-9}$$

Suppose we investigate the application of this law to the strain gage of Fig. 13-4. The illustration shows a coil mounted a nominal distance D

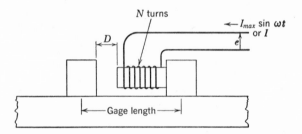

Fig. 13-4. A magnetic strain gage installed on a steel beam.

from a block of steel. This block and the coil with its supporting members are bolted or otherwise rigidly fastened to the steel structural member undergoing tests. The gage length depends to some degree on how the parts of the gage are attached to the member, but is roughly the distance between the center of the block and the center of the coil support. The entire system is assumed to be of ferromagnetic material except for the air gap D.

Now in any magnetic circuit

$$NI = \text{mmf} = \Phi\Re \tag{13-10}$$

where N is the number of turns in the exciting winding, I is the current in this winding, mmf is the magnetomotive force, Φ is the flux, and $\Re$ is the reluctance of the path. If we assume that $\Re$ is proportional to the length of the air gap and that the member under test is vibrating in a sinusoidal fashion, then

$$\Re = \Re(t) = k(D + d \sin \omega_0 t) \tag{13-11}$$

where D is the nominal air gap shown in Fig. 13-4, d is the amplitude of the variation in gap width, and ω_0 is the angular frequency of vibration. The constant k will be considered to absorb all physical and electrical proportionality factors. Now from Eq. (13-10), $\Phi = NI/\mathfrak{R}$, and substitution of this quantity into Eq. (13-9) leads to

$$e = N \frac{d}{dt} \frac{NI}{\mathfrak{R}(t)} \qquad (13\text{-}12)$$

The use of I in Eq. (13-12) indicates the case of d-c excitation in which a steady current flows in the coil of Fig. 13-4.

Substitute Eq. (13-11) for $\mathfrak{R}(t)$ in Eq. (13-12).

$$e = \frac{-N^2 I \omega_0 d \, \cos \omega_0 t}{D^2 k \left(1 + \dfrac{d}{D} \sin \omega_0 t\right)^2} \qquad (13\text{-}13)$$

Since $d/D \ll 1$, the squared quantity in the denominator may be approximated as $1 - (2d/D) \sin \omega_0 t$. Substitute this into Eq. (13-13) and expand the resulting sine-cosine product into the sum and difference frequencies. This results in

$$e = \frac{-N^2 I \omega_0 d}{D^2 k} \left(\cos \omega_0 t - \frac{d}{D} \sin 2\omega_0 t\right) \qquad (13\text{-}14)$$

Note the presence of a second-harmonic distortion term, which may be made as small as desired by increasing D. Note also that if D is made large for this or any other reason, e will be relatively small, since e decreases as D^2. The most important point to consider, however, is that if $d = 0$, i.e., there is no vibration with time, there is no output voltage. This strain gage operating with d-c excitation is therefore incapable of measuring extremely slow displacements that would be most logically considered a gradual change in D. The presence of ω_0 in the numerator is a nuisance, since it shows that amplitude depends on frequency. However, this need not cause much concern in a practical installation. It is only necessary to include between the transducer and oscilloscope or other recorder an amplifier stage with an upper half power frequency around a few cycles per second, i.e., an integrating amplifier. The drop in amplifier gain with increasing frequency will exactly offset the increasing value of e as ω_0 becomes larger. The net result is that for constant values of N, I, k, and D, the voltage at the output of the amplifier will be directly proportional to d, neglecting the second-harmonic distortion term of Eq. (13-4).

Now suppose that the strain gage is excited with alternating rather than direct current. This problem is treated by introducing $I_{max} \sin \omega t$, where the quantity I originally appeared in Eq. (13-12). The analysis is far more complicated, although the method of attack is much the same as that used in arriving at Eq. (13-14). A great number of distortion terms appear, but all are associated with a multiplying factor $D(d^2/D^2)$. Since d^2/D^2 is usually extremely small with respect to unity, it is quite safe to omit these terms from the final answer. Also, during the development we encounter two terms that are identical, save that one includes a factor ω and the other ω_0. Since the use of a-c excitation constitutes a carrier-frequency system, it is probably safe to assume $\omega_0 \ll \omega$, so the lesser of these terms may be omitted. The final result is

$$ e \cong \frac{N^2 I_{max} \omega}{kD} \left(1 - \frac{d}{D} \sin \omega_0 t \right) \cos \omega t \qquad (13\text{-}15) $$

This is the expression for a standard amplitude-modulated signal, with carrier and both sidebands. It may therefore be demodulated by any standard AM detector circuit. If the displacement occurs so slowly that D may be considered to change but $d = 0$, the a-c excited system is still useful. Note that when $d = 0$, there is an output proportional to D^{-1}. As long as the *change* in D is small compared with the nominal value of D, the voltage e will appear to vary linearly with D rather than as the reciprocal of D. Consequently, a-c excitation leads to a system that is at least approximately linear with respect to both d and D, and produces an easily demodulated output signal. Note further that the amplitude of e in Eq. (13-15) is proportional to ω rather than ω_0. Since ω is constant in any particular case, an integrating amplifier is not required between the strain gage and the recorder.

13-3. The linear variable differential transformer

A very useful transducer for measuring small displacements (i.e., of the order of a fraction of an inch) is sketched in Fig. 13-5. This is the linear variable differential transformer. It consists of a tube of non-ferromagnetic material, often phenolic or another plastic, about which three windings are wrapped. Two windings are connected series bucking, and are located physically on opposite ends of the tube. In the middle is a third winding, which acts as an exciting winding, and to which the input voltage is applied. Inside the plastic tube is a steel core, free to move up and down. A push rod made of plastic or a nonferromagnetic

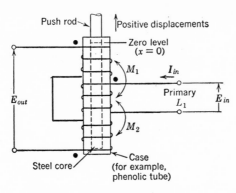

Fig. 13-5. The linear variable differential transformer (LVDT).

material is attached to this core. A second nonmagnetic tube (not shown in the figure) is slipped over the outside of the whole assembly to protect the windings and provide a place for attaching mounting clamps or screws.

If the steel core extends the same distance above the primary winding as below, the two outside windings are coupled equally tightly to the primary. Since these windings are connected series bucking, no output voltage is developed. On the other hand, if the core is moved up or down, one of the end windings will be coupled more tightly than the other to the primary, and there will be a net output voltage. The magnitude of the output is proportional to the amount of the displacement, and its phase depends on the direction. Since it is almost always desired to preserve the directional sense of the displacement, the output voltage must be passed through a phase-sensitive rectifier before going into an oscillograph or other recording system.

If we assume the output is connected to an amplifier with high input impedance, no secondary current will flow. The output voltage therefore depends entirely on the mutual inductances M_1 and M_2 and on the primary current and frequency. This voltage is

$$E_{out} = -j\omega M_2 I_{in} + j\omega M_1 I_{in} \qquad (13\text{-}16)$$

The current I_{in} is in turn given by

$$I_{in} = E_{in}/j\omega L_1 \qquad (13\text{-}17)$$

whence

$$E_{out} = \frac{E_{in}}{L_1}(M_1 - M_2) \qquad (13\text{-}18)$$

Now if the displacement of the core is small relative to the total length of the tube covered by windings, we can say that

$$M_1 = K + ax \tag{13-19}$$

$$M_2 = K - ax \tag{13-20}$$

where a and K are constants, and x is the core displacement from its zero level. Substitute Eqs. (13-19) and (13-20) into Eq. (13-18).

$$E_{out} = \frac{2aE_{in}}{L_1} x \tag{13-21}$$

This equation shows that the output voltage is linearly proportional to the displacement x, subject to the assumptions stated in regard to Eqs. (13-19) and (13-20). Here E_{out} and E_{in} are expressed in volts rms. The frequency of the driving voltage may be selected almost at will, from 60 cycles up to about 100 kc. The majority of differential transformers are designed for a frequency of around 1 to 2 kc, with E_{in} from 3 to 10 or 15 volts rms. They are available in various sensitivities to measure displacements from about 0.0001 in. to 0.25 in.

Both static and dynamic displacements are measured with equal ease. However, it is recommended by LVDT manufacturers that the highest frequency component in the mechanical motion should not exceed about 15 per cent of the electric supply frequency. This requirement is based on the assumption that diode detectors, whether phase-sensitive or conventional, will recover the information contained in the output voltage. Fifteen per cent is possibly on the generous side. A general rule of thumb for diode detectors is that modulating frequencies should be no higher than 1/10 the carrier frequency.

Differential transformers are very rugged, dependable, and relatively inexpensive. If x and E_{in} are large (say 0.1 in. and 10 volts for example), the output voltage may be as high as several volts. Thus in many cases little or no amplification is needed.

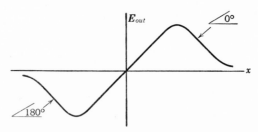

Fig. 13-6. E_{out} as a function of x in the LVDT. Phase of E_{out} shifts 180° at origin.

The hole for the core is usually bored through both ends, so if the displacement is larger than expected, the core simply moves outside the transducer and no damage is done. However, the linear relationship between output voltage and displacement prevails only when the core is moderately near the center of the winding assembly. Figure 13-6 shows the manner in which output voltage varies with displacement.

Differential transformers may be used in many applications. For example, they could be used to control an automatic machine tool by attaching the core to the cutting head to measure how far a cut has gone into the work. They have been used also in research on machine tool design (see Fig. 1-5 and accompanying discussion). In a study conducted by Purdue University for the Joint Highway Research Board, differential transformers were attached to concrete paving slabs to measure the displacement of the road when vehicles of various speeds and weights were driven by (2).

13-4. Accelerometers (3)

As the name implies, an accelerometer is a transducer to convert acceleration to an electric signal. Acceleration is directly related to force ($F = ma$), so any device responsive to force might be used as an accelerometer. This opens a great number of possibilities. For example, a strain gage could be cemented to a cantilever beam. Acceleration in such a direction as to bend this beam will be converted by the strain gage to a change of electric resistance. A differential transformer might be used in the same way, i.e., to determine how far the beam is bent, and from this to compute the force and finally the acceleration.

Piezoelectric crystals generate a voltage when stressed mechanically. This principle may be employed to measure force and hence acceleration. However, the piezoelectric crystal can detect dynamic forces only. Unless the crystal were connected to an amplifier of infinite input impedance, the charges produced by a permanent deformation of the crystal would soon leak away, and there would be no steady voltage to indicate the permanent displacement. The piezoelectric crystal accelerometer is therefore useful primarily in such applications as shaking tables and other forms of shock and vibration testing.

The transducers we have already treated in this chapter could all be adapted to accelerometer duty, as we have noted. Consequently, the following discussion is devoted to description and analysis of a special transducer designed exclusively as an accelerometer. This is the accelerometer tube developed by Ramberg of the Bureau of Standards (4,5,6).

It consists of a vacuum diode with a common cathode and two anodes sketched in Fig. 13-7. The cathode is mounted rigidly, while the

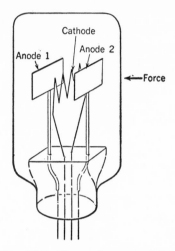

Fig. 13-7. The accelerometer tube.

anodes are capable of moving on spring-like mountings. A force applied as shown in the sketch causes anode 2 to move away from the cathode, while anode 1 moves closer. Then anode 2 will receive less current, while anode 1 conducts more heavily. If the tube is used in a circuit such as that of Fig. 13-8, the motions of the plates will throw the bridge

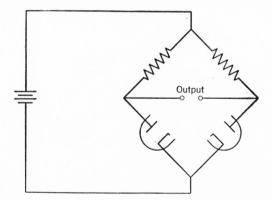

Fig. 13-8. Bridge circuit for the accelerometer tube.

out of balance, and an output voltage will appear. This voltage may be amplified and studied with an oscillograph, voltmeter, or any other instrument that will display the desired information.

The analysis of the accelerometer tube is largely a mechanical problem. It deals with the response of a system to a driving force. A number of factors must be considered, and the exact approach is to treat each anode as a mass concentrated at its center of gravity and supported by stiff bars subject to flexure and torsion. The complete analysis of the structure is therefore fairly complicated.

A simplified treatment giving at least an idea of the nature of the motion may be based on the assumption that the anodes act like masses mounted on springs. Such an arrangement is shown in Fig. 13-9. Sup-

Fig. 13-9. A simplified mechanical equivalent of the accelerometer.

pose that this system is subjected to a steady acceleration, tending to displace the mass to the position shown by dotted lines. The force applied is balanced by three components in the mechanical system: acceleration of the mass, damping, and the restoring force of the spring.

$$F = M \frac{d^2x}{dt^2} + K \frac{dx}{dt} + \frac{x}{lS} \tag{13-22}$$

where F is the constant applied force, M is the concentrated mass, K is the damping constant, l is the length of the spring from the clamped base to the center of gravity, S is the spring constant, and x is the displacement; M is grams, S is cm/cm/dyne, K is dynes/cm/sec, F is in dynes, and x and l are centimeters.

Equation (13-22) is a rather common one in all branches of engineering. The solution is given in many handbooks, or may be easily worked out with the Laplace transform or other methods. The final result is

$$x = \frac{F}{M}\left[\frac{1}{\alpha^2 + \omega^2} - \frac{\epsilon^{-\alpha t}}{(\alpha^2 + \omega^2)\omega}(\alpha \sin \omega t + \omega \cos \omega t)\right] \qquad (13\text{-}23)$$

where
$$\alpha = K/2M \qquad (13\text{-}24)$$

and
$$\omega = \sqrt{\frac{1}{MlS} - \frac{K^2}{4M^2}} \qquad (13\text{-}25)$$

Note that x eventually attains a steady value as the exponential term in Eq. (13-23) dies out. This is to be expected if the transducer is subjected to a steady acceleration. However, there will be a period of time when the output exhibits a "ringing" due to the decaying sinusoidal terms. Critical damping is not possible within the evacuated tube envelope, as there is no air to set up friction with a vane.

Another problem of practical importance is subjecting the accelerometer to a force of nonconstant magnitude. For example, a rocket engine might deliver a very high initial thrust, with the force decreasing as the fuels are exhausted. Such a force might be of the form $F(t) = F\epsilon^{-\lambda t}$. If this expression is substituted for F in Eq. (13-22) and the resulting differential equation solved, we find

$$x = \frac{F}{M}\left[\frac{\epsilon^{-(\alpha - j\omega)t}}{2j\omega(\lambda - \alpha + j\omega)} + \frac{\epsilon^{-(\alpha + j\omega)t}}{-2j\omega(\lambda - \alpha - j\omega)}\right.$$
$$\left. + \frac{\epsilon^{-\lambda t}}{(\alpha - j\omega - \lambda)(\alpha + j\omega - \lambda)}\right] \qquad (13\text{-}26)$$

It will be noted that terms involving exp $-j\omega t$ appear here just as in the case with steady acceleration. These terms are generally eliminated by a low-pass filter. If we drop them out, Eq. (13-26) simplifies to

$$x = \frac{F}{M}\frac{\epsilon^{-\lambda t}}{(\alpha - \lambda)^2 + \omega^2} \qquad (13\text{-}27)$$

It will be seen at once that this is a bit oversimplified, for Eq. (13-27) implies that at $t = 0$, $x \neq 0$. We know this must be incorrect, since it would require an infinite force to obtain a finite displacement in zero time. The terms we threw away would make $x = 0$ at $t = 0$. In spite of this obvious fallacy, Eq. (13-27) is a good approximation to the displacement of the mass after t exceeds a few time constants of $1/\alpha$. A sketch of $x(t)$ is shown in Fig. 13-10.

Now we must consider the action of the tube itself, if its anodes are displaced in a manner such as shown in Fig. 13-10. We need consider only one anode; the other anode acts in a similar manner, except that its displacement at any time is in the opposite direction from the first.

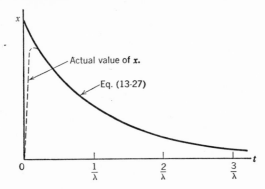

Fig. 13-10. Displacement of accelerometer mass subjected to exponentially decreasing force.

Since we are dealing with a diode having planar electrode structures, the simplest form of Child's law will express the anode current as a function of displacement.

$$I_b = \frac{2.335 \times 10^{-6} A E_b^{3/2}}{x^2} \tag{13-28}$$

where E_b is anode voltage, x is the distance between anode and cathode, and A is the area of the electrodes, assuming anode and cathode have the same area, are solid planes, and end effects are neglected. Since these assumptions will not be entirely true in the actual accelerometer

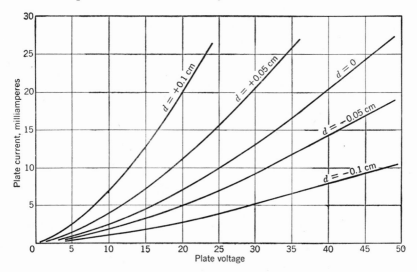

Fig. 13-11. Plate current as a function of displacement d in an accelerometer tube. $I_b = (5 \times 10^{-6} E_b^{3/2})/(x-d)^2$ amperes.

tube, the numerical constant will be less than 2.335×10^{-6}. However, the basic dependency of I_b on $E_b^{3/2}$ and x^{-2} still applies.

The Ramberg tube was developed specifically for driving a galvanometer without the use of amplifiers. However, the tube itself may be regarded as an amplifier in which a change in x corresponds to a change in the control grid voltage of a conventional tube. If various values of x are used as parameters to construct a family of characteristic curves, a typical result is given in Fig. 13-11. These curves were constructed by taking the numerical constant of Eq. (13-28) as 2×10^{-6}, A as 2.5 cm², and the undisplaced value of x as 0.25 cm. They apply to the voltage-current relationship between cathode and *one anode* only. The parameter of the family is displacement d. Positive values indicate the anode is moved closer to the cathode.

By the use of these curves, the accelerometer tube may be treated as a conventional triode, with d substituted for grid voltage. Accordingly, we may modify the conventional definitions of μ, r_p, and g_m to obtain the following:

$$\mu = \frac{\partial E_b}{\partial d}\bigg|_{I_b \text{ const}} \qquad \text{(volts/cm)} \qquad (13\text{-}29)$$

$$g_m = \frac{\partial I_b}{\partial d}\bigg|_{E_b \text{ const}} \qquad \text{(amps/cm)} \qquad (13\text{-}30)$$

$$r_p = \frac{\partial E_b}{\partial I_b}\bigg|_{d \text{ const}} \qquad \text{(volts/amp = ohms)} \qquad (13\text{-}31)$$

If the tube is in a circuit with an undisplaced operating point at $I_b = 10$ ma, $E_b = 25$ volts, the quantities listed above may be found by graphical analysis from Fig. 13-11 as

$$\mu = 138 \text{ volts/cm}, \qquad g_m = 0.086 \text{ amp/cm}, \qquad r_p = 1660 \text{ ohms}$$

The product $g_m r_p = \mu$ as in any tube.

The definitions of Eqs. (13-29) to (13-31) allow us to treat the accelerometer like any other tube in small-signal analysis. For example, the discussion of Sections 3-3 and 3-4 applies directly to the circuit of Fig. 13-8. The only difference is in the interpretation of μ, r_p, and g_m, and in the fact that the only possible quiescent operating point is on the curve for $d = 0$. Also, it must be borne in mind that as far as manufacturing tolerances permit, the two anodes of the accelerometer behave symmetrically. If one undergoes a displacement of $+0.1$ cm, the other must simultaneously be displaced -0.1 cm.

The resonant frequency of the mechanical system should be high to prevent useful data being masked by free vibrations. Also, the higher the natural frequency, the less chance of its being excited by vibration from nearby mechanical equipment. In general, a resonant frequency between 500 and 1000 cycles is considered satisfactory. Another advantage in having a high resonant frequency is that it is easier to design a low-pass filter to remove the free oscillations without intruding on the part of the spectrum where bona fide information is present.

13-5. Mechano-electronic transducers

Another type of tube closely related to the Ramberg accelerometer is the mechanoelectronic transducer. This tube employs a flexible seal through which the anode lead, a rigid rod, is brought to the outside of

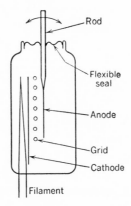

Fig. 13-12. Mechanical arrangement of the mechanoelectronic transducer.

the tube. The arrangement is sketched in Fig. 13-12. Moving the rod back and forth moves the anode nearer to or farther from the cathode and grid assembly, causing a change in plate current. The motion is essentially rotary rather than rectilinear. It must be held to a very small amount, of the order of $\pm 1°$ or less, to avoid cracking the seal or bending the internal anode structure.

A set of curves similar to that of Fig. 13-11 is obtained for this transducer for *every value of control grid voltage*. The normal mode of operation is with the grid at zero volts relative to the cathode. However, the presence of the control grid makes possible a very convenient method of inserting carrier voltage if carrier rather than direct-coupled circuitry is desired. In this case, a volt or two of fixed bias is applied to the grid in series with the carrier signal. This carrier is amplified by the tube and at the same time modulated by the motion of the anode. The output thus consists of an AM signal whose envelope is proportional to the angular position of the anode shaft. The type 5734 tube is typical of transducers of this class.

13-6. Conclusions

The transducers discussed in this chapter are of rather general applicability to a great many mechanical systems. With a little ingenuity, they can be made to perform a vast variety of measurements. For example, the output of a differential transformer's phase-sensitive detector could be differentiated to indicate velocity. Or a magnetic strain gage may be used to measure the thickness of a coat of baked enamel on steel by employing a-c excitation so that static displacements are indicated.

Many examples of specialized transducers will be found in subsequent chapters. In some cases, only a special transducer can do a given job. But it is essential, if one wishes to get the most out of electronic instruments, to keep alert to the possibilities of adapting one transducer to many tasks.

Likewise, one should keep in mind the many possible ways to process the information obtained from a given transducer. For example, a strain gage is used primarily for determining the microdisplacements in members under stress and thus computing the stress itself. But the output of a strain gage instrumentation system (i.e., the voltage obtained after reinserting the carrier and demodulating) could just as well be connected to a frequency counter to find the frequency of vibration in the member. Or the demodulated outputs of two separate strain gage systems might be connected to a phase meter to determine the phase relationships between different members of a structure vibrating at the same frequency. Such a problem might arise in the study of mechanical filters for vibration isolation.

Finally, mention should be made of a particularly complete list of transducers, covering not only mechanical measurements, but almost any quantity one might wish to study in the general area of physical sciences. This is a book entitled *Transducers*, published by the Instrument Division of Allen B. DuMont Laboratories, Inc., Clifton, New

Jersey. This lists hundreds of transducers classified by the quantity they measure. Since new editions are printed from time to time, the publisher should be contacted directly for information regarding availability and price. The reader's attention is also called to the "Institute of Radio Engineers Standards on Transducers" appearing in the August 1951 issue of the *Proceedings of the I.R.E.*

REFERENCES

1. C. C. Perry and H. R. Lissner, *The Strain Gage Primer* (New York: McGraw-Hill Book Company, Inc., 1955).
2. G. R. Partridge, J. W. Dunkin, R. L. Anderson, and R. C. Geldmacher, "A 14-Channel Displacement Measuring Device Utilizing Magnetic and Paper Tape Recording," *Transactions of the AIEE, Part I, Communications and Electronics*, no. 32, September 1957, p. 461.
3. Anthony Orlacchio and George Hieber, "Accelerometers—Which Type For the Job?" *Electronic Industries*, vol. 16, March 1957, p. 75.
4. Walter Ramberg, "A Vacuum Tube for Acceleration Measurement," *Elec. Eng.*, vol. 66, June 1947, p. 555.
5. Walter Ramberg, "The Measurement of Acceleration with a Vacuum Tube," *Trans. AIEE*, vol. 66 (1947), p. 735.
6. Walter Ramberg, "Vacuum Tube Acceleration Pickup," *J. Research Natl. Bur. Standards*, vol. 37, December 1946, p. 391.
7. Karl R. Spangenberg, *Vacuum Tubes* (New York: McGraw-Hill Book Company, Inc., 1948), p. 171.

Chapter 14

SOME PROBLEMS IN VELOCITY
MEASUREMENT

The measurement of velocity usually implies the problem of finding how long it takes a moving object to travel over a given distance. But this is really a problem in the measurement of *time interval*, since the distance is usually known. Consequently, this chapter is restricted to instruments for determining the velocity of an object or a fluid while it is en route. We shall not admit the question of determining distance per unit time over a measured course.

As always, emphasis will be on electronic instruments to accomplish the task. Therefore a great many common devices for velocity measurements are omitted from detailed discussion. These include such things as flow meters employing small propellers which turn at an angular velocity proportional to the linear velocity of fluid moving past them, and conventional tachometers for determining angular velocity.

It is true, of course, that the outputs of such transducers can be measured by electronic instruments. Thus the voltage developed in a tachometer could be measured with a vacuum tube voltmeter; or a magnetic strain gage mounted near a gear could determine the speed of rotation if the pulses produced as each tooth sweeps by are connected to a frequency meter or counter. These are bona fide examples of electronic instruments at work, but are also logical and fairly obvious applications of instruments discussed earlier in the test. Therefore let us turn our attention to illustrations of systems in which the transducer and its associated circuitry function as a single instrument.

14-1. Hot wire anemometers—I *(1,2)*

A hot wire anemometer is a device for determining the velocity of moving air by the cooling effect of the air upon a heated wire. There are two general types of hot wire anemometers: the first drives the wire from a constant current source, and measures the air velocity by noting the change in wire resistance; the second keeps the wire resistance constant by means of a feedback system to vary the current. The wire current is then a measure of the air velocity. In this section, we shall treat the first principle, i.e., change of resistance.

We shall not go into the theory of hot wire anemometry, which is a rather complicated subject, but well covered in the technical literature *(3,4,5,6)*. The pertinent points to bear in mind for present purposes are that the resistance is a nonlinear function of velocity; and that because of the thermal time constant of the wire, it loses sensitivity at 6 db per octave above a given cutoff point, which is at a distressingly low frequency—a few hundred cycles per second at best.

The inherent nonlinearity of the wire may be taken into account in the calibration of the instrument. The drop in output at high frequencies is more serious. Frequency components of 100 kc or higher are of interest in the study of air turbulence in wind tunnels. This means we must deal with frequencies some two and a half decades above the cutoff frequency of the wire itself, and therefore overcome about 50 db attenuation.

Figure 14-1 illustrates in block diagram form the main parts of a hot-wire anemometer of the constant current type. The hot wire is

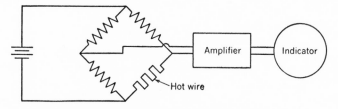

Fig. 14-1. The constant-current hot-wire anemometer.

connected in a Wheatstone bridge. The resistor in the same leg is made large enough to convert the d-c supply into the equivalent of a constant current source. Since the hot wire may demand several hundred milliamperes, practical considerations of supply voltage and power rating usually limit the series resistance to a few hundred ohms. The hot wire itself is surprisingly small—about 80 mils long and 0.2 mil in diameter, with a resistance of perhaps 100 ohms. It is usually made of tungsten to provide as much mechanical strength as possible. The diameter must be narrow to achieve a short thermal time constant. However, too thin a wire may be shattered by the impact of a particle of dust moving at high velocity. Therefore the wire can seldom be made smaller than about 0.1 mil.

The equivalent circuit of the hot wire in terms of its thermal lag is shown in Fig. 14-2. This is a familiar RC circuit, with an upper half-

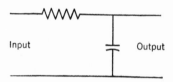

Fig. 14-2. An equivalent circuit representing the thermal lag of the hot wire.

power frequency (in radians per second) equal to the reciprocal of the time constant RC. Such a circuit has a pole on the negative real frequency axis. In the case of the hot wire, the pole lies at a few hundred to a couple of thousand radians per second.

Now if we wish to extend the frequency response of the instrument, we must place a zero on the real frequency axis in such a position as to

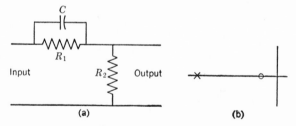

Fig. 14-3. A compensating network of the "lead" type: (a) the circuit; (b) the pole-zero constellation of this network.

coincide with, and therefore cancel out, the pole. Another pole is inevitably introduced by stray capacitance if nothing else, and the trick is to move this new pole as far to the left as possible. One suggested circuit is shown in Fig. 14-3. The transfer function is

$$\frac{E_{out}}{E_{in}} = \frac{sC + 1/R_1}{sC + 1/R_1 + 1/R_2} \tag{14-1}$$

This has a zero at $-1/CR_1$ and a pole at $-\dfrac{1}{C}\left(\dfrac{1}{R_1} + \dfrac{1}{R_2}\right)$. Such a lead network would make a perfectly satisfactory compensating system in a single-ended amplifier. However, a differential amplifier is required in this application because of the very low level of input signal, possibly as little as 100 μv. Therefore two lead networks would be required, with the resultant problem of making two components track together perfectly if the compensation must be adjusted to match different wires. A more satisfactory approach in this case is a feedback compensating circuit, shown in Fig. 14-4.

The action of the feedback is thus: at high frequencies, the capacitor C_x acts as a perfect by-pass, placing both cathodes at the same potential. Current flows through the two 100,000-ohm resistors and C_x. If the circuit is balanced, the anode potentials of T_2 and T_4 are equal and exactly out of phase. Therefore ground potential exists at both sides of

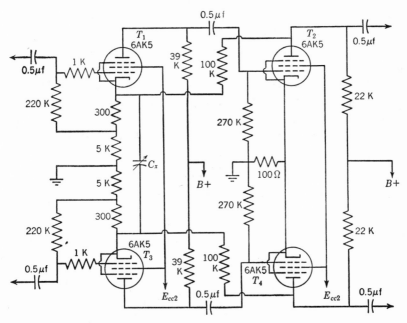

Fig. 14-4. Compensating differential amplifier. (After Sarture, by permission of Purdue University.)

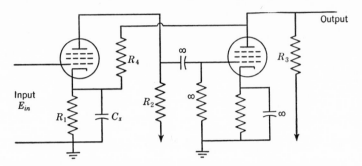

Fig. 14-5. A simplified single-ended version of the amplifier of Fig. 14-4.

C_x, no voltage is fed back to the cathodes, and the gain is very high. As the frequency drops, C_x starts to present a significant amount of impedance. Voltage is developed across the cathodes through the feedback path in such phase as to cause degeneration, or a reduction in gain. Finally, at very low frequencies the gain asymptotically approaches a minimum value.

The mathematical analysis of the circuit of Fig. 14-4 is quite complicated. The approach is straightforward, but there are many meshes and nodes in the equivalent circuit, and the results are so unwieldy as to be useless. A somewhat simpler single-ended circuit acting in about the same way is shown in Figs. 14-5 and 14-6, the former being the actual circuit and the latter an equivalent circuit. Components marked ∞ in Fig. 14-5 are presumed to be large enough to act as either short circuits or open circuits. The parameters g_m and r_p are assumed the same in both tubes.

If the equivalent circuit of Fig. 14-6 is used to compute the ratio of

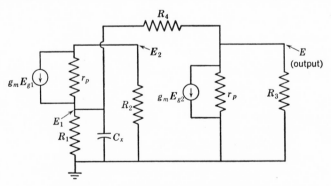

Fig. 14-6. Equivalent circuit of Fig. 14-5.

E/E_{in}, we may determine the radian frequency of the zero and the pole. The analysis is easily performed by using the node voltage approach, bearing in mind that $E_{g1} = -E_1 + E_{in}$ and $E_{g2} = E_2$. Even so, the results are rather lengthy. It is found that the zero lies at

$$s_{zero} = -\frac{1}{C_x}\left(\frac{1}{R_1} + \frac{1}{R_4} + \frac{1}{g_m R_2 R_4}\right) \tag{14-2}$$

The expression for the pole is a very long equation, but for numerical values comparable with those of the components in Fig. 14-4, only one term makes any really significant contribution. This term gives an approximate frequency of the pole as

$$s_{pole} \cong -\frac{g_m^2}{C_x(R_4/r_p + R_4/R_3 + 1)(1/r_p + 1/R_2)} \tag{14-3}$$

For example, if $C_x = 0.4$ μf, $R_1 = 5000$ ohms, $R_2 = 40,000$ ohms, $R_3 = 20,000$ ohms, $R_4 = 100,000$ ohms, $r_p = 500,000$ ohms, and $g_m = 4000$ μmhos, Eq. (14-2) gives the zero as -525 radians per second, and Eq. (14-3) places the pole at $-280,000$ radians per second. (The exact expression for the pole gives $-290,000$, an error of about 4 per cent.)

The important fact to note from this example is that the pole lies about 500 times farther to the left than the zero. Therefore, if the zero is placed at the break frequency of the hot wire, the over-all combination of hot wire and amplifier will have its upper half-power frequency some 500 times higher than without compensation. The position of the zero is easily adjusted by varying C_x. This also changes the *position* of the pole, but does not affect the *ratio* between the frequencies of pole and zero.

Figure 14-7 illustrates the frequency response of the amplifier of Fig. 14-5. It is somewhat idealized at the high-frequency end, for eventually stray and interelectrode capacitances in the circuit will cause a drop. The gain cannot remain at a high constant value indefinitely. This curve is drawn for the case where the frequency of the pole lies exactly 100 times above the frequency of the zero. It is assumed in Fig. 14-7 that by varying C_x, the frequency of the zero was made to coincide exactly with the upper half-power frequency of the hot wire.

The output of a hot wire anemometer system is usually displayed with a true rms-reading voltmeter when the total turbulence is to be found, or with a cathode ray oscilloscope. The latter is useful when one suspects the existence of a repetitive pattern in the air fluctuations, as

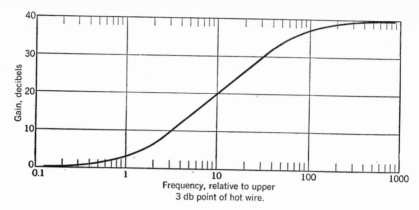

Fig. 14-7. Frequency response of amplifier of Fig. 14-5.

near a propeller. It is also of value when studying shock waves in the air, as when a projectile passes by or a missile enters the atmosphere after a flight in essentially free space.

14-2. Hot wire anemometers—II (7)

The second type of hot-wire anemometer employs a feedback system to adjust the wire current, thus keeping the resistance constant. This technique has not been so successfully reduced to practice as standard compensation, but is nevertheless worthy of some consideration.

One embodiment of the method is shown in Fig. 14-8. Here the hot-wire bridge is driven by a radio frequency oscillator. As the wire

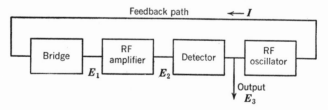

Fig. 14-8. Block diagram of a feedback method for extending the frequency range in hot wire anemometry. (After Waterman, by permission of Purdue University.)

resistance changes, the radio frequency is modulated, detected, and the resulting envelope is used to vary the output of the oscillator (8). The result is that as the air stream tends to cool the wire, the driving voltage increases, raising the input power in an effort to keep the resistance constant.

The effect of feedback in raising the upper half-power frequency of the over-all system is as follows: define the forward gain as

$$K_f = \frac{A}{1 + j\omega\tau_w} \tag{14-4}$$

where ω is the frequency of the air turbulence, τ_w is the time constant of the hot wire, and A is the low-frequency forward gain. By low frequency, we mean frequencies well below the cutoff frequency of the wire, yet still high enough so that attenuation is not introduced by interstage coupling networks such as capacitors or transformers.

$$A = \frac{\Delta E_3}{\Delta I}, \qquad \omega \ll 1/\tau_w \tag{14-5}$$

where E_3 is the output voltage, and I is the bridge supply current.

Now let the feedback loop be closed, introducing the feedback factor β.

$$\beta = \frac{\Delta I}{\Delta E_3} \tag{14-6}$$

We shall suppose the response of the oscillator to a change in E_3 is instantaneous, so that the only time lag is that associated with the hot wire in the bridge. For all practical purposes, this is true.

With feedback, the system gain is

$$G = \frac{A/(1 + j\omega\tau_w)}{1 + \beta \, A/(1 + j\omega\tau_w)} = \frac{A}{1 + j\omega\tau_w + \beta K_f} \tag{14-7}$$

The upper half-power frequency in Eq. (14-7) is

$$\omega_2 = (1 + \beta A)/\tau_w \tag{14-8}$$

This is higher by the factor $(1 + \beta A)$ than the case with no feedback. Therefore the action of the complete anemometer circuit is equivalent to that of a system without feedback or compensation, but employing a wire with a time constant only $1/(1 + \beta A)$ as long.

The use of a radio frequency carrier is another advantage, in that most of the amplification can be done at approximately the same frequency. Furthermore, d-c components in the air velocity may be measured, provided there is direct coupling between the detector and oscillator so that feedback still operates at zero frequency. This was not possible in the anemometer of Section 14-1 because drift in even the best direct-coupled amplifier could mask the very low input signals often encountered. Direct coupling between the detector and oscillator of Fig. 14-8 should not be difficult in practice, as at this point the signal level is as high as it gets, and the effects of drift will be at a minimum.

Applications of this anemometer are the same as described in Section 14-1. Only the method of achieving compensation differs.

14-3. Ultrasonic measurement of fluid velocity (9)

The measurement of fluid velocity by ultrasonics is based on determining the change in phase of the sound wave as it first moves in the

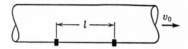

Fig. 14-9. Placement of transducers for velocity measurement in fluids.

direction of fluid flow, and then as it moves in the counter direction. Figure 14-9 illustrates the necessary mechanical configuration. Two transducers, marked A and B, are placed a distance l apart in a pipe. The pipe contains a fluid moving in the direction shown with velocity v_0. If sound is injected into the pipe at transducer A and received at B, the transit time will be shorter than expected because the fluid is moving in the same direction as the sound waves. On the other hand, propagation from B to A will take longer than if the fluid were motionless because now the sound must travel counter to the velocity of its medium of propagation. Define V_0 as the velocity of sound in the fluid itself. Then the net velocity for travel from A to B is

$$v = V_0 + v_0 \tag{14-9}$$

while propagation in the opposite direction is at a velocity of

$$v' = V_0 - v_0 \tag{14-10}$$

Figure 14-10 shows the circuitry necessary to reduce the principle to a practical instrumentation system. A switch is provided for alternating the functions of transducers A and B. In one setting, A is the sound source and B the receiver; in the other switch position, the functions are opposite. A phase-angle meter indicates the phase difference between the transmitted and received sounds. The oscillator, amplifier, and phase angle meter may be of practically any type. However, it is important that the oscillator frequency be constant and free of drift,

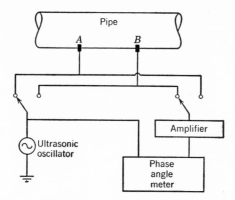

Fig. 14-10. Block diagram of ultrasonic fluid velocity measuring system.

since as will be shown, the interpretation of the results requires that ω be known accurately. The transducers should be of a bilateral type so that a given transducer may be used as either a sound source or receiver. Piezoelectric crystals are commonly used in this application.

Suppose that the switches are as shown in Fig. 14-10, so that A is the source. Then a wave of sound going from A to B will arrive at B with a phase angle of $\omega t - \omega l/v$. The indication of the phase angle meter is

$$\angle B - \angle A = \left(\omega t - \frac{\omega l}{v}\right) - \omega t = -\frac{\omega l}{v} \qquad (14\text{-}11)$$

When the transducer functions are reversed,

$$\angle B = \omega t \quad \text{and} \quad \angle A = \omega t - \frac{\omega l}{v'}$$

The phase angle meter then indicates

$$\angle B - \angle A = \omega t - \left(\omega t - \frac{\omega l}{v'}\right) = \frac{\omega l}{v'} \qquad (14\text{-}12)$$

Now add algebraically the angles represented by Eqs. (14-11) and (14-12). Call the sum ϕ.

$$\phi = -\frac{\omega l}{v} + \frac{\omega l}{v'} = \omega l \frac{v - v'}{vv'} \qquad (14\text{-}13)$$

Substitute the values of v and v'.

$$\phi = \omega l \frac{V_0 + v_0 - (V_0 - v_0)}{V_0^2 - v_0^2} = 2\omega l \frac{v_0}{V_0^2 - v_0^2} \qquad (14\text{-}14)$$

In most liquids, V_0 is close to one mile per second, so v_0 is almost certain to be negligible by comparison. We may then drop v_0^2 from Eq. (14-14), and obtain

$$\phi = \frac{2\omega l}{V_0^2} v_0 \qquad (14\text{-}15)$$

or

$$v_0 = \frac{\phi V_0^2}{2\omega l} \qquad (14\text{-}16)$$

It may be shown from Eq. (14-14) that v_0 must become 9.95 per cent of V_0 before Eq. (14-16) is in error by 1 per cent. This would make v_0 about 300 mph, so for velocities likely to be encountered in practice, Eq. (14-16) is a very good approximation.

The velocities and length l may be in any consistent system of units, such as metric or English. The important thing is to know them accurately. The value of V_0 is readily found if it is possible to stop the flow of liquid for a few minutes so that $v_0 = 0$. Then either Eq. (14-11) or (14-12) gives an angle of magnitude $\omega l/V_0$. It is well to check V_0 from time to time, since it varies with temperature and other factors such as air bubbles or impurities.

14-4. Electromagnetic flow metering (*10*)

In principle, the system shown in Fig. 14-11 can be used to determine the velocity of any moving material. It is based on the law that an emf is induced in any body traveling normal to a magnetic field.

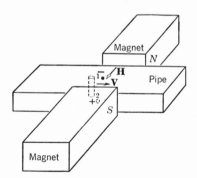

Fig. 14-11. The principle of the electromagnetic flow meter.

Suppose that the pipe, shown rectangular purely as a matter of convenience, contains a fluid moving with velocity **V**. A magnetic field **H** is placed normal to the direction of flow. Now consider a small rod-shaped element of the fluid, shown by dotted lines in the figure. As this moves through the magnetic field, an emf is induced in it according to the law

$$\mathbf{E} = \mathbf{V} \times \mathbf{H} \qquad (14\text{-}17)$$

Let a pair of terminals, 1 and 2, be fixed to the top and bottom of the pipe. As the element of fluid sweeps by these terminals, a voltage will appear between them according to Eq. (14-17), and in the polarity shown, i.e., terminal 1 negative and 2 positive. Naturally, the pipe must be made of a nonconducting material like glass or plastic. Since the actual fluid fills the pipe completely, and is presumably always flowing, there will be not just a pulse of voltage, but a steady emf developed between the terminals. This voltage may be measured, and from it the velocity of the fluid computed.

There are some very major difficulties in reducing this system to practice. If the fluid is a conductor, the emf is "short-circuited" by the fluid itself. If it is a nonconductor, then there appears to be an extremely high source impedance between the terminals, with the result that the emf is short-circuited by the measuring circuit. Moreover, the voltage is extremely small. For example, in a 2-in. diameter round pipe with a flow of 100 gal per minute, the emf is about 16 millivolts for a field of 1000 gausses. Still another problem is that with a d-c magnetic field, the current drawn by the metering circuit tends to polarize the electrodes and make them inoperative. For this reason, it is advantageous to use an alternating magnetic field. But this a-c field is a mixed blessing, for spurious voltages may be induced in nearby conductors and components. These voltages may completely mask the small signal one is trying to measure. These difficulties may be solved by the use of amplifiers of extremely high input impedance (essentially electrometers); and by careful shielding, balancing, and the judicious insertion of bucking voltages to counteract spurious signals.

A number of instruments using this principle have been reported in the literature: numerous examples are given in the bibliography of the Hogg, Mittelmann, and Schover paper (10). However, reduction of the principle to practice still requires great care.

14-5. Doppler velocity measurements (11)

The velocity of moving objects may be measured in a number of ways, but as noted at the start of this chapter, most of them require a *time* determination. One exception is the doppler method illustrated

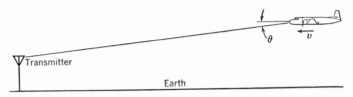

Fig. 14-12. Placement of elements in aircraft velocity measuring system using doppler effect.

in Fig. 14-12. The manner of operation may best be explained in terms of the frequencies involved.

Assume the ground transmitter sends a signal of a frequency f_s. Then the plane receives a frequency of

$$f_0 = \frac{1 + \dfrac{v}{c}\cos\theta}{[1 - (v/c)^2]^{1/2}} f_s \qquad (14\text{-}18)$$

where v is the velocity of the plane, and c is the speed of light, 3×10^8 meters per second.

The received frequency is a function of θ, so it is necessary to consider two situations: first, when the effect of θ is negligible, and second, when θ is relatively large. If the angle is small, $\cos\theta$ equals unity. It is safe to take $(v/c)^2$ as entirely negligible with respect to unity in any physical objects larger than atomic particles. Then Eq. (14-18) simplifies to

$$f_0 = f_s\left(1 + \frac{v}{c}\right) \qquad (14\text{-}19)$$

or
$$f_0 - f_s = \Delta f = \frac{v}{c} f_s \qquad (14\text{-}20)$$

The frequency shift is very small. For example, if f_s is 200 megacycles and $v = 200$ mph, Δf is about 60 cycles.

Now if θ is larger than zero, the factor $\cos\theta$ may have to be taken into account. In this case, Eq. (14-18) becomes

$$f_0 = f_s\left(1 + \frac{v}{c}\cos\theta\right) \qquad (14\text{-}21)$$

Then
$$\Delta f = f_0 - f_s = f_s\frac{v}{c}\cos\theta \qquad (14\text{-}22)$$

The fractional change in frequency is $\Delta f/f_s$.

$$\frac{\Delta f}{f_s} = \frac{v}{c}\cos\theta \qquad (14\text{-}23)$$

If θ is to cause less than 5 per cent error, $\cos \theta$ must be equal to or greater than 0.95, so θ can be no larger than 18.2 degrees. This is not so serious a limitation as might be supposed. For example, if a plane is flying at an altitude of 42,240 feet (8 miles), the ground distance between transmitter and plane is 24.3 miles for $\theta = 18.2$ degrees. Accuracy improves as the plane flies lower or is farther from the transmitter.

The discussion thus far has established only that a doppler frequency shift occurs in proportion to the speed of the plane. There is no way the airborne equipment can determine the amount of this shift. The plane is aware only of receiving a signal at the frequency f_0. If an airborne reference frequency of f_s were available, the frequency shift could be found in the plane, and the velocity determined there. However, such a reference would have to be of secondary standard quality. A frequency drift of only one part in 10^5 would completely mask Δf. Therefore it is necessary to make the frequency shift measurement at the ground station.

This is accomplished as follows: The ground transmitter sends a signal at f_s. The plane receives $f_s + \Delta f$. The received frequency is passed through a frequency-doubling circuit and the result, $2f_s + 2\,\Delta f$, is transmitted from the plane back to the ground station. The purpose of the frequency doubling is to avoid interference between the ground transmitter and the airborne transmitter.

The doppler effect operates on the return trip just as it did in converting the original frequency f_s to f_0. The fractional change is the same, but since the returning carrier frequency is twice as high, the actual shift in cycles per second will be twice as large. Thus the return frequency received at the ground station is $2f_s + 4\,\Delta f$. For example, let $f_s = 200$ megacycles and $\Delta f = 60$ cycles. Then $f_0 = 200,000,060$. The doubled frequency transmitted back from the plane is $400,000,120$; the received signal at ground is approximately $400,000,240$.

This total shift of 240 cycles is made up of two components: 120 cycles due to doubling the initial 60-cycles shift, and an additional 120 cycles obtained on the assumption that the plane transmitted back not $400,000,120$ cycles, but rather simply $2f_s$ or $400,000,000$. The error in this last assumption is entirely negligible; if the return trip shift had been computed on the basis of $400,000,120$ cycles, the total shift would have been the original 120 cycles plus 120.000036, or 240.000036.

A block diagram of the electric system showing pertinent frequencies is given in Fig. 14-13. The actual measurement of velocity is accom-

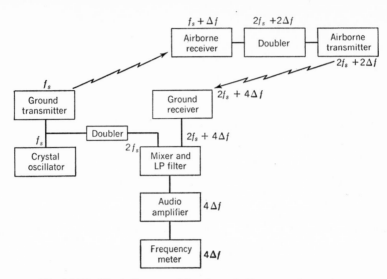

Fig. 14-13. Block diagram of doppler velocity measuring system.

plished by mixing the returned signal with the second harmonic of the crystal oscillator. The difference frequency is retained by a low-pass filter and determined with a frequency meter. This meter will ordinarily be calibrated directly in velocity.

Doppler radar systems operate in much the same manner as the system just described. The principal difference is that the object whose velocity is measured does not send back a signal from its own transmitter. Rather, the return signal is purely a reflection of the original one. The value of Δf is identical to that given by Eq. (14-22). The frequencies involved are therefore f_s at the transmitter and $f_s + 2\,\Delta f$ at the receiver. The transmitter and receiver are mounted side by side, both aimed at the target by a common antenna.

The transmitted and received frequencies are mixed (but without the frequency-doubling step shown in Fig. 14-13), and the difference indicated on a frequency meter. Since f_s will be of the order of a few thousand rather than a few hundred megacycles per second, the difference frequency will be much higher than in the system discussed earlier. For example, with a transmitted frequency of 2000 megacycles, an object moving toward the radar installation at only 20 mph will give a difference of 60 cycles for each one-way trip of the radar beam, or a total of 120 cycles. Note this is twice rather than four times the one-way shift because no frequency doubling is involved.

REFERENCES

1. Charles W. Sarture, "A Compensated RMS-Reading Hot Wire Anemometer" (Master's Thesis, Purdue University, 1955).
2. L. S. G. Kovasznay, "Development of Turbulence-Measuring Equipment," *Natl. Advisory Comm. Aeronaut. Tech. Note 2839*, January 1953.
3. L. V. King, "On the Convection of Heat from Small Cylinders in a Stream of Fluid: Determination of the Convection Constants of Small Platinum Wires with Applications to Hot Wire Anemometry," *Phil. Trans. Roy. Soc.* (London), Series A, vol. 214, November 12, 1914, p. 373.
4. R. C. Dean, Jr., *Aerodynamic Measurements* (Gas Turbine Laboratory, Massachusetts Institute of Technology, 1953).
5. H. L. Dreyden and A. M. Keuthe, "The Measurement of Fluctuation of Air Speed by the Hot Wire Anemometer," *Natl. Advisory Comm. Aeronaut. Rept. 320* (1929).
6. L. S. G. Kovasznay, "Calibration and Measurement in Turbulence Research by the Hot Wire Method," *Natl. Advisory Comm. Aeronaut. Tech. Note 1130*, June 1949.
7. Joseph R. Waterman, "A New Electronic Anemometer with Wide Frequency Range and Increased Stability" (Master's Thesis, Purdue University, 1952).
8. Hendrik W. Bode, *Network Analysis and Feedback Amplifier Design* (Princeton: D. Van Nostrand Company, Inc., 1945), pp. 479-480, 493-498.
9. W. B. Hess, R. C. Swengel, and S. K. Waldorf, "Measuring Water Velocity by an Ultrasonic Method," *Elec. Eng.*, vol. 69, November 1950, p. 983. See also R. C. Swengel, W. B. Hess, and S. K. Waldorf, "Principles and Application of the Ultrasonic Flowmeter," *Power Apparatus and Systems*, April 1955; and R. C. Swengel, W. B. Hess, and S. K. Waldorf, "Demonstration of the Principles of the Ultrasonic Flowmeter," *Elec. Eng.*, vol. 73, December 1954, p. 1082.
10. Walter R. Hogg, Eugene Mittelmann, and Donald S. Schover, "Electronic Circuit Problems in Electromagnetic Flow Measurements," *Proc. Natl. Electronics Conf.*, vol. 8 (1952), p. 127.
11. Leonard R. Malling, "Radio Doppler Effect for Aircraft Speed Measurements," *Proc. I.R.E.*, vol. 35, November 1947, p. 1357.

Chapter 15

INSTRUMENTS FOR THE MEASUREMENT
OF TIME

As was pointed out in Chapter 9, the quantities *frequency* and *time* are very closely related, are served by the same set of primary standards, and are measured the same way in some cases. Therefore the material in this chapter will have certain points of similarity to that of the previous chapter. The differences between time and frequency measurement are principally a matter of viewpoint. A measurement of time, as we use the term in this chapter, is actually *time interval*. That is, we shall deal with the matter of determining how long it is between two events, and not with such problems as finding exactly when it is high noon.

One of the most satisfactory instruments for general-purpose time studies is the cathode ray oscilloscope. We shall not discuss this instrument in detail, since it is really a combination of two systems: a time base generator, and high-quality amplifiers. Any signals that can be converted to voltage can be applied to the vertical amplifiers, and the time between them determined with an accuracy limited only by the linearity and precision of calibration of the time base generator. It is with these time base generators that we shall first be concerned.

15-1. The thyratron sweep circuit

An old circuit, but still a useful one when relatively slow repetition rates are required, employs a thyratron tube to control an integrating circuit. The basic idea is that constant current is permitted to flow into a capacitor. This develops a linearly increasing voltage, provided the time allowed for the current to flow is small compared with the RC time constant. When the voltage reaches a high enough value to ionize the gas in the thyratron, the tube discharges the capacitor, and a new sweep starts. The circuit of this sweep generator is shown in Fig. 15-1. The ignition or firing voltage of the thyratron is a function of the grid bias.

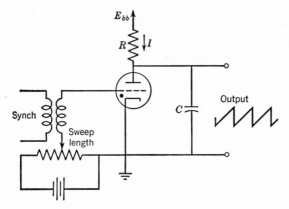

Fig. 15-1. The thyratron sweep generator.

The more negative the grid, the higher the voltage required to ionize the gas, and therefore the longer it will take for the capacitor voltage, e_C, to reach this value. Thus the sweep length may be controlled by the potentiometer.

The firing may also be initiated by a positive pulse applied to the control grid. This pulse is known as a *synchronizing* signal. It is usually derived from the waveform being observed on the oscilloscope. For example, if we are observing a sine wave, the synchronizing circuits may be adjusted to produce a sync pulse when the sine wave crosses zero in the positive-going direction. Then each new time base is started at the same time as the wave we wish to observe, with the result that the latter appears to remain stationary on the phosphor.

Our present interest, however, is in the time base itself. We shall define E_a as the anode voltage while the thyratron conducts, and E_f as the firing voltage. The value of E_a is usually around ten or fifteen volts, depending mostly on the gas with which the tube is filled, and to some extent on temperature and miscellaneous factors. The firing voltage is the potential required to ionize the gas initially. This may vary from around 50 to 400 or 500 volts in thyratrons commonly used in sweep generators. The exact value is primarily a function of grid bias, but also depends on temperature and other factors. Within a few microseconds after firing, the voltage drops to E_a, following path FA' in Fig. 15-2. This discharges the capacitor C of Fig. 15-1, and the tube ceases to conduct. The extinguishing mechanism is usually explained on the assumption that enough stray inductance exists in the wiring to drop the voltage e_C a trifle below E_a; i.e., the inductance prevents the capacitor discharge current from stopping instantaneously when $e_C = E_a$.

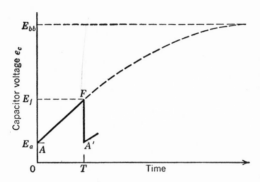

Fig. 15-2. Detail of the output waveform of the time-base generator of Fig. 15-1.

Frequently a few microhenries of inductance are placed intentionally between the anode of the tube and the capacitor C. A few ohms of series resistance may be inserted also to prevent the discharge current from exceeding the peak current rating of the thyratron.

In any event, we shall assume the capacitor starts to charge toward E_{bb} as an asymptotic limit as soon as the thyratron extinguishes after the previous sweep. The capacitor will have an initial voltage equal to E_a for all practical purposes. During the generation of the sweep, path AF in Fig. 15-2, the thyratron is an open circuit. Then the expression for the capacitor voltage may be set down by inspection as

$$e_C = E_a + (E_{bb} - E_a)(1 - \epsilon^{-t/RC}) \tag{15-1}$$

The sweep ends when the voltage E_f is reached. This occurs at the time $t = T$. Substitute E_f for e_C and T for t in Eq. (15-1).

$$E_f = E_a + (E_{bb} - E_a)(1 - \epsilon^{-T/RC}) \tag{15-2}$$

Solve for T.

$$T = RC \log_e \frac{E_{bb} - E_a}{E_{bb} - E_f} \tag{15-3}$$

Equation (15-3) is useful for determining the total sweep time, or the frequency of the sweep which is the reciprocal of T.* Thus if one expects to observe a signal with a frequency of 1 kc or period of 10^{-3} second, Eq. (15-3) tells how to pick values of R and C that give this value for T. Usually T would be made somewhat longer than the nominal value so that the *sync pulse* will trigger the new sweep.

A matter of at least as much importance as the sweep repetition rate is the sweep linearity. If a method of calibrating the sweep is available, i.e., accurately determining e_C vs time, linearity is not essential; but a linear trace makes life a great deal easier for the user of the equipment. Therefore let us determine the relationship between the time constant RC and linearity. It is obvious that the nearer e_C approaches E_{bb}, the more nonlinear the time base becomes, but we should like to quantify this fact.

The per cent deviation from linearity may be computed with the

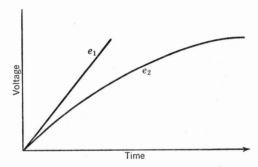

Fig. 15-3. Comparison between a linear sweep voltage and an exponential.

aid of the two curves of Fig. 15-3. Here e_1 is a straight line or linear sweep, while e_2 is an exponential.

$$e_2 = 1 - \epsilon^{-t/RC} \tag{15-4}$$

assuming it approaches 1 volt as an asymptote. This is purely a matter of convenience, and does not affect the final conclusions.

Voltage e_1 will have the same initial *slope* as e_2, but remains linear. This initial slope is de_2/dt evaluated at $t = 0$. The value is found by inspection from Eq. (15-4) to be $1/RC$, so the equation for e_1 is

$$e_1 = t/RC \tag{15-5}$$

* The statement that $f = 1/T$ implies the capacitor discharges and the thyratron deionizes in zero time. Typically 50 to 100 μsec may be required for these operations.

Now define the deviation from linearity as

$$\delta = \frac{e_1 - e_2}{e_1} \qquad (15\text{-}6)$$

Substitution of the expressions for e_1 and e_2 leads to

$$\delta = 1 - \frac{RC}{t} \left(1 - \epsilon^{-t/RC} \right) \qquad (15\text{-}7)$$

The results are plotted in Fig. 15-4 as a percentage. Time is normalized on the basis of the time constant RC. It is seen that for 5 per

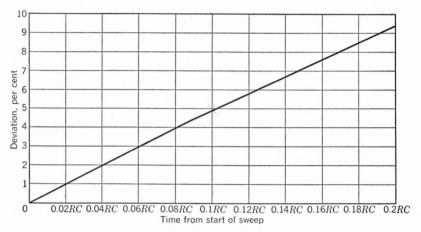

Fig. 15-4. Deviation from linearity of exponential time base.

cent deviation from linearity, the firing potential E_f must be reached at about $t = 0.1RC$.

15-2. High-vacuum pentode sweep generators

The inherent nonlinearity of the thyratron time base circuit has caused it to fall into disuse in many applications. An even more serious drawback is the fact that the gas, once ionized, requires considerable time to deionize and turn the tube off. This means that the thyratron sweep circuit is limited to low repetition rates. Small thyratrons, such as the 2D21 and the 2050, deionize in about 30 to 100 μsec, depending on the operating conditions. If we take 50 μsec as a typical value, the maximum repetition rate of the sweep is limited to 20 kc by the time required for deionization. Furthermore, under these conditions, *all* the time is spent in deionizing the tube, and none is left for generating a sweep.

When rapid repetition rates and good linearity are required, it is essential to employ high-vacuum time-base generators. There are a number of circuits that may be used for this purpose. One example is shown in Fig. 15-5. It consists of a one-shot multivibrator fired by a

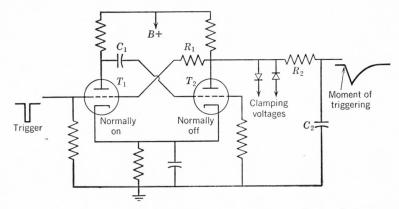

Fig. 15-5. Time base generator employing vacuum tube one-shot multivibrator and integrating circuit.

trigger pulse to initiate the sweep. The sweep repetition rate is equal to the frequency of these triggering pulses. The sweep length is adjustable by varying C_1, which determines how long T_2 remains conducting. Clamping diodes at the anode of T_2 insure that a square wave of voltage will be produced at that point. If the integrating circuit time constant R_2C_2 is long compared with the sweep length, a linear sweep appears at the output. This is followed by the recovery of capacitor C_2 along an exponential path. This circuit can operate appreciably faster than the thyratron sweep generator, but poses the same problem of nonlinearity.

If the capacitor in an integrating circuit can be charged with a true constant current, then a perfectly linear time base will be generated. This is because the capacitor integrates the current, and the time integral of a constant is a linearly increasing function of time.

One possible circuit for providing a constant charging current is shown in Fig. 15-6. This employs a pentode as the current source. Over a wide range of anode voltages, the plate current of a pentode is virtually constant for given potentials on the screen and control grids.

The operation is thus: Suppose a large negative pulse is applied to the grid of T_2, so that this tube is cut off. Then point B rises in potential, and diode D becomes conducting. Capacitor C discharges through the diode and resistor R, and point A approaches a potential equal to $E_{bb} - I_b R$, where I_b is the anode current of the pentode. As soon as

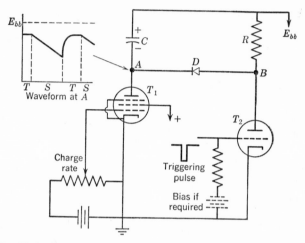

Fig. 15-6. A pentode time base circuit to provide a linear sweep.

this triggering pulse ends, tube T_2 starts to conduct heavily, and the potential at B drops well below that of point A. The diode cuts off, and C starts charging in the polarity shown with the constant current I_b. The grid bias of the pentode determines the value of this current. When another trigger pulse occurs, the sweep is terminated and the cycle repeats.

Figure 15-6 shows a sketch of the voltage waveform at point A. During times marked T, a trigger pulse is present. During time intervals S, the capacitor is charging through the pentode. Interval T would usually be much shorter than S; it has been exaggerated in the sketch to show the exponential waveform during the time of the triggering pulse.

There are many variations of this basic pentode charging circuit (*1,2*). Usually the greatest problem in reducing it to practice is resetting the capacitor at the end of the sweep. If this is to be done quickly, it requires a low-impedance high-current source. In Fig. 15-6, for example, suppose $E_{bb} = 200$ volts, we desire a sweep of 5 volts per microsecond slope, a duration of 10 μsec, and reset in 5 μsec. Let us at least tentatively design the circuit.

Suppose the pentode current is set to 5 ma. The capacitor voltage after 1 μsec is

$$e_C = \frac{I_b t}{C} = \frac{0.005 \text{ amp} \times 10^{-6} \text{ sec}}{C} = 5 \text{ volts} \qquad (15\text{-}8)$$

From this, C is found to be 1000 $\mu\mu$f. If the reset must occur in 5 μsec, the time constant RC should be about one-fifth this, or 1 μsec. Then $R = 1000$ ohms, which includes the forward resistance of the diode. This resistance is very low with modern diodes such as silicon junction types, and may be safely neglected.

The pentode anode voltage at the start of the sweep is $E_{bb} - I_b R = 200 - 0.005 \times 1000 = 195$ volts. At the end of the sweep, it is 195 volts $-$ (5 volts/μsec $\times$ 10 μsec) $= 145$ volts. The anode of the triode must still be below this potential at the end of the sweep. Suppose it is at 140 volts. Then the triode current during the sweep time is (200 v $-$ 140 v)/1000 ohms $= 60$ ma. Therefore we must find a triode that will draw 60 ma with 200 volts for E_{bb} and a 1000-ohm load. The 6V6 or 6AQ5 connected as triodes come very close, with 58 ma current for the above conditions and zero grid volts. This would result in 142 volts at the anode of the diode, which is still below 145. Tube T_2 could be a pentode also if desired.

It will be seen from this example that T_2 draws a very heavy current. If the reader wishes to repeat the above example, trying different recovery times, but always letting the time constant RC be one-fifth the allowed reset interval, it will be found that resetting the sweep in 2 μsec requires 150 ma in T_2, and a 1-μsec reset demands 333 ma.

15-3. The Miller integrator as a time base generator

There is no real objection to integrating an *approximately* constant current derived from a voltage source by a series resistance if the approximation is good enough. As long as the time for integrating is much less than the RC time constant, the deviation from linearity is not objectionable. The Miller integrator shown in Fig. 15-7 achieves this result. It operates on the well-known principle that the grid-plate capacitance of a tube is increased in proportion to the gain of the amplifier stage. In the construction of amplifiers, this so-called Miller effect may be a source of serious difficulties at high frequencies. However, in the integrator we take advantage of it. A capacitor may be made to look tens or hundreds of times its actual size, with the result

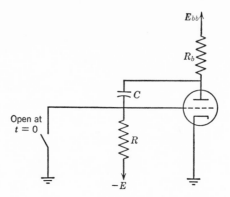

Fig. 15-7. A Miller integrator. Tube may also be a pentode.

that the effective time constant is very much greater than RC. It might appear at first glance that this would lead to very low output voltages, since with a long effective time constant, C would charge very slowly. However, the gain of the amplifier provides an adequate output.

We can study the performance of the integrator as a function of time by analyzing the equivalent circuit of Fig. 15-8. This differs from

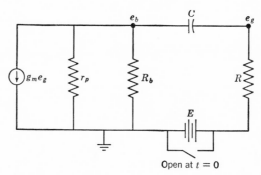

Fig. 15-8. Equivalent circuit of Fig. 15-7, except that battery is connected at $t = 0$ and short-circuited prior to that time.

Fig. 15-7 only in the placement of the switch. It is convenient to think of the voltage E as suddenly being turned on at $t = 0$, and on paper this is most readily accomplished by short-circuiting the battery prior to $t = 0$.

The node equations are written below in the Laplace transformed state, in which the step function of voltage is expressed as $\mathcal{E}/\boldsymbol{s}$. The script style of type shows a quantity is in the transformed condition.

$$\varepsilon_b\left(\frac{1}{r_p} + \frac{1}{R_b} + sC\right) + \varepsilon_g(g_m - sC) = 0 \qquad (15\text{-}9)$$

$$\varepsilon_b(-sC) + \varepsilon_g\left(sC + \frac{1}{R}\right) = -\frac{\varepsilon}{sR} \qquad (15\text{-}10)$$

If these equations are solved for e_b and the inverse transform taken, we find

$$e_b = kE\,\frac{(a_0 - \alpha)\epsilon^{-\alpha t} - a_0}{\alpha} \qquad (15\text{-}11)$$

where $$k = \frac{1}{R(1/R + 1/r_p + 1/R_b + g_m)} \qquad (15\text{-}12)$$

$$a_0 = -g_m/C \qquad (15\text{-}13)$$

$$\alpha = \frac{1}{RC}\,\frac{1/r_p + 1/R_b}{1/R + 1/r_p + 1/R_b + g_m} \qquad (15\text{-}14)$$

The denominator of Eq. (15-14) is obviously larger than the numerator, so α is smaller than $1/RC$. The time constant in Eq. (15-11) is $1/\alpha$, so we see from Eq. (15-14) that the Miller integrator has a longer time constant than RC. For example, suppose that in Fig. 15-7 we use a pentode rather than a triode and have the following circuit parameters: $r_p = 10^6$ ohms, $R_b = 10^5$, $R = 10^4$, $C = 10^{-8}$, $g_m = 10^{-3}$ mho, and $E = 110$ volts. Then $k \cong 1/11$, $\alpha = 100$, and $a_0 = 10^{-5}$. The effective

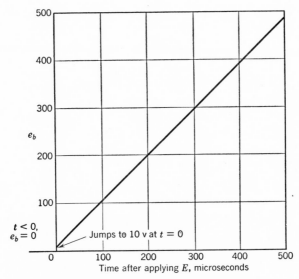

Fig. 15-9. Plate voltage e_b vs. time in circuit of Fig. 15-8.

time constant is $1/\alpha = 0.01$ sec, while the product RC is 0.0001 sec. Note the effective time constant is increased by a factor of 100. The value of e_b as a function of time is plotted in Fig. 15-9.

For convenience, it is assumed that the plate voltage at $t = 0-$ is zero. This is not quite true, since we are neglecting the quiescent plate voltage that exists at that time. Figure 15-9 should actually be interpreted as the *rise* in plate voltage as a function of time. However, this is a detail. The point to note is that the sweep is extremely linear, and of generous amplitude. The sweep must end either when the anode reaches the supply voltage E_{bb} or when switch S is closed again. Figure 15-9 does not show the end of the trace, but assumes in effect that E_{bb} is at least 500 volts, and S is left open for at least 500 μsec.

After 500 μsec, $t = 5RC$. But t is only $0.05(1/\alpha)$. Thus the effective lengthening of the time constant by the Miller integrator results in essentially linear operation. As can be seen from Fig. 15-4, when $t = 0.05RC$, the deviation from linearity is only 2.5 per cent.

One version of the Miller circuit as it is used in the Tektronix Model 545 cathode ray oscilloscope is shown in Fig. 15-10. The integration is performed by the 6CL6 tube. Instead of connecting the integrating capacitor C directly to the anode of the integrator tube, it is isolated by a cathode follower. The 55-volt neon tube between the 6BQ7A grids and the 6CL6 anode is for the purpose of establishing the correct d-c operating point for the cathode follower. It has no direct bearing on the sweep generation.

The sweep is initiated by applying a trigger pulse to the direct-coupled flip-flop. This drops the voltage on the anodes of the 6AL5 below the cathode potentials. Prior to this, both sides of capacitor C are clamped at approximately ground potential. After the trigger pulse, they are free to seek their own level. Current starts to decrease in resistor R, and the control grid of the 6CL6 starts going negative. This causes the anode potential to rise, and the cathode follower pulls up the potential of the top plate of capacitor C at almost the same rate. Capacitor C is thus charged primarily through the cathode follower, and the potential of the 6CL6 control grid remains almost constant. Such small decrease in potential with time as does occur at this point is due to the contribution of capacitor-charging current that flows through R. Because the potential across R is so nearly constant, this charging current is approximately constant, and the decrease in grid voltage proceeds linearly with time. This grid voltage appears at the 6CL6 anode

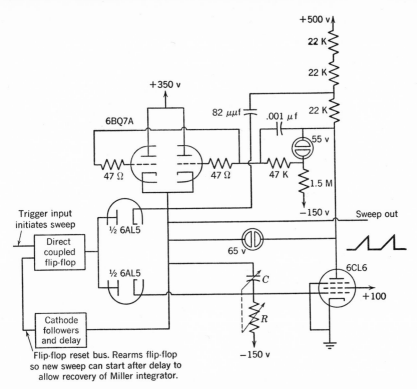

Fig. 15-10. Integrator circuit of main sweep generator as used in Tektronix Type 545 oscilloscope.

(amplified) as the desired linear sweep. The sweep speed is changed by adjusting C and R with front-panel controls. The repetition rate is controlled by the frequency of the initiating trigger pulses.

Initiating pulses are blocked from the time of the start of a sweep until the sweep is completed and the Miller integrator has time to recover. At the end of each sweep, the cathode followers and delay circuit near the bottom of the drawing inject a reset pulse into the flip-flop to arm it for the next trigger.

The sweep voltage is sketched at the right-hand edge of Fig. 15-10. The fastest basic sweep rate in this circuit is 0.1 μsec per centimeter; this may be enlarged by additional amplification to 0.02 μsec per centimeter.

The Miller integrator is also extremely useful when a very long time constant is required. One method of making a long time constant is to use large resistors and large capacitors. But a capacitor larger than about 10 to 20 μf becomes of unwieldy physical size unless it is an electrolytic type, and even the best electrolytic capacitors tend to have large leakage currents. By the use of a Miller circuit, a high-quality, low-leakage capacitor of say 10 μf may be made to look like several thousand microfarads, and very long time constants may be achieved. The author recalls one sinusoidal oscillator that operated at a frequency of 1 cycle per half hour. This was a demonstration unit constructed for classroom use to illustrate the Miller effect.

Since the apparent increase in grid-to-plate capacitance depends on the voltage gain between the two terminals of the capacitor, a Miller integrator can be considered an amplifier with capacitance between its input and output terminals. Any number of stages may be included in this amplifier, provided there is a phase inversion between input and output. The over-all assembly is obviously one type of feedback amplifier, and care must be exercised to prevent oscillation when more than one tube is used.

15-4. Timing markers

The modern oscilloscope is a time-measuring instrument of great versatility and usefulness. A good laboratory model will have sweep speeds and sweep linearity of the order of 3 per cent accuracy. However, there are cases when still greater accuracy is required. In this case, auxiliary timing markers or pips are useful.

One method of producing an auxiliary timing reference is shown in Fig. 15-11. A square wave of voltage is applied to the control grid of a pentode amplifier in which the plate load is a high-Q resonant circuit. This provides a decaying sinusoidal waveform with a repetition rate

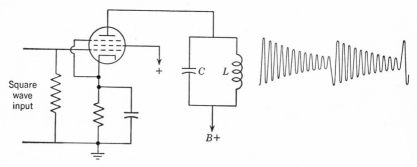

Fig. 15-11. Decaying sinusoid for calibration of time interval.

equal to the square wave frequency and a period for individual cycles determined mostly by L and C. If L, C, and the square wave frequency are properly adjusted relative to one another, the square wave can be made to repeat in some convenient multiple of the sine wave frequency. For example, each burst of sinusoids might be made 10 cycles long, so that the individual cycles provide one time calibration and the repetition rate a second calibration exactly 10 times as long.

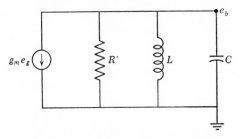

Fig. 15-12. Equivalent circuit of Fig. 15-11.

The equivalent circuit for Fig. 15-11 is shown in Fig. 15-12. Here

$$R' = R||r_p \qquad (15\text{-}15)$$

where R is $Q^2 R_{ser}$, with Q the figure of merit of the inductor (we assume the capacitor free of losses), and R_{ser} the inductor series resistance. The plate voltage as a function of time is determined easily by writing the node equation for e_b in Fig. 15-11. This is

$$\varepsilon_b \left(\frac{1}{R'} + \frac{1}{sL} + sC \right) = -g_m \frac{\varepsilon_g}{s} \qquad (15\text{-}16)$$

with all quantities in the s domain, i.e., Laplace transformed. ε_g is the amplitude of the square wave applied to the control grid. The corresponding function of time is

$$e_b(t) = -\frac{g_m E_g}{\omega C} \epsilon^{-t/R'C} \sin \omega t \qquad (15\text{-}17)$$

where

$$\omega = \sqrt{\frac{1}{LC} - \frac{1}{4R'^2 C^2}} \qquad (15\text{-}18)$$

In any really useful circuit of this type, the value of R' is sufficiently large that $\omega = 1/\sqrt{LC}$ for all practical purposes. We may define an over-all circuit Q as

$$Q' = R'/\omega L = R'\omega C \qquad (15\text{-}19)$$

Then

$$R'C = Q'/\omega \qquad (15\text{-}20)$$

$$\omega = 2\pi/T \tag{15-21}$$

where T is the period of the sinusoidal cycles. Substitute Eq. (15-21) into Eq. (15-20).

$$R'C = Q'T/2\pi \tag{15-22}$$

When t equals one time constant, the amplitude of the timing wave has dropped to $1/\epsilon$ of its maximum value. We might arbitrarily take this as the greatest allowable decrease. Suppose we postulate this occurs after n periods of the timing wave. Then

$$t = nT = \text{one time constant} = Q'T/2\pi \tag{15-23}$$

$$n = Q'/2\pi \tag{15-24}$$

Equation (15-24) is useful in determining the required Q' for the over-all circuit if a given number of sinusoids is desired before the amplitude drops to $1/\epsilon$ the maximum value. For example, if $n = 10$, then Q' must be 63.

Another method of generating a timing pattern is the use of an oscillator and pulse-forming circuit. This is shown in block diagram form in Fig. 15-13. A sinusoidal oscillator is followed by a Schmitt

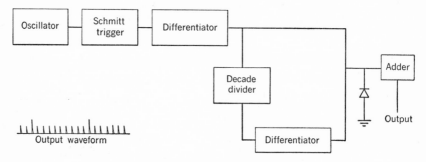

Fig. 15-13. A timing comb generator.

trigger or similar circuit to produce square waves. These are differentiated, producing a sequence of positive and negative pulses. One set of pulses goes directly to an adding circuit; the other set goes to a decade divider. For every ten pulses applied to this divider, one positive-going step of voltage is obtained. This is likewise differentiated, and the resulting pip is sent to the adding circuit, where it combines with the tenth pulse of the high-frequency train. Thus every tenth pulse is a double-amplitude one. A typical timing comb is shown at the lower left of Fig. 15-13.

Negative as well as positive pips are produced at the differentiating stage. These negative pulses are removed by the diode at the input of the adding circuit.

The timing pattern is as accurate as the oscillator employed to produce it. When first-class accuracy is necessary, the oscillator will be crystal-controlled. A decade divider is shown as a matter of convenience, but division by any desired factor can be employed.

The divider could be of the counting type employing cascaded binary stages, or it might consist of multivibrators dividing by the appropriate ratio. Multivibrators cannot divide by too large a number if they are to remain synchronized reliably. For example, division by ten would probably be accomplished by dividing first by five and then by two.

The circuits employed in this block diagram have already been described in detail in Chapter 9. We shall say nothing further about them here.

15-5. Types of display

A number of types of display are possible with cathode ray oscilloscopes (3). Workers in the field of radar have contributed especially heavily to the development of these techniques. Most of the examples listed in this section are drawn from the radar art.

(a) *The Type A Display.* This display is sketched in Fig. 15-14(a). The time base is swept out by a linear sawtooth in the conventional manner, and timing pips are added for greater accuracy. The sweep is initiated at one event (such as the transmission of a radar pulse), and the time of the second event (such as the return echo) produces the large pip. The time between events is proportional to the distance along the x axis from the origin.

(b) *The Type J Display.* This is a polar version of the type A display, shown in Fig. 15-14(b). It may be generated in various ways. One is by the use of the special cathode ray tube sketched in Fig. 15-14(c). This tube has a wire entering from the center of the faceplate and running axially a short distance down the tube. A metal ring or conductive coating is placed on the inside perimeter of the tube close to the faceplate and concentric with the wire. A potential difference between the ring and wire deflects the electron beam in a radial direction. A

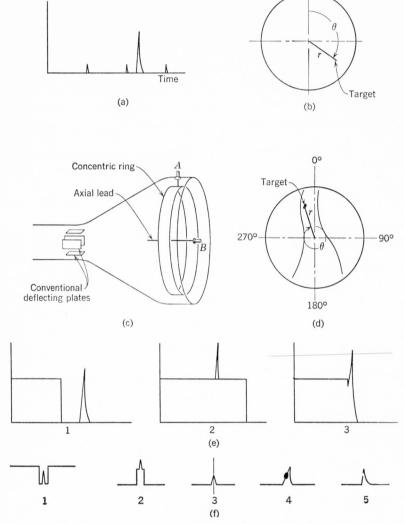

Fig. 15-14. Various types of displays. See text for description.

circular trace is produced by the conventional deflecting plates (cf. Section 9-2, and esp. Fig. 9-8). This determines the angular coordinate θ, while the radial coordinate is specified by the voltage between terminals A and B. The trace starts at $t = 0$, and ends with the return echo. The radial distance r is a measure of the amplitude of the echo, and θ is time, or in radar applications, distance.

(c) *The Type B Display.* The type *B* display is similar to the type *J* in that a polar coordinate system is employed. An example of this display is shown in Fig. 15-14(d). However, the circular trace is generated by voltages 90 degrees out of phase synchronized by a servomechanism with the angular position of a rotating radar antenna.

These voltages are generated by a device known as a *resolver*, shown in Fig. 15-15. It contains an input winding known as the *stator* and an output winding known as the *rotor* with two legs 90 electrical degrees out

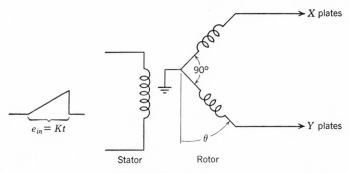

Fig. 15-15. A resolver.

of phase. The output winding is mounted on a shaft, and may be rotated mechanically with respect to the stator. The angle θ in Fig. 15-15 represents the displacement of the rotor relative to some arbitrary reference point.

The input voltage is a linear sweep of the form

$$e_{in} = Kt \tag{15-25}$$

The voltage at the X plates is

$$e_x = e_{in} \sin \theta = (K \sin \theta)t \tag{15-26}$$

and that at the Y plates is

$$e_y = e_{in} \cos \theta = (K \cos \theta)t \tag{15-27}$$

The voltages e_x and e_y are parametric equations for a straight line with slope equal to cot θ. Therefore as θ varies in synchronism with the antenna, a sequence of straight line radial traces is produced. If $\theta = \omega t$ where ω is the speed of rotation of the antenna, and ω is much less than the repetition rate of the input sweep voltage, the trace appears to be a rotating straight line sweeping around the face of the cathode ray tube, similar to the hand of a clock.

When a radar echo is received, the trace is momentarily brightened by a positive pulse of voltage on the cathode ray tube control grid. This causes the object from which the echo returns to appear as a bright dot, such as the point marked "target" in Fig. 15-14(d). Any other object capable of returning an echo pulse is also displayed on the tube. For example, Fig. 15-14(c) shows the outlines of a river bank, with the target ahead of the radar and somewhat to the port side. The angle 0° coincides with the heading of one's own ship or aircraft. Some of the newer radars employ a doppler principle to determine if a target is moving, and display it only if it is. This has the advantage that fixed objects, such as the riverbank, will not appear on the display to distract the operator's attention.

(d) *Type M Displays.* Type M displays employ a square wave of length controlled by the operator. An example is shown in Fig. 15-14(e). The start of the square wave is triggered by the transmitted pulse. The length is adjusted until the edge coincides with the pip from the return echo. A dial calibrated in time, or more likely distance, is used to set the square wave length, and the range to the target is then read from this dial. Figure 15-14(e)1 shows the appearance of the display when the dial is set for too short a distance; part 2 of this figure shows too long a setting; and 3 is correct, with the range adjustment on target.

Figure 15-14(f) shows a number of variations of the type M display. Parts 1, 2, and 3 are correctly adjusted; in parts 4 and 5, the range is just a trifle short of the target. Part 1 is the so-called "notch" display. The adjustment of the range potentiometer moves a down-going pulse along the cathode-ray tube X axis. When the range is correct, the return pip is centered in the pulse, producing a notch. A "pedestal" display is shown in sketch 2. This is similar to the notch, except that the return pip adds instead of subtracts. Part 3 shows a hairline moved mechanically instead of electronically across the face of the tube. This line is centered on the pip for correct range. In part 4, the trace is brightened at the moment in time controlled by the range potentiometer. This bright spot should be made to coincide with the top of the pip. In number 5, the trace is blanked momentarily; otherwise, this is similar to display 4.

All of these displays have been used for radar. However, any of them might be used for measurements of time interval in other applications. They are all really time measurements anyway, correlated with distance through the speed of light, which is the velocity at which the radar beam travels to its target and back.

15-6. Direct-reading time interval meters

We have discussed in considerable detail methods of generating time bases and displays. This is the most important part of oscillographic time interval measurement, since accuracy is either achieved or lost in the sweep generator. The next question is how to convert the time base to a time interval measurement in the absence of a cathode ray oscilloscope.

Most approaches to this question involve methods of initiating the sweep at the occurrence of one event and terminating it when the time interval being measured has elapsed. In most applications, various auxiliary transducers are required. For example, the time required for a flashbulb to reach peak light output could be measured by triggering the sweep with the same voltage that fires the bulb. A photocell connected to a differentiating circuit would give a measure of the light intensity. When this reaches its peak, the output of the differentiator goes through zero. The zero crossing could be sensed by a Schmitt trigger circuit, which delivers a pulse to the timing circuit to terminate the sweep.

Figure 15-16 shows one possible configuration for a direct-reading time-interval meter. A flip-flop is arranged with both positive and negative supply potentials so that when T_2 is conducting, its plate is very negative relative to ground, say -50 volts. When a negative trigger pulse is applied to the starting terminal, T_2 cuts off. Its plate attempts to go positive, but is clamped by the diode at the grid of T_3 and remains at zero voltage. Tube T_3 is now able to conduct, and starts to charge capacitor C. Note the similarity to Fig. 15-6. The voltage on C increases linearly with time until a stop pulse at the grid of T_1 turns T_1 off and T_2 on. The grid of T_3 is then at -50 volts again, and T_3 stops conducting. C retains the charge it acquired while T_3 conducted, and this is measured with an electrometer. An electrometer is almost essential, as it allows C to lose its charge only over a long period of time. Thus the user has an opportunity to read the capacitor voltage which is a measure of the time interval. A reset switch or pushbutton simultane-

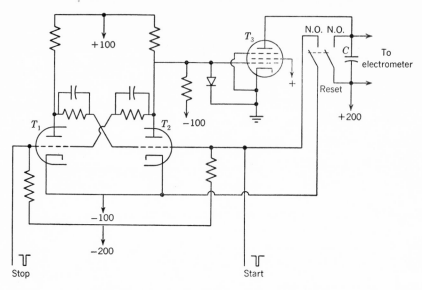

Fig. 15-16. A direct-reading time interval meter.

ously discharges the capacitor and momentarily connects the grid of T_2 to its cathode so that T_2 conducts and T_3 remains off until the arrival of the next starting pulse.

The great disadvantage of a circuit of this type is that C will lose its charge eventually, even with an electrometer as the measuring instrument. This difficulty might be eliminated in several ways, all of which involve giving the instrument a memory. For example, the voltage across the capacitor might be used as the input to a mechanical encoder of the type shown in Fig. 12-17. The encoder would have to operate rapidly to finish encoding the voltage on C at the end of the sweep before this voltage drops appreciably. Also, it would have to operate in one direction only so that it would display the highest value that was reached, and not follow the capacitor voltage back down as C discharges. After the result is written down at leisure, the mechanical encoder would be reset by an extra contact on the switch in Fig. 15-16.   .

Another technique based on the circuit of Fig. 15-16 is to omit T_3 and its associated components, and place a ballistic galvanometer in series with the anode of T_1. The swing of the galvanometer is a measure of the total charge that passed through it, which in turn is proportional to the time interval. This method also lacks a memory. The operator must pay constant attention to the galvanometer in order to observe how far it deflects.

15-7. Time interval by counting

The subject of time interval measurements with electronic counters has been mentioned before in Chapter 9. The interval that can be measured accurately by counting depends on the maximum operating rate of the counter. For example, if a time interval is 10 μsec, it can be measured to 1 per cent accuracy by a 10-megacycle counter. The 10-megacycle pulses are gated into the decade counters at the start of the time interval, and the gate is closed again 10 μsec later. During this time, 100 pulses should enter the counters. Since the count may be in error by plus or minus one, it follows that the accuracy is 1 per cent. Accuracy improves as the time interval becomes longer. Counting circuits are described in Chapter 9; the reader is referred to the material there for details.

A somewhat simplified counter for time interval measurements is presented in a paper by Sturtevant (4). This counter employs a 1-kc tuning fork as the timing element. It is useful for moderately long intervals, of the order of a few tenths second or more. There are many applications where this less elaborate counter would be entirely satisfactory. The general principles of operation are the same as those described in Chapter 9.

REFERENCES

1. John M. Cage, *Theory and Application of Industrial Electronics* (New York: McGraw-Hill Book Company, Inc., 1951), p. 143.
2. Owen S. Puckle, *Time Bases* (New York: John Wiley & Sons, Inc., 1951), 2nd ed.
3. Britton Chance, Robert I. Hulsizer, Edward F. MacNichol, Jr., and Frederick C. Williams, *Electronic Time Measurements* (New York: McGraw-Hill Book Company, Inc., 1949), vol. 20 of the Radiation Laboratory Series.
4. Julian M. Sturtevant, "A Millisecond Timer," *Rev. Sci. Instr.*, vol. 22 (June 1951), p. 359.

Chapter 16

SOUND

16-1. The nature of sound

Sound is defined by the American Standards Association (*1*) in these words: "Sound is an alteration in pressure, particle displacement, or particle velocity propagated in an elastic material or the superposition of such propagated alterations. Sound is also the sensation produced through the ear by the alterations described above." The first sentence is the one of most interest to engineers and physicists. The second is of concern primarily to the biologist. Naturally, there is joint work between the two fields. Engineers and physiologists are both concerned with the effects of sound upon the human animal. Some sources of sound, such as jet aircraft, produce pressures capable of rupturing the eardrums at close range or doing other physical damage.

There are several general categories into which sound falls.

1. The simplest sound is the pure sinusoidal tone, which rarely occurs in nature. Most sounds contain at least a few harmonics.

2. White noise is a very common natural sound. This is characterized by the same properties that are present in white electric noise: Gaussian distribution of amplitude, and a frequency spectrum having uniform energy density per cycle. Such sounds as wind and splashing water are very close to white noise.

3. Combinations of white noise and discrete frequencies are widely found. Most industrial noise is in this category. A rotating motor furnishes a good example. The armature produces sound of a given fundamental frequency, such as 30 cycles in an 1800-rpm motor. Vibrations in the bearings, hum in the stator laminations, brush clicks against the commutator bars, etc., all combine to produce harmonics of this

fundamental frequency. White noise is added by air swishing through the cooling louvers.

4. Combinations of discrete frequencies in the absence of white noise. The most obvious example of this type of sound is music. String and reed instruments produce a fundamental and various harmonics characteristic of the instrument. Drums, chimes, and similar percussion instruments produce a fundamental and a number of inharmonically related overtones.

A simple sound (pure sine wave) is usually described completely by stating its frequency and amplitude. It is rarely necessary to specify the phase as well. A more complex sound is described by giving the frequency and amplitude of each of its components. White noise is an exception, as this can be specified only in a statistical fashion.

The measurement of sound has as its usual objective the determination of loudness and pitch, since these quantities are the things to which the ear responds. Unfortunately, the brain comes into the picture also, making loudness and pitch subjective quantities, not truly subject to measurement in the tidy, unequivocal manner physical scientists are accustomed to. The purely physical quantities corresponding to loudness and pitch are intensity and frequency. These can be determined accurately, and from them fairly good estimates of the subjective quantities are made.

Intensity is the strength of a sound field propagating in a given direction. It is expressed as watts per square centimeter. This is a vector quantity, as the direction of propagation is part of the definition. For measurement purposes, the scalar quantity *intensity level* is more useful. This is expressed as

$$\text{intensity level} = 10 \log_{10} \frac{I}{I_0} \qquad (16\text{-}1)$$

where I is the intensity and I_0 is a reference level equal to 10^{-16} watt/cm². Note that intensity is a measure of sound power. Another useful reference is *pressure level*.

$$\text{pressure level} = 20 \log_{10} \frac{P}{P_0} \qquad (16\text{-}2)$$

where P is pressure in dynes/cm² and P_0 is the reference pressure of 0.0002 dynes/cm². This value of P_0 was selected so that sounds of a given intensity would have the same value in decibels whether expressed in terms of pressure or intensity. Both references are based on subjective tests. They express the sound intensity or pressure of a sine wave of 1 kc that can just be detected by a listener with good hearing in the absence of any other sounds.

16-2. The significance of sound analyzer readings

Sound analyzers are devices to measure the contribution to the total intensity made by sounds in a frequency band Δf wide, centered upon the frequency f to which the analyzer is tuned. We shall consider sound analyzer circuits later in this chapter. A discussion of interpreting their readings is included at this point to illustrate the calculation of total intensity from discrete samples.

The sound analyzer scale is calibrated in a quantity A such that

$$A = 10 \log_{10} \frac{\Delta I}{I_0} \tag{16-3}$$

where ΔI is the contribution to the total intensity from the pass band Δf wide. The concept of *intensity level per cycle* is usually more useful. In mathematical terms this is

$$B = 10 \log_{10} \frac{\Delta I/\Delta f}{I_0} = 10 \log_{10} \frac{\Delta I}{I_0} - 10 \log_{10} \Delta f \tag{16-4}$$

In many sound analyzers, Δf is adjustable. This is why the instruments are calibrated to indicate A. Then B is obtained for the particular value of Δf by using Eq. (16-4).

The total sound intensity is determined from values of B by a rather roundabout method. From Eq. (16-4), it is seen that

$$\frac{\Delta I}{\Delta f} = I_0 \times 10^{B/10} \tag{16-5}$$

$$\text{total intensity} = I = \int_0^\infty \frac{\Delta I}{\Delta f} \, df = I_0 \int_0^\infty 10^{B/10} \, df \tag{16-6}$$

In a practical case, the limits of integration may usually be taken as 20 cycles and 20 kc because these correspond to the limits of hearing. Normally the intensity calculation will require numerical integration of the curve of B vs f. Such a curve is known as a *noise spectrogram*. It is usually plotted on semilog paper. The intensity calculated from Eq. (16-6) is finally converted to intensity *level* so that the result of sound analyzer readings will correspond at least fairly well with the subjective impression of loudness that a listener would have.

16-3. Acoustic transducers

Before getting into the matter of circuits for sound measuring instruments, we should consider at least briefly the problem of transducers to convert sound into an electric signal. Since the definition of sound is not restricted to pressure alterations in air, it follows that transducers must be available for operation in a number of different media.

A pressure-to-voltage transducer for operation in air is known as a *microphone*. Transducers for detecting sound in solid bodies are *vibration pickups*. Those used in underwater sound measurements are generally referred to simply as *"transducers"*; it is perfectly obvious to the person using it what transducer he has in mind.

(a) *Summary of Types of Microphones.* We do not propose to develop the theory of microphone design or operation, which is a rather specialized field. There are many excellent references dealing with this topic (*2,3*). However, it seems worth while to list the main types of microphones and summarize briefly their properties.

There are five types of microphones in relatively common use. These are the dynamic, capacitor, ribbon, crystal, and carbon varieties. The dynamic microphone sketched in Fig. 16-1 consists of a coil of wire

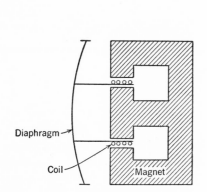

Fig. 16-1. The dynamic microphone.

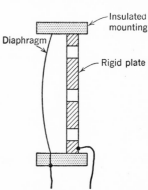

Fig. 16-2. The capacitor microphone.

moved in a magnetic field by the pressure of sound waves striking the diaphragm. An emf is induced in the moving coil of wire, and this is amplified by conventional audio amplifiers of a few hundred thousand ohms input impedance. This microphone can be used also as a loud-speaker by driving the coil with audio frequency current. Most intercom sets use the same small speaker, about 3 or 4 inches in diameter, for the microphone.

The capacitor microphone, Fig. 16-2, is the acknowledged queen of laboratory microphones. It is the accepted standard for precise acoustical measurements. It operates on the principle that sound waves striking the conducting diaphragm change the capacitance between it and a metal plate mounted close behind. The electrical theory of this action will be examined in detail in Chapter 18, where we consider a similar device as a pressure transducer, unrestricted to acoustical measurements. In brief, however, a direct bias voltage is applied to the input terminals, and as the diaphragm moves, an alternating voltage is superimposed on this direct voltage. The a-c signal is amplified and delivered to the measuring instruments.

The capacitor microphone must operate into as high an impedance as possible. A cathode follower is almost invariably placed in the same housing as the microphone itself. A laboratory capacitor microphone is usually detachable from its mounting and cathode follower preamplifier. Thus, when not in use, it may be stored in a desiccating container to keep out moisture and prevent a low-impedance leakage path between diaphragm and plate.

The ribbon microphone of Fig. 16-3 is similar in principle to the dynamic microphone. The conductor is a thin metal ribbon rather than a coil. This ribbon is mounted between the poles of a long, narrow mag-

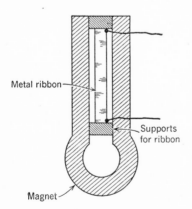

Fig. 16-3. The ribbon microphone.

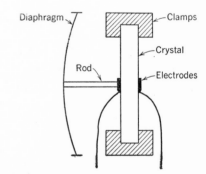

Fig. 16-4. The crystal microphone.

net. Variations in air pressure cause it to move and an emf is induced. The source impedance looking back into this microphone is very low, of the order of a fraction of an ohm. An impedance step-up transformer is often assembled in the same case as the ribbon and magnet assembly.

Figure 16-4 shows the arrangement of a crystal microphone. Various piezoelectric materials can be used. Rochelle salt and quartz crystals are the most common. Quartz is a superior material, but much more expensive. Rochelle salt melts at 65°C, and is adversely affected by high humidity. Therefore some consideration must be paid to the operating environment of a crystal microphone if there is any question as to the type of crystal material. Piezoelectric crystals are characterized by the fact that an emf is developed between the faces of the crystal when it is stressed mechanically. Air pressure variations are transmitted to the crystal by mechanical coupling with a diaphragm and the emf is taken from electrodes attached to opposite faces. These electrodes may be plated or vaporized onto the crystal. The crystal is mounted in clamps to hold it by the edges or corners.

The crystal microphone is second in quality only to the capacitor type. It is widely used in laboratory instruments if the extraordinary precision of a good capacitor microphone is not essential. Crystal microphones require an amplifier of relatively high impedance—a few hundred thousand ohms.

The carbon microphone of Fig. 16-5 would not in general be used in instrumentation applications. It exhibits both nonlinearity and hysteresis. The carbon granules tend to be very noisy electrically. The principle of operation is very simple: namely, air pressure changes the

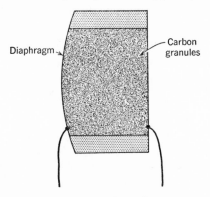

Diaphragm

Carbon granules

Fig. 16-5. The carbon microphone.

resistance by packing the carbon granules more or less tightly as the diaphragm moves in and out. The change of resistance modulates a direct current passed through the microphone. This produces an a-c component that is usually coupled out through a transformer.

The carbon microphone has been included for completeness in our survey of microphones. Although it is not recommended for instrumentation, it is perfectly suitable for voice transmission. Carbon microphones are used by the tens of millions in the world's telephones. They are inexpensive, dependable, and virtually indestructible.

For applications in extremely high sound levels, up to 200 db, special capacitor and crystal microphones are available (4). The chance of encountering 200 db is relatively rare, but in some cases, as jet engine testing, it might happen. Exposure to sound intensities much above 120 db will result in various types of temporary or permanent damage to the auditory system. Rupture of the eardrum is a definite possibility. Therefore any testing done in sound levels above 120 db must be carried out by microphones monitored at remote locations.

(b) *Vibration Pickups.* Most vibration pickups employ a piezoelectric principle, similar to the microphone of Fig. 16-4. Instead of a mechanical connection to a diaphragm, a rod in contact with the crystal extends through the case. This rod is touched against the vibrating body to transmit vibrations to the crystal. The general appearance is somewhat similar to a large phonograph cartridge with a greatly enlarged needle.

Magnetic vibration pickups are also available. They are similar in principle to the magnetic strain gage described in Chapter 13.

As a matter of fact, *any* transducer capable of measuring small displacements might be used in vibration analysis. This includes all types of strain gages and the differential transformer. However, in most cases when one speaks of a vibration pickup, he visualizes the piezoelectric type.

(c) *Ultrasonic and Underwater Transducers (5).* This is a highly specialized topic; we shall discuss it only briefly. Two main classes of transducers are used in this service: the piezoelectric and the magnetostriction. Magnetostriction transducers operate on the principle that in some materials, such as nickel, a magnetic field causes a change in dimensions. The process is reversible: if the dimensions are distorted,

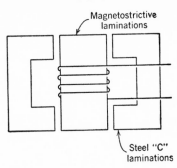

Fig. 16-6. Principle of the magnetostrictive transducer.

a magnetic field is created. The general arrangement of such a transducer is shown in Fig. 16-6. The magnetostrictive laminations are surrounded by a current-carrying coil, and steel C laminations are placed along the sides to reduce the size of the air gap. Magnetostrictive transducers are usually designed for relatively low frequencies, in the audio range or slightly above. There are two reasons for this. First, the laminations should be excited with current at their natural resonant frequency, which for nickel is equal to 2440 kc divided by the length (i.e., the dimension in the direction parallel to the magnetic field) in millimeters. High frequencies require short laminations, which are difficult to handle in assembly. Second, eddy current losses become higher and higher as the frequency goes up.

Crystal transducers are used at frequencies from a few hundred kilocycles to a few megacycles per second. Quartz and barium titanate ceramic are most common. Other materials such as Rochelle salt may be used, but have to be sealed in a sound-transmitting enclosure for protection against humidity.

Crystal transducers may deliver appreciable power, of the order of hundreds of watts in commercial ultrasonic generators. Submersible transducers for industrial applications, such as ultrasonic cleaning, homogenizing otherwise immiscible liquids, etc., are usually of the crystal type. Crystals are also used for transducers in ultrasonic equipment for detecting faults in castings. More will be said of this application later in the chapter.

Magnetostrictive transducers are available in ratings of many kilowatts. They are well suited to such applications as depth sounding, where distances of the order of hundreds of feet are involved and low frequencies must be used because of the increasing attenuation of water as frequency rises. Sonar is one very obvious example of underwater measurement by acoustical methods. However, it is basically similar to depth sounding or ultrasonic fault locating. Since it is a rather specialized application, largely of a military nature, it will not be discussed here.

16-4. Sound level meters (6,7,8)

A sound-level meter is basically a vacuum tube voltmeter calibrated to indicate the voltage from a microphone in terms of the incident sound intensity. It is used to correlate the subjective impression of *loudness* with the physical quantity *intensity*. A number of design features are involved that would not be required if a purely physical measurement were desired.

In order to determine how the meter should respond to sounds of different intensities, it is necessary to see how the ear itself responds.

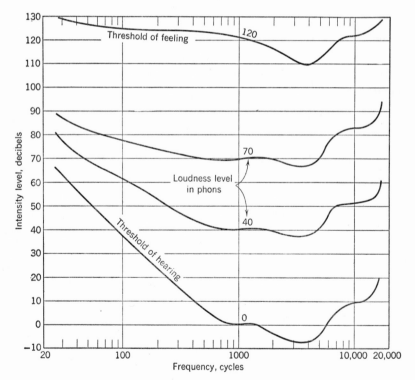

Fig. 16-7. The Fletcher-Munson equal loudness contours.

It turns out that we hear loud sounds of all frequencies equally well, but faint sounds appear to be especially weak at low and high frequencies. These facts are shown in quantitative fashion in Fig. 16-7, which illustrates four of the so-called Fletcher-Munson equal loudness contours. Loudness is measured in a unit called the *phon*, so chosen that at 1000 cycles, a sound *n* phons loud is produced by an intensity level of *n* db. As the frequency varies on either side of 1000 cycles, the intensity must be higher to make the sound have a given loudness. For example, a loudness of 70 phons requires 80 db intensity at 70 cycles.

Because the ear is relatively insensitive at very low and very high frequencies, a sound level meter should also be insensitive at these frequencies if it is to indicate loudness rather than intensity. Therefore *weighting* networks are placed in sound level meters to simulate the frequency response of the ear. Weighting networks specified by the American Standards Association are designed to simulate the ear at loudness levels of 40 and 70 phons. They also provide a "flat" setting for the measurement of very loud sounds where the ear itself has an almost flat response. The flat setting is also used for purely physical testing when one wishes to measure intensity level rather than loudness level. The 40, 70, and "flat" networks are designated *A*, *B*, and *C*, respectively. The American Standards Association design objective for these networks is shown in Fig. 16-8. These curves are approximately

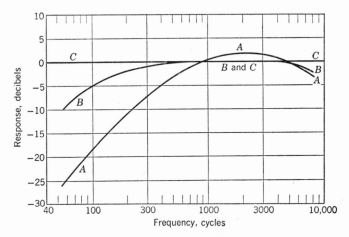

Fig. 16-8. Design objectives for *A*, *B*, and *C* weightings of sound level meters. (Adapted from *American Standards Association Bulletin Z24.3-1944.* Courtesy of American Standards Association.)

the inverse of the 40-, 70-, and 120-db curves in Fig. 16-7. A certain
amount of tolerance from the design objectives is allowed. The reader
should refer to the current edition of *American Standards Bulletin Z24.3*
for exact specifications.

A design within the required tolerances can be readily achieved with
RC-coupled amplifiers by placing the poles of their transfer gain functions at appropriate points. Often the poles in two amplifier stages must
be specified to obtain the desired result.

One possible arrangement of a sound-level meter is shown in Fig.
16-9. Feedback stabilized amplifiers provide a constant amount of gain,

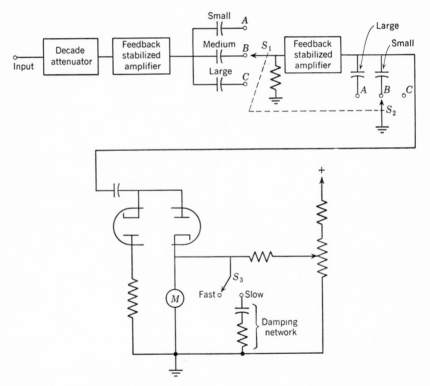

Fig. 16-9. Typical sound-level meter construction.

independent of the particular weighting characteristic connected into
the circuit. The characteristic is selected by switches $S1$ and $S2$. For
the A characteristic, the coupling capacitor selected by $S1$ is relatively
small, causing a drooping low-frequency response. Likewise, $S2$ selects
a large shunt capacitor to worsen the high-frequency response. For

"flat" (*C* type) operation, the interstage capacitor is very large, and the shunt capacitance is nonexistent save for the amplifier output capacitance and miscellaneous stray capacitance. A decade attenuator at the input provides range selection. This attenuator is calibrated in terms of the approximate sound level at the input. The exact level is the algebraic sum of the attenuator dial setting and the meter indication. The meter is almost invariably calibrated with a linear decibel scale. When the input level has been determined with the *C* weighting network, the weighting control is switched to the characteristic that comes closest to the prevalent level. For example, if exploratory measurements with the *C* setting give a level of 80 db, the weighting network would probably be switched to the *B* position before any permanent data are written down.

The *A* and *B* networks are usually used when the sound intensity is within ±15 db of 40 or 70 db, respectively. The majority of measurements in homes, stores, and offices would be made on the *B* weighting.

A fast-slow switch is provided to control the damping of the meter. The slow position introduces heavy damping, and results in an indication averaged over a fair portion of a second. The fast setting allows the meter to follow rapidly-varying fluctuations. The potentiometer at the right of the meter provides for injecting just sufficient current into the meter circuit to compensate for current in the diodes associated with electrons emitted with high initial velocity.

16-5. Sound analyzer circuits (*9,10,11*)

The extremely narrow pass band of crystal wave analyzers is not well suited to routine analysis of sound. The crystal analyzer must be tuned with great precision, and frequently one or more components of a complex sound may be overlooked. It is much more convenient to employ sound analyzers especially built for acoustical work with bandwidths of at least 100 cycles. There is some advantage in having the pass band increase in width in proportion to the center frequency. Sound analyzers incorporating this feature are known as constant-percentage bandwidth types. A particularly useful arrangement, both for sound and vibration studies, is to provide octave bandwidth filters. For example, one filter passes 20-40 cycles, the next 40-80, etc.

The main part of a sound analyzer is a frequency-selective amplifier followed by a vacuum tube voltmeter to indicate the value of *A* defined

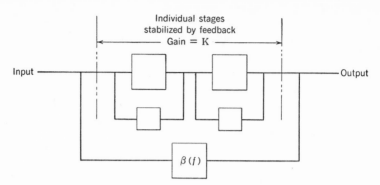

Fig. 16-10. Block diagram of a frequency-selective feedback amplifier.

in Eq. (16-3). The block diagram of one such amplifier is shown in Fig. 16-10. To insure constant forward gain and therefore stability of calibration, the active stages employ negative feedback. A frequency selective feedback path $\beta(f)$ or $\beta(\omega)$ is placed around the entire amplifier chain. The gain of the complete assembly is

$$G = \frac{K}{1 - \beta(\omega)K} \qquad (16\text{-}7)$$

We shall consider K in the remainder of this section to be purely a numerical constant; i.e., the forward gain is provided by an ideal amplifier of constant gain and zero phase shift at all frequencies of interest.

If at some frequency, or over a small range of frequencies, $\beta(\omega) = 0$, the gain $G \equiv K$. At frequencies outside this range, $\beta(\omega) \neq 0$, and $G \ll K$. One possible beta characteristic is shown in Fig. 16-11. The frequency at which β becomes zero may be selected by adjusting certain circuit parameters with a front-panel control.

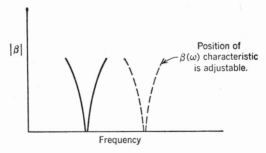

Fig. 16-11. A typical curve of $|\beta|$ as a function of frequency for sound analyzer applications.

A feedback network widely used in sound and vibration analyzers is the *twin T* or *parallel T*. This can be tuned to a fairly sharp null at any desired frequency by the adjustment of resistors and capacitors. No inductors are used in the twin T, so it is normally less expensive to build than an LC filter. Also it has good immunity to hum pickup from stray magnetic fields.

The twin T circuit is shown in Fig. 16-12. Our analysis of this network assumes the output is open-circuited. This condition may be

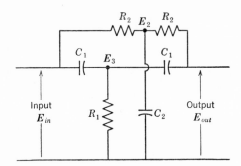

Fig. 16-12. The twin T network.

closely approximated by connecting the output to a cathode follower amplifier. The input impedance of a twin T is not constant with frequency. Therefore, if this network is driven from a high impedance (i.e., approximately constant current) source, the input voltage will be a function of frequency. This problem may be averted by driving the network from a low-impedance source, such as another cathode follower.

The output voltage may be determined as with any other circuit by solving the mesh or node equations. The latter are more convenient to use in this case. They are

$$E_{out}(-1) + E_2(2 + sC_2R_2) + E_3(0) = E_{in} \qquad (16\text{-}8)$$

$$E_{out}(-1) + E_2(0) + E_3(2 + 1/sR_1C_1) = E_{in} \qquad (16\text{-}9)$$

$$E_{out}(1 + sC_1R_2) + E_2(-1) + E_3(-sC_1R_2) = 0 \qquad (16\text{-}10)$$

The feedback factor β is the ratio E_{out}/E_{in}. We shall not go through the routine algebra, but the result is

$$\beta = \frac{s^3R_1R_2^2C_1^2C_2 + 2s^2R_1R_2C_1^2 + 2sR_1C_1 + 1}{s^3R_1R_2^2C_1^2C_2 + s^2(2R_1R_2C_1C_2 + 2R_1R_2C_1^2 + C_1C_2R_2^2) + s(2R_1C_1 + R_2C_2 + 2R_2C_1) + 1} \qquad (16\text{-}11)$$

This has a rather formidable appearance, but fortunately only the numerator is of immediate concern. In particular, we are interested in the zeros of the numerator, since these determine when the amplifier gain is at a maximum.

If the amplifier is operating in the steady state, i.e., frequencies of the form $j\omega$ are applied, then terms involving s raised to odd powers are imaginary and those with s to even powers are real. To find the zeros in the numerator, we must equate the reals and imaginaries separately to zero. From the real terms,

$$2s^2 R_1 R_2 C_1^2 C_2 + C_2 = 0 \tag{16-12}$$

$$s^2 = (j\omega)^2 = -\frac{1}{2R_1 R_2 C_1^2} \tag{16-13}$$

$$\omega^2 = \frac{1}{2R_1 R_2 C_1^2} \tag{16-14}$$

From the s^3 and s terms in the numerator of Eq. (16-11),

$$s^3 R_1 R_2^2 C_1^2 C_2^2 + 2s R_1 C_1 C_2 = 0 \tag{16-15}$$

and

$$\omega^2 = \frac{2}{R_2^2 C_1 C_2} \tag{16-16}$$

If at some particular frequency we are to have a null in β, it follows that the ω of Eq. (16-14) and Eq. (16-16) must be the same frequency. Therefore, we may equate these two expressions in order to determine the requirements for a null.

$$\frac{2}{R_2^2 C_1 C_2} = \frac{1}{2R_1 R_2 C_1^2} \tag{16-17}$$

Simplifying this expression as much as possible gives

$$4C_1 R_1 = C_2 R_2 \tag{16-18}$$

Equation (16-18) specifies a relationship among the circuit parameters that will produce a null in β at the frequency

$$\omega = \sqrt{2/R_2^2 C_1 C_2} = \sqrt{1/2R_1 R_2 C_1^2} \tag{16-19}$$

Example: Let $R_1 = R_2 = R$, $C_1 = 0.01$ μf and $C_2 = 0.04$ μf. The resistors are varied in value, and the tuning characteristic of Fig. 16-13 results. This figure shows the frequency for a null in β as a function of R. Other tuning characteristics are possible (12).

The variable resistors are usually of the precision wire-wound type, ganged together to facilitate tuning. If the entire range of frequencies of

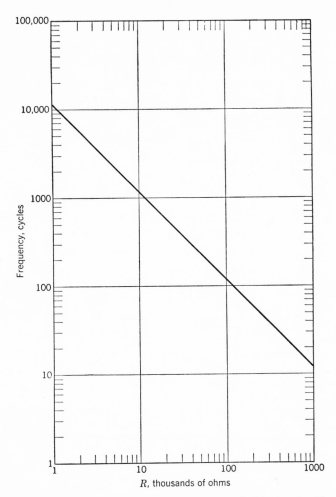

Fig. 16-13. Frequency at which $\beta = 0$ for a twin T network with equal resistances and $C_1 = 0.01$ μf, $C_2 = 0.04$ μf.

Fig. 16-13 is to be covered, the problem of tracking resistors together from 1000 ohms to 1 megohm becomes difficult. The tuning circuit might provide instead for a limited adjustment of resistors to obtain vernier tuning, and coarse range switching by changing the capacitor values.

For the very special case we are considering here, where $R_1 = R_2 = R$ and $C_2 = 4C_1$, there is a common root in the numerator and denominator of the expression for β, Eq. (16-11). This may be factored out to obtain

$$\beta \text{ (special case)} = \frac{2s^2R^2C_1^2 + 1}{2s^2R^2C_1^2 + 6sRC_1 + 1} = \beta_X \qquad (16\text{-}20)$$

We have added the subscript X to distinguish this from the general expression for β in Eq. (16-11).

The equation for the gain of a feedback amplifier is given in Eq. (4-3), repeated here as Eq. (16-21), except that β_X is used instead of the general quantity β.

$$G = \frac{K}{1 - \beta_X K} \qquad (16\text{-}21)$$

We may think of β_X as a polynomial in s. Thus

$$\beta_X = \frac{A(s)}{B(s)} \qquad (16\text{-}22)$$

If Eq. (16-22) is substituted into Eq. (16-21),

$$G = \frac{KB(s)}{B(s) - KA(s)} \qquad (16\text{-}23)$$

With Eq. (16-23), it is relatively easy to determine the response to be expected from the sound-analyzer amplifier. For example, suppose $K = 100\angle180°$, and $RC_1 = 10^{-4}$. The poles and zeros of Eq. (16-23) are easily found, since the numerator and denominator are merely quadratics. The values are

$$\text{poles:} \qquad -148.5 \pm j7070$$

$$\text{zeros:} \qquad -28200, \ -1800$$

The relatively small real term in the poles indicates that fairly sharp tuning is to be expected, and this is indeed the case. But it is not nearly so sharp as it would be with a crystal filter. The 3-db bandwidth of an amplifier having a relatively isolated pole, as in the present example, is approximately

$$\text{B.W.} = \left|\frac{\sigma}{\pi}\right| \quad \text{cycles} \qquad (16\text{-}24)$$

where σ is the real part of the complex frequency of the pole. Here $\sigma = -148.5$ and the bandwidth is therefore 47 cycles.

Moderately sharp tuning is often desirable, although there seems to be an increasing trend toward octave bandwidths. Octave-band sound analyzers are usually not intended to have continuously variable frequency adjustments. Therefore the octave range is generally selected by a front panel switch that inserts a suitable band-pass filter at the input or output of an amplifier. The filter and amplifier sections are followed by a vacuum tube voltmeter to indicate the value of sound intensity within the octave band. Usually the meter is designed to give a linear indication in decibels (see Sections 6-6 and 6-7).

16-6. Reverberation time meters (*13,14*)

An important acoustic property of rooms and auditoriums is *reverberation time*. This is the time required for a sound pressure level to drop by 60 db. The reverberation time is a measure of the "liveness" of a room. A long reverberation time is generally recommended for music, and a shorter one for speech. Reverberation adds fullness and depth to music, but tends to create a garbled effect with speech. The optimum time is a function of the volume of the room, as well as the nature of

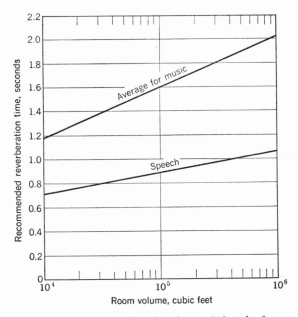

Fig. 16-14. Optimum reverberation time at 512 cycles for rooms of various volumes. (By permission from *Acoustical Designing in Architecture* by Vern O. Knudsen and Cyril M. Harris. Copyright, 1950, John Wiley & Sons, Inc.)

sound to be heard therein. Figure 16-14 gives recommended reverberation times for auditoriums. It may be extrapolated downward to include ordinary-sized rooms. However, there is an implication that if the reverberation time is not close to the recommended value, some acoustic treatment should be provided. This is not always feasible in small rooms.

There are several ways reverberation time may be measured. One method is with a high-speed level recorder. This is essentially a sound-level meter designed for rapid response, which plots its readings on chart paper. A sound source, such as a loudspeaker, is operated in the room until the level recorder reaches a constant value. The sound is then turned off. As it decays, the level drops approximately linearly (on a decibel scale) with time. The time required for a decrease of 60 db is the quantity we must determine. In noisy areas, the full 60 db drop may not occur. For example, if the sound source used for testing is capable of raising the sound level in a room to 100 db, and the ambient noise level is 50 db, there is no possible way of realizing the full 60 db drop after the source is turned off. In that case, the reverberation time may be estimated by extrapolating the initial linear slope of the decay curve.

There are numerous ways to construct direct-reading reverberation-time meters. Several such instruments are shown in Beranek. However, any reverberation-time meter must include a system for sensing a drop in sound level of 60 db or some other reference value.

The sensing circuit for reverberation-time measurements is shown in Fig. 16-15. This figure shows a principle; it does not apply specifically

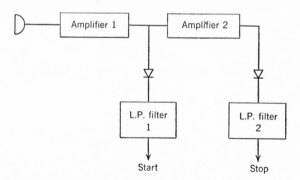

Fig. 16-15. Sensing circuit of reverberation time meter.

to any one reverberation time meter. Amplifier 1 is a preamplifier with sufficient gain to produce a certain voltage at the output of filter 1 when the sound level is high. For example, if the sound pressure is at 110 db due to a test tone in the auditorium, the output of the first filter might be 31.6 volts. When the sound pressure drops to 100 db, the output will be 10.0 volts. Suppose at this level something sets a time interval measuring circuit into operation. The "something" might be a mechanical relay that opens when the voltage across its coil reaches 10 volts; or it might be a Schmitt trigger that delivers an initiating pulse to the time interval meter when its input voltage crosses 10 volts. There are several possibilities.

Amplifier 2 has a gain of exactly 60 db. This amplifier will be driven into saturation by a sound level capable of producing 10 volts at the output of filter 1. However, as the sound level decays, amplifier 2 will eventually come out of saturation. When the level has dropped by 60 db, the output of filter 2 will also be 10 volts. A relay or trigger circuit identical to that employed after filter 1 terminates the time interval measurement.

There are two considerations that must be borne in mind in designing the filters and amplifier 2. First, it is not always possible to obtain the full 60-db drop. Amplifier 2 might provide only 30-db gain, for example, in which case the reverberation time measurement would be one-half the correct value. Or a high ambient noise level might necessitate a measurement based on less than the full 60-db drop. Second, the time constant of the filters must be chosen rather carefully. If sound level is plotted as a function of time with a high speed level recorder, it is found that the sound dies *on the average* at a uniform rate in decibels per second. But a number of little wiggles are superimposed on the decay curve. The filters should have a long enough time constant to average these ripples. Something like 0.05 to 0.1 sec would be about right. If relays are used for starting and ending the time interval, their coils will act as LR filters, and additional filtering may not be required. The rectifiers may be omitted also if a-c operated relays are chosen.

A very long time constant would give satisfactory averaging action, but leads to a different type of error. This is shown in Fig. 16-16. Suppose we have two filters, A and B. Filter A has a rather short time constant, and B is very long. The trigger circuits operated by the filters will have a certain amount of tolerance because of changes in line voltage, aging of components, etc. As a result, the trigger associated with filter A might fire anywhere between points 1 and 2, and there could be a timing error of $\Delta_1 t$. Filter B's trigger might operate anywhere between points 3 and 4, and the possible error is $\Delta_2 t$. It is seen that as the time constant becomes longer and longer, the possible error in sensing the exact moment when the sound level crosses a specified value in-

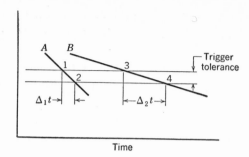

Fig. 16-16. The effect of an excessive filter time constant.

creases. Therefore the filter time constants should be as short as possible consistent with performing the required averaging.

Several time interval measuring circuits were described in Chapter 15. Any of these could be adapted to operate with the basic reverberation time sensing system of Fig. 16-15. The interval range will extend from a few tenths of a second to possibly 5 sec as a maximum, and the measuring circuit should be selected with this fact in mind. A fast-operating electric clock of the type sold for stop-watch applications would be satisfactory in many cases. This clock could be turned on and off by mechanical relays controlled by the start and stop buses in Fig. 16-15. A rather simple electronic counter could be used also. This might be assembled from three low-speed decade counters. The input pulses could be derived by clipping and differentiating the 60-cycle line frequency, which would be perfectly adequate for measuring times of the order of several tenths of a second or more. Three decades would give a capacity of 1000 counts, or 16.7 sec if the counting rate is 60 cps.

16-7. The supersonic reflectoscope (15)

The supersonic reflectoscope is an instrument to locate internal flaws in solids by means of reflected sound waves. The principal parts are

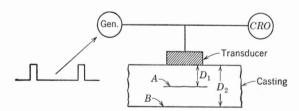

Fig. 16-17. Basic principle of ultrasonic reflectoscopes.

shown in the block diagram of Fig. 16-17. A generator produces short pulses or short bursts of sine waves at a relatively slow repetition rate. A transducer of the piezoelectric crystal type converts the electric signal to mechanical vibration which propagates down the casting. If there is a flaw, such as a void or internal crack, the pulse of sound is reflected just as an electric pulse is reflected from a discontinuity in a transmission line. The reflected pulse is received by the crystal transducer and displayed on the oscilloscope. The time between the input pulse and the

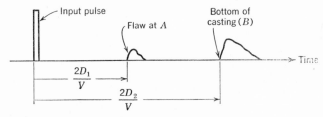

Fig. 16-18. Pulse pattern displayed by an ultrasonic reflectoscope.

returning echo gives the distance to the flaw. Still later, another echo identifies the bottom of the casting. Both times are usually read from the calibrated time base of the oscilloscope. An example of the displayed pattern is shown in Fig. 16-18.

There may be a number of minor echoes in addition to the major ones from the flaw and the bottom of the piece. These are caused by multiple internal reflections. They may require a rather long time to die out, and for this reason the repetition rate of the generator must be rather slow.

Example: The velocity of sound in steel is of the order of 6×10^5 cm per second. Suppose a steel casting 30 cm thick has a flaw 12 cm from the transducer. The round-trip distance to the flaw is 24 cm, and will require 4×10^{-5} sec. The time for the return echo from the bottom is 10×10^{-5} sec. Thus, the initial pattern of reflections is completed in 100 μsec. An appreciably longer time should be allowed to permit the decay of miscellaneous multiple reflections. Suppose that we allow 900 μsec for this purpose. Then the total time per "shot" is 1000 μsec, and the repetition rate of the pulse or tone burst is 1000 cycles. Suppose it is known that the first half centimeter of the casting will be removed by machining operations later on. Then flaws nearer the surface than

0.5 cm are of no concern. A flaw exactly 0.5 cm from the surface will send back an echo after 1.67 μsec. Therefore if the instrument must be able to detect faults as close as 0.5 cm from the surface, the maximum input pulse length is 1.67 μsec. In summary, the size of the casting determines the repetition rate, and the minimum detectable distance to the first defect fixes the length of the pulse or tone burst.

It sometimes happens that a flaw lies so close to the surface that its return echo is not resolved, even with short pulses, but appears to be simply an elongation of the input pulse. Where it is essential to locate faults near the top surface, a shim may be placed between the transducer and the casting. This increases the effective distance to the flaw. Naturally, a shim sends back an echo at its juncture with the casting. This echo may be minimized by coating the interface with mercury, thus amalgamating the casting to the shim. It may then be possible to pinpoint the flaw.

A skilled operator can determine not only the position of defects, but something of their size and character from the echo.

REFERENCES

1. Harvey Fletcher and W. H. Munson, "Loudness, Its Definition, Measurement, and Calculation," *J. Acoust. Soc. Am.*, vol. 5, October 1933, p. 82.
2. Leo L. Beranek, *Acoustics* (New York: McGraw-Hill Book Company, Inc., 1954), chap. 6.
3. Harry F. Olson, *Acoustical Engineering* (Princeton: D. Van Nostrand Company, Inc., 1957), chap. 8.
4. Arnold Peterson, "Sound Measurements at Very High Levels," *Gen. Radio Exptr.*, vol. 29, September 1954, p. 1.
5. Oskar Mattiat, "Transducers for Producing Ultrasonic Waves," *J. Acoust. Soc. Am.*, vol. 25, March 1953, p. 291.
6. Leo L. Beranek, *Acoustic Measurements* (New York: John Wiley & Sons, Inc., 1949), chap. 20.
7. *Sound Level Meters for Measurement of Noise and Other Sounds, Bulletin Z24.3-1944.* (Available from the American Standards Association, Inc., 70 East 45th St., New York 17, N. Y.)
8. Arnold Peterson, "The Sound Survey Meter," *Gen. Radio Exptr.*, vol. 26, April 1952, p. 1.

9. H. H. Scott, "The Degenerative Sound Analyzer," *J. Acoust. Soc. Am.*, vol. 11, October 1939, p. 225.

10. Glenn E. Tisdale, "Continuously Adjustable Electronic Filter Networks," *Proc. I.R.E.*, vol. 38, July 1950, p. 796.

11. Leo L. Beranek, *op. cit.* (Reference 6), pp. 519 ff.

12. George E. Valley, Jr., and Henry Wallman, *Vacuum Tube Amplifiers* (New York: McGraw-Hill Book Company, Inc., 1948), vol. 20 of the Radiation Laboratory Series, sec. 10-1.

13. Vern O. Knudsen and Cyril M. Harris, *Acoustical Designing in Architecture* (New York: John Wiley & Sons, Inc., 1950), pp. 153 and 192 ff.

14. Leo L. Beranek, *op. cit.* (Reference 6), sec. 18-2.

15. F. A. Firestone, "Supersonic Reflectoscope," *J. Acoust. Soc. Am.*, vol. 17 (1946), p. 287.

Chapter 17

LIGHT

17-1. General properties of light

Light, like any other electromagnetic radiation, may be specified in terms of two physical properties: *intensity* and *wavelength*. Intensity is that property of light called brightness in everyday speech, and wavelength corresponds in a general way to the sensation of color. Most of us fall into inaccurate terminology when discussing light; more will be said of this in a moment. The situation is like that in the field of sound, where purely physical quantities such as intensity and frequency become subject to interpretation by the brain.

Another property of light sometimes of interest is *polarization*. The human eye is not sensitive to this quantity, nor are most of the transducers we employ in light-sensitive instruments. If polarization *is* important in a given application, we can take it into account by the use of polarizing material between the transducer and light source. Certain natural crystals such as tourmaline and manufactured products such as those sold under the trade-mark "Polaroid" have the property of polarizing light. For purposes of this chapter, polarization is neglected completely; our topics will deal with the measurement of intensity and wavelength only. These are sufficient to define a light source completely as far as its physical nature is concerned. The psycho-optical situation is a bit more involved.

The sensation of light as interpreted by the eye and brain is more conveniently expressed in terms of three quantities. These are the dominant wavelength or *hue*, brightness or *brilliance*, and purity or *saturation*. The meaning of these terms may be most easily explained by an example.

318

Take the color we call pink. This has a dominant hue somewhere in the red region of the visible spectrum. Many other wavelengths are present also—in fact, if we think of the entire continuum of wavelengths as being a single color called "white," then we may say pink is a mixture of red and white. This is easily proved by taking a red lamp, surrounding it by several white lamps, and looking at a white card held some distance away. The illumination falling on the card looks pink because the red light is diluted with white. The relative amount of such dilution of the dominant hue is what we mean by saturation. Pink is an unsaturated color; so is "baby" blue. "Royal" blue, on the other hand, is highly saturated, or "pure."

Brilliance refers to the magnitude of the stimulation of the optic nerve produced by a given light. For example, a source of pink light might be viewed first with the naked eye and then through a neutral gray filter glass. It would have the same dominant hue and the same saturation in both cases, but when seen through the gray filter we would say it was less brilliant than when we looked with the naked eye.

The specification of color in terms of brilliance, hue, and saturation is most useful to workers in the field of color, such as in the manufacture of paint, dyes, or photographic products. For most purposes, the engineer and physicist will find it easier to consider light in terms of intensity and wavelength only. This is the viewpoint taken in this chapter.

17-2. Photocells and their characteristics

If we are entirely honest, it must be confessed that precise measurements of light can often be performed better by conventional optical instruments than by electronic equipment. This is especially true in color measurements. A photocell is no substitute for a good diffraction grating or prism. However, as the state of the electronic art moves on, photocells are becoming more and more useful in applications where extreme precision is not required.

Photocells make very satisfactory transducers for determining light intensity. By the use of external colored filters and the proper choice of sensitized cathode surfaces, they may be employed for color measurements also. Certainly photoelectronic instruments are more rugged than most purely optical devices, and they are often easier for unskilled personnel to use.

Three different principles of operation are found in photocells. These are photo*voltaic*, photo*conductive*, and photo*emissive*.

A photovoltaic material is one that develops an emf in the presence of light. Copper oxide is an example, as is selenium (selenium is also photoconductive). Selenium cells are widely used in portable light meters and photographic exposure meters. In such applications, their terminals are short-circuited through a microammeter. The meter is calibrated either in foot-candles or arbitrary numbers that indicate how long an exposure to allow for a photograph.

Photoconductive materials are substances that change their resistance in the presence of light (*1*). Selenium, zirconium oxide, and aluminum oxide are examples. Cadmium sulfide is another good photoconductive material. It has low electric noise, and permits relatively little *dark current*; i.e., in total darkness its resistance is extremely high and very little current can pass for a given applied emf. Some other photoconductive materials are cadmium selenide (CdSe), cadmium telluride (CdTe), and the sulfides, selenides, and tellurides of zinc and lead. These photoconductive substances are incorporated into practical circuit components by various methods. Photoconductive cells can be made from layers of powered material "potted" in clear plastic or sintered onto a base material. It is also possible to grow single crystals of the photoconductive material by techniques similar to those used in preparing germanium and silicon chips for transistors.

The characteristics of photoconductive cells vary a great deal with temperature, applied voltage, and light. Their response time to a step function of luminous flux is long compared with high-vacuum phototubes. For light intensities in the range of 10 to 100 foot-candles, the time required to reach 90 per cent of the final current is in the range of 10 to 50 millisec for cadmium sulfide. Sensitivities are intermediate between ordinary phototubes and photomultipliers; a few amperes per lumen is typical. Under some operating conditions, the photoconductive cell may exhibit a pronounced nonlinearity, the current varying either more or less rapidly than the incident light.

Commercially available photoconductive cells are usually of very small physical dimensions—of the order of a few tenths of an inch in any direction. The photoconductive area itself may be only a few hundredths of an inch on each side. This miniature package, plus their good sensitivity, makes them very satisfactory for such applications as reading the data punched in cards and tape. It appears that photoconductive materials may become extremely important components in instrumentation and control systems within a very few years.

Photoemission is the property most widely encountered in the photocells used for general electronics work. It is characteristic of certain materials, chiefly mixtures of the rare earth elements and their oxides, to liberate electrons under the bombardment of light. The mechanism is explained on the basis of an energy transfer from a photon of light to an atom close to the prepared photocathode surface. An outer orbit electron in the atom is excited by the energy it receives. If the energy is sufficiently large, of the order of an electron volt, the electron escapes its bond to the atom and is emitted. Cesium oxide on silver is an example of a photocathode surface. It is prepared by exposing a layer of silver oxide to cesium vapor.

An effect more closely related to photoemission than the other two categories is phototransistor action. If light shines on a *p-n* junction, holes are emitted just as they would be if a complete transistor were energized by a current flowing between its emitter and base.

The transducers we shall be concerned with in this chapter are high-vacuum photoemissive tubes. Spangenberg (*2*) is recommended as a reference for those seeking further details on the construction and internal physics of these devices.

Phototubes are manufactured with various cathode surfaces depending upon the color at which maximum sensitivity is desired. The surface designations and corresponding colors for some of the most common cathode types are listed in Table 17-1.

TABLE 17-1. IDENTIFICATION OF PHOTOCATHODE SURFACES

Surface type	Color for maximum response
S1	Infrared
S3	Blue-violet (not ultraviolet)
S4	Long-wave ultraviolet in presence of white light. Green in presence of tungsten light source
S5	Short-wave ultraviolet
S8	Blue-violet ranging to long-wave ultraviolet
S9	Blue-green

Type S1 is the most common surface by far. Almost as many tube types are made with this characteristic as all others put together. The reason for this predominance is that many phototubes in commerical equipment are used in relay circuits or sound reproducing systems in conjunction with beams of *incandescent* light.

Figure 17-1 shows the spectral sensitivity characteristic of an S1 surface (*3*) together with the relative distribution of energy from an incandescent lamp operating at a color temperature of 2870°K. The

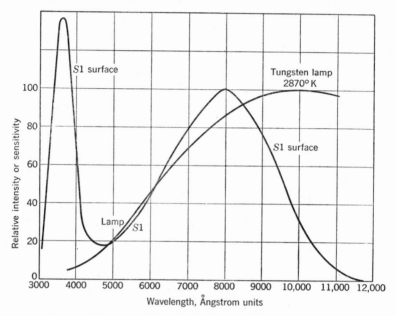

Fig. 17-1. Spectral characteristics of incandescent lamp at 2870°K color temperature and S1 photosensitive surface. (Courtesy, Radio Corporation of America.)

term *color temperature* refers to the color a "black body" radiator would have if heated to the stated temperature. Low color temperatures are reddish or yellow, and high color temperatures are bluish. Tungsten lamps normally operate at color temperatures between 2800 and 2900 degrees Kelvin. Mean noon sunlight has a color temperature of about 4800°K; average daylight, including reflections from the blue sky as well as direct sunlight, runs around 6500°K.

The technique of determining the response of a phototube to a given light source is as follows: find the relative response of the cathode surface at every wavelength from published or experimental data, multiply this by the relative intensity of the light source at the same wavelength, and plot as a function of wavelength the products obtained from all such multiplications. The area under the resulting curve is an index of the over-all response of the phototube-and-light-source combination.

The results may sometimes be surprising. In particular, care must be given to the effects of invisible ultraviolet and infrared. The eye can lay a serious booby trap for those who attempt to estimate results on the basis of visible light alone. We can show this by an example. Suppose a dark blue filter, such as the Wratten 49, were placed between a tungsten source and a phototube with a type S1 cathode. It would appear that virtually no response should be obtained from the phototube, since S1 cathodes are not responsive to visible blue and the tungsten source is relatively poor in blue light anyway. On the other hand, if a clear red filter such as the Wratten 25 were used, we would expect almost as much response from the phototube as if there were no filter at all. Suppose we examine these two cases quantitatively.

Figure 17-2 shows the relative transmission of the Wratten 49 and 25 filters. Figure 17-3 gives the product (tungsten intensity × filter response × S1 sensitivity) for the cases of no filter, Wratten 25 filter, and Wratten 49 filter. The relative areas under the curves are: no filter, 2887; #25 filter, 2355; and #49 filter, 1420. Then if we take the current from the phototube with no filter as 100 units, the relative current with the number 25 filter is 81.5, and with the number 49 filter it is 49.2. Note that almost all the response in the last case is due to infrared light. If we considered the area under the curves from 4000 Å to 7000 Å only,

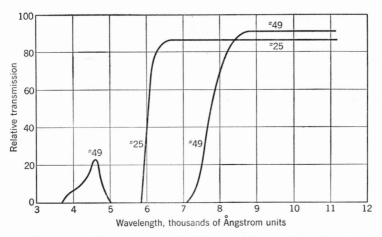

Fig. 17-2. Transmission of two Wratten filters. (Reproduced with permission from the *Kodak Data Book*, "Kodak Wratten Filters for Scientific and Technical Use.")

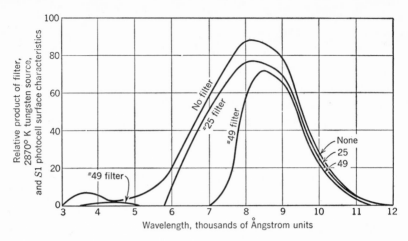

Fig. 17-3. Combined response of photocell, light source, and filters.

i.e., the *visible* part of the spectrum, we would incorrectly predict zero output from the phototube with the blue filter. The curve for this case in Fig. 17-3 is of zero height below 7000 Å, except for the slight elevation around 4500 Å.

An experimental check using a type 930 phototube, tungsten source, and number 25 and 49 filters gave these results: no filter, anode current 2.0 μa; filter #25, 1.61 μa; and filter #49, 0.96 μa. These currents are in the ratio 100:80.5:48, agreeing almost perfectly with predicted performance.

17-3. Photo bridge and comparison circuits

The simplest circuit for the measurement of light is shown in Fig. 17-4. The principle of operation is obvious: varying light intensity

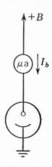

Fig. 17-4. The simplest light-measuring circuit.

causes a change in the current of the phototube, and this is indicated by the microammeter.

This circuit is identical in principle to the elementary d-c vacuum tube voltmeter of Fig. 3-1. The only difference is that luminous flux is the independent variable, rather than grid direct voltage. Transfer characteristics relating plate current I_b to luminous flux Φ are illustrated in Fig. 17-5. Note that even when Φ is zero, a small current flows. This is

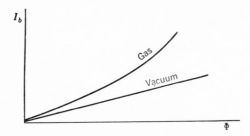

Fig. 17-5. Typical transfer characteristics of high-vacuum and gas-filled phototubes.

known as the "dark current." It may or may not be troublesome, depending on the application. It usually lies between about 0.0005 and 0.1 μa, and is a function of the plate voltage. Dark current is usually higher in gas-filled phototubes by one or two orders of magnitude than in vacuum types of comparable dimensions and voltage ratings.

The disadvantages inherent in the transfer-characteristic vacuum tube voltmeter of Fig. 3-1 are present also in the light-measuring instrument of Fig. 17-4. However, they are much less severe, especially when high-vacuum phototubes are employed. Over a wide range of plate voltage, the vacuum phototube delivers an almost constant current for a given incident flux. Furthermore, the cathode sensitivity remains unchanged over long periods of time, as there is no heated coating to vaporize or decompose during the life of the tube. Photocathodes are subject to certain characteristic troubles of their own, however. They are poisoned by slight traces of oxygen. Prolonged exposure to intense light reduces the sensitivity through a fatigue effect. The cathode usually recovers almost completely after a period of inoperation. In the case of gas-filled phototubes, the cathode is destroyed very rapidly by positive ion bombardment if the voltage across the tube becomes high enough to ionize the gas. To insure against ionization, the supply voltage for a gas-filled tube should not exceed 50 or possibly 75 volts.

While the simple transfer-function circuit is superior to its vacuum tube voltmeter prototype, there are cases where a bridge arrangement is very useful. The basic circuit is illustrated in Fig. 17-6. If the phototubes and resistors are identical, no current flows in the galvanometer

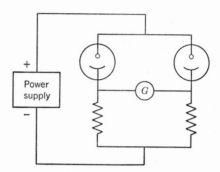

Fig. 17-6. The basic phototube bridge.

for equal incident light on the tubes. If one tube receives more light than the other, the galvanometer deflects. If we define μ, r_p, and g_m for the phototube as

$$\mu = \left.\frac{\partial e_b}{\partial \Phi}\right|_{i_b \text{ const}} \tag{17-1}$$

$$r_p = \left.\frac{\partial e_b}{\partial i_b}\right|_{\Phi \text{ const}} \tag{17-2}$$

$$g_m = \left.\frac{\partial i_b}{\partial \Phi}\right|_{e_b \text{ const}} \tag{17-3}$$

then the equations derived for bridge-type vacuum tube voltmeters in Chapter 3 apply directly to the phototube bridge.

The bridge circuit is especially adapted to comparison measurements, since it eliminates or at least minimizes the effects of small variations in the intensity of the light source. For example, it may be desired to compare the translucency of a sample of drafting paper with that of a standard. The method would be as follows: Illuminate both phototubes from the same light source. Place the standard sample of paper between one tube and the light, and the sample to be tested in front of the second tube. If the two are equally translucent, the galvanometer will not deflect. Differences will be indicated by the amount and direction of the deflection.

This description of the test is a bit oversimplified, for no method has been included to achieve the initial balance of the bridge. In the vacuum tube voltmeter prototype, initial balance is achieved by adjusting the grid voltage on one tube with a potentiometer. We must look to a different technique here. Probably the easiest method is to employ neutral gray photographic wedges. These are placed between the phototubes and the light source and moved back and forth until a balance is achieved. Then the wedges are fastened in place by a setscrew (or more probably were adjusted by a rack and pinion or worm gear in the first place and hence not subject to accidental motion) and the samples to be tested are inserted between the phototubes and light source. The galvanometer deflection indicates the difference between their light transmitting properties, as we noted above. (See also Section 1-2d.)

A substitution method is also useful. This consists of placing the unknown sample across one tube, and rebalancing the bridge by changing a calibrated wedge at the opposite tube. The optical density of the unknown is equal to the *change* in the calibrated wedge setting.

The real advantage of the bridge arrangement in measurements of the type just described is its inherent immunity to small changes common to both sides. Thus if the intensity of the common light source changes slightly, both phototubes will change their currents by approximately the same amount. Likewise, small variations in supply voltage will be compensated by the bridge. The circuit of Fig. 17-4 could be used for optical density measurements, but there might always be some question as to whether the light source remained constant in intensity during a series of tests. The eye cannot judge this: human beings have exceedingly poor judgment of both light and sound intensities, especially if changes take place slowly.

The bridge circuit is also useful for comparing the colors of two slightly different light sources. In this type of comparison, phototubes of different surface characteristics could be employed. The tubes selected should have similar electrical characteristics, only the cathode surfaces differing. For example, the type 921 with an S1 surface and the type 5582 with an S4 surface meet this requirement.

The comparison is performed thus: a standard light is shone on both phototubes, and the bridge is balanced by gray wedges as before. Then the unknown source, of approximately equal intensity, is used as the illuminant. The bridge will not become unbalanced by a slight intensity difference. But it *will* become unbalanced if the color of the unknown source affects the two phototubes differently from the standard source. For example, suppose the bridge had been balanced initially with a

"standard cool white" fluorescent light source. If it is then exposed to incandescent light, the tube with the S1 surface will respond with more
current, while the S4 cathode emits less. Therefore the bridge will become unbalanced in one direction. Illuminating the two tubes with daylight would cause unbalance in the opposite direction, since daylight is
more blue in color than standard cool white fluorescent illumination.

The bridge is not so satisfactory for color comparison as it is for
intensity comparison. We have assumed the phototubes were linear,
and the different light sources of approximately equal intensity so that
only color differences cause a change in bridge balance. Neither of these
assumptions is necessarily valid. In particular, it is very difficult to
determine if two lights of different colors are of equal intensity.

One way around this difficulty is to use a resetting scheme as shown
in Fig. 17-7. A standard light source is used as the first illuminant, and

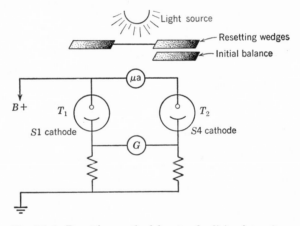

Fig. 17-7. Resetting method for standardizing intensity.

the resetting wedges are placed so a medium gray is above both tubes.
The initial balance wedge is then adjusted to obtain a null on the galvanometer, and the reading of the microammeter is recorded. Then the
source of unknown color is substituted for the standard, and the *resetting*
wedges are adjusted until the microammeter gives the same indication.
Then we know tube 2 is responding in exactly the same manner as
before. Any change in intensity alone has been neutralized by the resetting wedge over this tube.

The reset wedge above tube 1 is coupled to the wedge over tube 2,
and in so far as possible both wedges are identical. Then any difference

in *intensity* is likewise compensated as far as tube 1 is concerned. If the unknown light is of the same color as the standard, the bridge should still be in balance. Therefore any change in the galvanometer reading is due entirely to color differences.

It is not essential that tubes of different cathode characteristics be employed. Comparable results can be obtained by using filters of different colors between tube 1 and the source and between tube 2 and the source. One may then use identical tube types on both sides of the bridge. This insures symmetrical electrical characteristics on both sides.

Also, it might be noted that there are other methods than gray wedges for obtaining variable light. An iris diaphragm provides a continuously variable adjustment in light intensity. Or two polarizing crystals could be used. If their axes of polarization are parallel, the light transmission through the pair is high; when the axes are at right angles, the transmission is very low.

All these methods present certain practical difficulties. Wedges may fade or darken with time, and change their calibration. An iris diaphragm cannot be closed fully. Therefore if a balance requires a very small quantity of light, the iris may not provide sufficient reduction. In the case of polarized crystals, the problem is a bit more involved. The crux of the difficulty is this: When the crystals are exactly at 90 degrees, presumably no light can pass. The slightest change away from 90 degrees passes a finite amount of light. Now optical density is defined as

$$D = \log_{10} \frac{\Phi_1}{\Phi_2} \tag{17-4}$$

where Φ_1 is the luminous flux proceeding directly to a surface from a light source, and Φ_2 is the flux that reaches the surface if a light-absorbing material is placed in the path of the light beam. If Φ_2 is zero, the density is infinite, but if Φ_2 is finite, the density is finite. It can be seen that as the axes of the crystals move the slightest bit away from 90 degrees, there is almost an infinite change in optical density. (We say *almost* because the crossed crystals cannot present an absolutely impervious block to the passage of light.) Therefore using crossed polarizing crystals as an adjustment for light intensity means that as we approach high densities, adjustment and calibration are difficult. Manufactured substances are less effective than natural crystals as polarizers of light. In fact, the problem with manufactured polarizers may be one of getting a sufficiently wide change in optical density.

A word of warning: the worst possible way to adjust light intensity is with a rheostat. Varying voltage will inevitably change the color temperature of the source. The bridge circuit designed for intensity comparison is self-compensating for *small* variations in color temperature. But it will not, except as a matter of luck, remain compensated over the wide changes that occur when a light source is adjusted by varying voltage.

In most cases of measurements with *reflected* light, the light intensity is relatively weak. Therefore amplification is required. In Section 17-4 we shall discuss a type of chopper action by which the direct current in a phototube can be converted to alternating for amplification. However, there is another technique for avoiding d-c amplifiers that is especially adapted to use with phototube circuits. This consists of using a fluorescent lamp as the light source. The use of improved long-persistence phosphors in fluorescent lamps reduces their flicker a great deal. But there is still enough modulation of the light intensity to produce an a-c component in the anode current when phototubes are exposed to fluorescent light. This modulation occurs at twice the line frequency, i.e., 120 cycles in most areas.

An example of an instrument that takes advantage of this fact is shown in Fig. 17-8. This device is employed for the photoelectric grad-

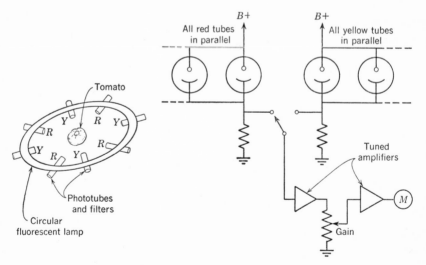

Fig. 17-8. An instrument used for photoelectric grading of tomatoes at the Purdue Agricultural Experiment Station. (By permission of Purdue University.)

ing of tomatoes to determine the degree of ripeness. As we have all observed, a "green" tomato is green or yellow, and a ripe tomato is deep red. The tomato being graded is placed within a circular fluorescent lamp, and banks of phototubes so placed that they cannot receive light *directly* from the lamp pick up *reflected* light from the tomato skin. Half the phototubes are fitted with red filters and the rest with yellow. Thus the ratio of reflected red to reflected yellow can be determined by comparing the indication from the bank of red tubes to that from the yellow tubes.

Obviously, the intensity of the light source will determine the absolute level of the indications. By the use of gray wedges or other methods already discussed, the intensity of the reflected light could be standardized. But since we have a light source with a time-varying intensity, it is necessary only to pass the output from the phototubes through an *a-c amplifier* and attenuator followed by another amplifier and the indicating meter. The amplifiers are first connected to one bank of phototubes, say the red. The attenuator is adjusted to bring the meter to a reference mark. This is equivalent as far as the meter can tell to having standardized the light intensity.

Next the amplifiers and attenuator are switched to the yellow phototubes. The attenuator setting is left unchanged. If the tomato has an abnormally high yellow reflectance, the meter will read well upscale. With a properly ripened tomato, the meter indication is rather small. Since the instrument is calibrated for both light intensity and *red reflectance* during the initial gain adjustment, the indication with the yellow tubes is an accurate measure of the *yellow to red ratio*. The meter scale may be marked in per cent reflectance or in some sort of "ripeness" units corresponding to standard grades of tomatoes.

The same general scheme would be possible but far more difficult if direct-coupled amplifiers were required. The problem of drift is always present in the d-c amplifier. Added circuit complexities would be introduced in the design of an attenuator that did not simultaneously change bias levels in a d-c amplifier. With modulated light, it is practical to employ standard *RC* coupling networks, or better yet use tuned amplifiers to minimize the effects of electric noise. All the information in the circuit of Fig. 17-8 is carried at the frequency of 120 cycles, and a wide bandwidth is of no value whatsoever.

Bridge circuits and calibrated comparison systems using modulated light have a host of applications in scientific research and quality control.

The color of blood, urine, paper, paint, cosmetics, dyes, foodstuffs, etc., can be determined by photoelectric instruments.

Transparent substances may be placed directly between the phototube and light source. Sample holders for liquids are available commercially. These are essentially test tubes, but rectangular in shape with their sides as nearly parallel as possible, and made of thin, especially clear glass.

17-4. Magnetic modulation for chopping

The effects of such spurious signals in phototube circuits as leakage, drift, and noise may be minimized by employing a-c rather than d-c amplification. This section describes a method for modulating the electron beam in the phototube with an a-c magnetic field (4). This eliminates mechanical or electric choppers. It also allows a wide choice of light sources. We are not restricted to fluorescent or similar lamps that produce modulated light at harmonics of the line frequency.

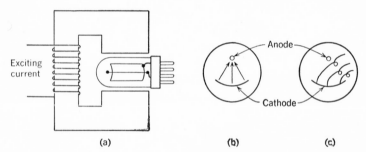

Fig. 17-9. A magnetic modulator for phototube current. Parts (b) and (c) show the electron paths with no magnetic field, and with an intense field. (After Kalmus and Striker.)

The magnetic modulator consists of a phototube mounted in a strong alternating magnetic field, as in Fig. 17-9(a). At any moment when the magnetic flux is zero, the electrons emitted from the photocathode travel directly to the anode. When the magnetic flux increases in one direction, the electrons follow curved paths that cause many of them to miss the anode. This effect is suggested by the sketch in Fig. 17-9(c); there is no attempt to illustrate accurate electron trajectories, but merely to show the general shape of the path. As the flux drops back to zero, the electrons travel to the anode again. The process repeats as the flux goes through its negative half cycle. True, the electron paths are deflected in the opposite direction, but the anode is aware only of a reduced current. Finally, at the end of the negative half cycle of flux, the anode current returns to full value. It is seen that the growth and fall of the anode current occurs at twice the frequency of the magnetic flux. This makes no particular difference, but must be borne in mind if one is designing a tuned amplifier to accept the output current of the phototube.

While many applications suggest themselves for this magnetic modulator, it was originally developed for measuring very low light levels. Photomultiplier tubes, discussed in the following section, are also available for this type of measurement. However, the photomultiplier tube has certain drawbacks which may influence the circuit designer against it. Very high supply voltages are a major practical difficulty.

It is informative to determine the minimum detectable light level by using the magnetic modulator principle. Suppose the phototube is connected to the first amplifier stage in the manner shown in Fig. 17-10.

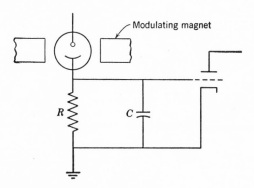

Fig. 17-10. Phototube and preamplifier. Bias and supply voltages neglected.

If we neglect any shot noise in the tube, and consider only noise due to thermal agitation in the grid circuit, the rms noise voltage is

$$E_n = \frac{\sqrt{4kTRB}}{(1 + R^2\omega^2C^2)^{1/2}} \tag{17-5}$$

where R and C are resistance in ohms and capacitance in farads, ω is the angular frequency of the alternating current in R, B is the amplifier bandwidth in cycles per second, k is Boltzmann's constant, 1.38×10^{-23} watt per degree Kelvin, and T is temperature in degrees Kelvin.

Assume the phototube current is 100 per cent modulated and sinusoidal in shape. The sensitivity of the phototube is S amp per lumen and Φ is luminous flux in lumens. If modulation were not taking place, the direct current sent through R by the phototube would be

$$I_{dc} = S\Phi \tag{17-6}$$

After 100 per cent sinusoidal modulation, the quantity of Eq. (17-6) becomes the *peak to peak current*, and the rms is this value divided by $2\sqrt{2}$. The RC network produces attenuation, so the *voltage* developed by the current is only

$$E_s = \frac{S\Phi R}{2.828(1 + R^2\omega^2C^2)^{1/2}} \tag{17-7}$$

It is usually assumed that the least detectable signal is one just equal to the noise. Following through with this assumption, we may equate Eq. (17-7) to Eq. (17-5) and solve for Φ.

$$\Phi = \frac{4\sqrt{2}}{S} \sqrt{\frac{kTB}{R}} \tag{17-8}$$

Example: Let $S = 100 \times 10^{-6}$ amp per lumen, $T = 300°K, B = 1$ cycle, $R = 10^9$ ohms. Then $\Phi = 1.15 \times 10^{-10}$ lumen. This is comparable to the least detectable light level in photomultiplier tubes.

In practice, a bandwidth as narrow as 1 cycle could be achieved only with the greatest difficulty. One hundred cycles is more likely, and this would increase the minimum detectable level by an order of magnitude. Also, there will be shot noise in the tube, and very likely some hum pickup from the magnetic assembly surrounding the phototube. These difficulties will cost one or two more orders of magnitude. Therefore the minimum light level might be about 10^{-8} or 10^{-7} lumen.

The effect of dark current must also be considered. If we let I_d represent the dark current in amperes and Φ_d the amount of luminous flux that produces a current equivalent to the dark current,

$$\Phi_d = I_d/S \tag{17-9}$$

Usually Φ_d will be appreciably larger than the minimum flux set by noise considerations in Eq. (17-8). However, dark currents vary a great deal, even among phototubes of the same type number. It may be possible to select a phototube in which Φ_d is less than Eq. (17-8). In any event, if more than one phototube is available in the stockroom, the one with the lowest dark current should be used in the magnetic modulator circuit.

17-5. A logarithmic photometer (5)

An interesting circuit for determining the value of light intensity over a wide range has been described by Sweet. This employs a photomultiplier tube and feedback circuit to obtain essentially logarithmic indications.

The photomultiplier tube consists of a cathode and anode separated by a number of additional plates known as "dynodes." The dynodes are made of material with high secondary emission (6), so that an electron striking a dynode causes an average of more than one electron to leave

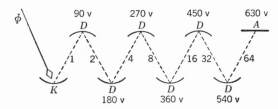

Fig. 17-11. Schematic construction of a photomultiplier tube. K = cathode; D = dynode; A = anode.

the surface. Figure 17-11 shows the arrangement of a photomultiplier tube with six dynodes. The voltages relative to cathode are shown at each electrode. If the incident photon of light liberates one electron, and the secondary emission coefficient of each dynode is 2, then 64 electrons will reach the plate. Thus there is a total secondary emission multiplication of 64.

A factor of 2 was selected at each stage to provide an easy example. It is also an extremely pessimistic example. With properly prepared surfaces, such as silver and cesium oxide on a silver-cesium base, secondary emission multiplication of about 3 to 5 per dynode is expected for typical applied voltages.

Sweet analyzes the operation of the photomultiplier tube as follows: Define the sensitivity as S amperes per lumen, V the dynode voltage per stage, and n the number of stages. The sensitivity is related to V and n by Eq. (17-10).

$$S = kV^{n/2} \tag{17-10}$$

where k is a proportionality constant. The anode current is

$$I_b = S\Phi \tag{17-11}$$

where Φ is the incident light flux in lumens. Solve Eq. (17-11) for S and substitute into Eq. (17-10).

$$I_b = k\Phi V^{n/2} \tag{17-12}$$

$$V = \left(\frac{k\Phi}{I_b}\right)^{-2/n} \tag{17-13}$$

For typical operating conditions with a type 931-A photomultiplier tube, the value of k may be calculated from published data. It is about 4×10^{-9}. This tube has nine dynode stages.

Now suppose that some sort of feedback regulator be devised that will keep I_b *constant.* This regulator circuit, as indicated by Eq. (17-13), must adjust the voltage per stage so that V is a function of $\Phi^{-2/n}$. Note the similarity in principle between this feedback requirement and that of the logarithmic voltmeter in Section 6-7.

Figure 17-12 shows curves for the value of V necessary to keep I_b constant for varying light levels. It will be seen that the relationship is

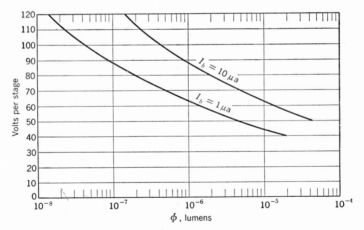

Fig. 17-12. Volts per stage required to maintain constant plate current for various light levels. Computed for type 931-A photomultiplier tube of median sensitivity.

at least roughly logarithmic. For this reason, a very large range of light levels can be measured with a moderate variation in V. For example, if $I_b = 1 \mu a$, a change of about 80 volts in the value of V corresponds to three decades (a factor of 1000:1) in luminous flux.

It is well to operate the photomultiplier tube with relatively low values of anode current. There is a type of fatigue effect noticed in phototubes that leads to a decreased sensitivity after prolonged operation at high anode currents. The lower plate current also has advantages from the safety standpoint, since the required voltages are not so high. However, the plate current should be one or two orders of magnitude greater than the dark current.

A circuit based on Sweet's, but different in many details, is presented in Fig. 17-13. The operation is thus: Suppose the incident light is in-

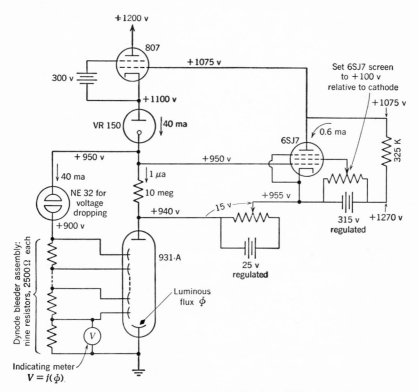

Fig. 17-13. Circuit for logarithmic indication of light intensity. Voltages and currents are values for tube of median sensitivity, when $\Phi = 4.35 \times 10^{-8}$ lumen.

creased. There will be a tendency for the 931-A plate current to increase. This makes the bias on the 6SJ7 somewhat less negative, and its plate current increases. This reduces the potential on the control grid of the 807 tube, and more of the 1200 volts from the high voltage power supply will appear across the 807 and less of this voltage across the dynode bleeder. Therefore the 931-A current is prevented from rising more than a very small amount. For all practical purposes it remains constant, and the voltage per stage as indicated by voltmeter V follows a curve similar to those in Fig. 17-12.

The quiescent phototube current may be set to the desired value by varying the potentiometer in the 6SJ7 grid circuit. The more this tap is moved to the right, the higher is the phototube current.

The 6SJ7 stage has a voltage gain of about 125, and the gain of the 807 tube is about 55. The total gain of the amplifiers is therefore about 7000. The 10-megohm resistor in the 6SJ7 grid lead will produce a change in potential of 10 volts per microampere. Therefore the total change in voltage across the dynode bleeder is 70,000 volts per microampere change in phototube current. On a *per stage* basis, with nine dynodes, the change per stage is about 8000 volts per microampere. Obviously the 931-A anode current will be held very close to its nominal constant value. A variation of only 0.01 μa will change the voltage per stage by 80 volts, which is the full range of V in Fig. 17-12.

Figure 17-13 is based on an anode current of 1 μa. This is at least one order of magnitude greater than the dark current, which is rated at a *maximum* value equivalent to 2.5×10^{-9} lumen of incident light. If we do not attempt to measure light levels less than 2.5×10^{-8}, dark current is no problem. Voltages and currents indicated in Fig. 17-13 are those that will be present when the incident light is 4.5×10^{-8} lumen; i.e., close to the minimum value we should try to measure.

Because of the great sensitivity of the photomultiplier tube, it is not useful for light levels of an appreciable part of a lumen. The circuit we have just described could be adapted to high light intensities by using dense gray filters as optical attenuators to bring the level of daylight or room light down to the range of the phototube.

17-6. Ballistic light measurements

In some applications, particularly testing of strobe lights, photoflash lamps, and the like, it is necessary to determine the total light delivered through the duration of the flash. The circuit of Fig. 17-14 was developed for this purpose (7).

This instrument operates on the principle that current from the phototube charges the capacitor at a rate proportional to the instantane-

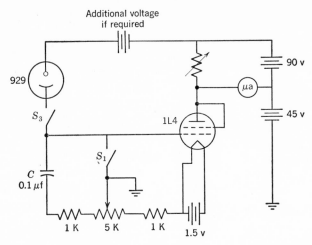

Fig. 17-14. Light integrating meter. (By permission from *Electronics*, June, 1948. McGraw-Hill Publishing Co.)

ous incident light. The capacitor voltage measured with a vacuum tube voltmeter at the end of the flash is proportional to the integral of this instantaneous light, and hence to the total lumen-seconds. Meters operating in this fashion are available commercially; the General Radio Type 1501-A Light Meter is an example.

The sequence of operation is this: Switch S_1 is closed until a moment before the reading is made. Then S_3 is closed and S_1 is opened, and the strobe light or photoflash bulb is fired. Current from the phototube flows into the capacitor in such a direction as to make the top plate rise in potential. This increases the anode current of the 1L4. Negative feedback is introduced by the cathode resistor network, giving improved linearity. At the end of the test, S_3 is opened again to prevent drift of charge into capacitor C. The unmarked potentiometer near the 1L4 anode provides bucking current through the microammeter so that the indication is zero when the voltage on C is zero.

The reading of the microammeter is proportional to the capacitor voltage, which in turn is the time integral of the phototube current. If the phototube sensitivity is S amp per lumen, the voltage across the capacitor at the end of the measurement is

$$E_c = \frac{1}{C} \int_0^T S\Phi(t)\, dt \qquad (17\text{-}14)$$

where $\Phi(t)$ is the luminous flux as a function of time, and T is the duration of a flash that started at $t = 0$.

The capacitor will eventually be discharged by grid current in the 1L4 tube. However, this grid current is relatively small, about 10^{-9} amp or less with about -1.3 volts grid bias and 0.5 ma plate current. It is necessary to provide a relatively high voltage for the phototube so that its current will be linearly related to the light intensity up to the highest expected levels of flux. Additional B supply voltage should be inserted for the phototube if required.

This instrument was originally designed for measurements with high intensity gaseous discharge strobe lamps. Edgerton's paper discusses the special requirements and calibration methods involved in this service.

17-7. An electronic spectroscope (8)

A very interesting characteristic of photoemission has been used for electronic spectroscopy in an instrument described by Sziklai and Schroeder. This instrument operates on the principle that the kinetic energy of a photoelectron depends on the wavelength of the light that liberated it. The energy after liberation is

$$\tfrac{1}{2}mv^2 = h\nu - \phi_P \tag{17-15}$$

where v is the velocity of the emitted electron, m the electron mass, h is Planck's constant (6.624×10^{-34} watt-seconds), ν is the frequency of the light, and ϕ_P is the photoelectric work function. If an *opposing* field is placed across the phototube, i.e., anode negative relative to cathode, the kinetic energy is converted to potential energy as the electron crosses the tube. Since electrons emitted by blue light have high kinetic energy, they can cross against a greater opposing field than electrons emitted by light from the red end of the spectrum. Equation (17-15) shows that the kinetic energy is linearly related to the frequency of the light. Therefore the opposing voltage against which an electron can cross the tube is linearly related to the light frequency.

There are certain difficulties in reducing the principle to practice. The electrons will have some thermal energy in addition to that imparted by photons, so there is no one precise go or no-go voltage corresponding to a given color of illumination. That is, the threshold for an electron transit is none too well defined. Photocathodes are inevitably somewhat heterogeneous, not all parts of their surfaces being equally good emitters. This effect would tend to average out if we have a large cathode, uniformly illuminated.

Suppose a photocathode is illuminated by two colors of light, blue and red, and we gradually reduce the opposing voltage. At point A in Fig. 17-15(a), a small current starts to flow as the blue-produced electrons with the most added kinetic energy are able to cross the tube. Along

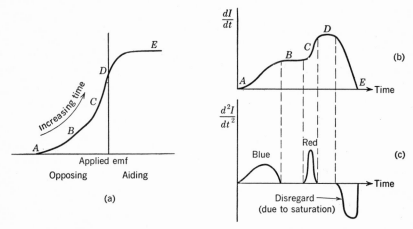

Fig. 17-15. (a) Growth of current with decreasing opposing emf. (b) and (c): first and second time derivatives of current curve in part (a).

the path from A to B, there is a considerable increase in the current as most of the high-energy "blue" electrons cross the tube. From B to C, there is a more or less uniform increase in current as the last of the blue electrons, the first of the red electrons, and miscellaneous strays are gathered up. From C to D, there is an abrupt increase again as the majority of the red electrons come across. Finally, a little beyond D, the field changes from opposing to aiding and saturation sets in.

Suppose we make the trip from point A to E with the voltage rising at a uniform rate in time. The *first* time derivative of the current will look like Fig. 17-15(b). The *second* derivative in Fig. 17-15(c) has a peak when blue electrons are drawn over, and a second peak when the red electrons cross the tube. Thus the second time derivative is a plot of the spectral distribution of the light. The negative peak is the result of entering saturation, and may be disregarded. Note that the red light in this example was more intense and of narrower bandwidth than the blue.

Figure 17-16 illustrates a circuit for the electronic spectroscope. The time base generator varies the phototube voltage to set the threshold for

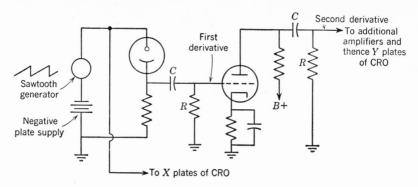

Fig. 17-16. Circuit of electronic spectrometer. (After Sziklai and Schroeder.)

electrons emitted by various colors of light. It simultaneously sweeps the cathode ray oscilloscope horizontal axis. Thus the X deflection is proportional to the color of the light. There are also two differentiating networks, and as much amplification as necessary to deflect the vertical plates of the oscilloscope.

If two of the spectroscopes we have just described are connected with phototubes in a push-pull arrangement and the same signals, both electric and luminous, applied to both, their outputs will neutralize each other. On the other hand, if different qualities of illumination shine on the two tubes, there will be a net output. This arrangement may be used for color matching.

Sziklai and Schroeder give complete circuit diagrams with values of components, and a detailed discussion of practical difficulties and possible remedies.

REFERENCES

1. R. H. Bube, "Photoconductivity of the Sulfide, Selenide, and Telluride of Zinc or Cadmium," *Proc. I.R.E.*, vol. 43, December 1955, p. 1836.
2. Karl R. Spangenberg, *Vacuum Tubes* (New York: McGraw-Hill Book Company, Inc., 1948), chap. 19.
3. Radio Corporation of America, *HB3 Tube Handbook, Phototube Section.* See drawings captioned, "Spectral Characteristic of Human Eye & of Tungsten Lamp at Color Temperature of 2870°K," and

"Spectral Sensitivity Characteristic of Phototube Having S1 Response."

4. Henry P. Kalmus and George O. Striker, "A New Radiation Meter," *Rev. Sci. Instr.*, vol. 19, February 1948, p. 79. See also U.S. Patent 2,429,933.

5. Monroe H. Sweet, "Logarithmic Photometer," *Electronics*, vol. 19, November 1946, p. 105. See also U.S. Patents 2,457,747; 2,478,163; and 2,492,901.

6. H. Bruining, *Die Sekundar-Elektronen-Emission fester Körper* (Berlin: Springer-Verlag, 1942; also Ann Arbor, Michigan: J. W. Edwards, 1944). One of the best treatments on the specialized subject of secondary emission.

7. Harold E. Edgerton, "Light Meter for Electric Flash Lamps," *Electronics*, vol. 21, June 1948, p. 78.

8. George C. Sziklai and Alfred C. Schroeder, "Electronic Spectroscopy," *J. Appl. Phys.*, vol. 17, October 1946, p. 763.

Chapter 18

PRESSURE AND TEMPERATURE

Although pressure and temperature are of very different nature and are measured with different types of instruments, it seems logical to group them together in one chapter. This is because in a great many applications these two quantities are interrelated and must be measured at the same time.

Most of the circuits used in pressure and temperature measurements have been treated earlier in this text. Accordingly, this chapter will deal primarily with transducers.

18-1. The variable capacitance pressure transducer

In Chapter 16, brief mention was made of the capacitor microphone as a transducer sensitive to small changes in air pressure. This microphone is but one example of a general class of capacitance pressure transducers, and accordingly detailed discussion was deferred to this chapter where we are considering pressure measurements in general.

All capacitance pressure transducers, whether microphones, high-pressure pickups, or for pressures approaching vacuum, are designed in the same general way. The basic mechanical configuration is shown in Fig. 18-1. A flexible metal diaphragm is mounted near a rigid metal plate, with electrical insulation separating the two around the edges. A pair of tubes permit pressures to be conveyed to each side of the diaphragm. If a measurement must be made relative to atmospheric pressure, one of the tubes is left open to the room, and the system under test is connected to the other. If a *differential* pressure measurement is desired, one tube is connected to one point and the other tube to the second point. The diaphragm then responds to the difference between

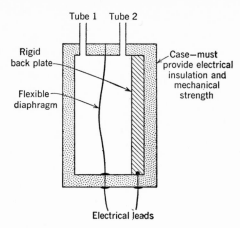

Fig. 18-1. The mechanical arrangement of a variable capacitance transducer.

the two pressure points. Diaphragms of various thicknesses and stiffnesses are available, permitting measurements from less than 1 psi to 10,000 psi or more.

As the distance between diaphragm and plate varies, the electric capacitance likewise changes as a function of the pressure. Specifically, the capacitance varies as $1/D$, where D is the distance from the diaphragm to the plate. For changes in D small compared with the nominal value of D, the change in capacitance is approximately a linear function of pressure. There are important electrical reasons for keeping changes in capacitance small, as we shall prove shortly.

The variations in capacitance are usually sensed in one of two ways. These are shown in Figs. 18-2 and 18-3. In Fig. 18-2, the variable

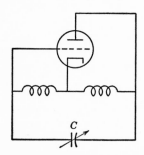

Fig. 18-2. The Hartley oscillator with a capacitance pressure transducer as the frequency-determining component.

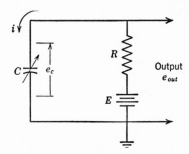

Fig. 18-3. A second method of sensing capacitance changes.

capacitor is used as the tuning element in a Hartley oscillator. Oscillators of other types would serve as well—the main requirement is that the oscillator be of a type that can be tuned by changing capacitance. As the value of C varies, the frequency of oscillation changes. Either static or dynamic pressures may be determined with this circuit. A static pressure results in a constant displacement of the diaphragm, and therefore a new steady-state frequency of the oscillator. Time-varying pressure changes cause time-varying frequency shifts; i.e., frequency modulation of the oscillator. The pressure information contained in these frequency variations may be recovered by demodulation with any of the conventional FM detector circuits.

One drawback in this arrangement is that any drift in the center frequency of the oscillator may be mistaken for a change in static pressure. Therefore an oscillator of inherently stable design must be employed. The center frequency may be varied by an additional tuning capacitance shunted across C. However, such a shunt capacitor reduces the per cent change of *total* capacitance for a given variation in C alone. The net result is to reduce the modulation index for a given pressure change. Therefore, if at all possible, the center frequency should be determined by selecting an inductor that gives the right frequency when shunted by C alone. A minor disadvantage is that the circuitry in Fig. 18-2 is more elaborate than in Fig. 18-3, and in addition an FM demodulator is required.

The circuit of Fig. 18-3 is simplicity itself. As the capacitance varies, a current flows in the resistor and develops an output voltage. It is essential that the output be connected to as high an impedance as possible. At least a good cathode follower should be used, and possibly an electrometer. Another operational difficulty is that the system of Fig. 18-3 will not respond to static pressure. If the value of C is suddenly changed by the application of a static pressure, there is a transient fluctuation in the output voltage. But the steady-state value of e_{out} is obviously E, and this is the value that must prevail shortly after a change in static pressure.

In an oscillator of the type shown in Fig. 18-2, the frequency is proportional to $C^{-1/2}$. If we also know C as a function of pressure, it is easy to construct a calibration curve for the whole assembly, giving frequency as a function of pressure. The technique is cut and dried, and there is very little more to say about it. The system of Fig. 18-3 is much more interesting, as it involves a nonlinear circuit. For this reason, and because it is of a bona fide practical as well as theoretical importance, we shall undertake a mathematical analysis of this circuit.

The current flowing in the capacitor, and therefore in the entire series circuit of C, R, and E, is equal to the time derivative of the charge in the capacitor. Thus

$$i = \frac{dQ}{dt} = \frac{d}{dt} Ce_c \qquad (18\text{-}1)$$

By Kirchhoff's laws,

$$E = iR + e_c \qquad (18\text{-}2)$$

Substitute i from Eq. (18-1).

$$E = \left(e_c \frac{dC}{dt} + C \frac{de_c}{dt} \right) R + e_c \qquad (18\text{-}3)$$

The next few equations are rather long and tricky, and it might be well to pause and establish what we hope to prove. It turns out that since Fig. 18-3 is a nonlinear circuit, a number of harmonics will be generated by the variable capacitor *even though its capacitance may vary in a perfectly sinusoidal manner*. The harmonic content increases as the change in capacitance becomes larger compared with the nominal value. This is the phenomenon we propose to investigate.

Assume the capacitance has an instantaneous value

$$c = C_0 + C_m \sin \omega t \qquad (18\text{-}4)$$

where C_0 is the static capacitance, and C_m is the peak change from the static value as a result of driving the capacitor with a sinusoidally varying pressure at the frequency ω. Let it be assumed also that harmonics *are* produced so that the capacitor voltage is

$$e_c = \alpha \sin \omega t + \alpha' \cos \omega t + \beta \sin 2\omega t + \beta' \cos 2\omega t$$
$$+ \gamma \sin 3\omega t + \gamma' \cos 3\omega t + \ldots + e_{c0} \qquad (18\text{-}5)$$

The Greek letter coefficients represent the amplitudes of the several harmonics, and e_{c0} is the quiescent value of e_c. It is seen by inspection of the circuit that $e_{c0} \equiv E$. Our next task is to determine the values of the α, β, γ, ... coefficients.

Substitute Eq. (18-5) into Eq. (18-3). Subtract E from each side of the resulting equation, since $e_{c0} \equiv E$. Perform all indicated differentiations and expand all sine and cosine products to obtain the sum and difference terms. Also assume that terms involving the third or higher harmonic are negligible. Therefore any quantities involving $\sin 3\omega t$, $\cos 3\omega t$, or γ are omitted. This leaves

$$0 = \frac{\alpha R\omega C_m}{2} \sin 2\omega t + \frac{\alpha' R\omega C_m}{2} \cos 2\omega t + \frac{\beta R\omega C_m}{2} \sin \omega t + \frac{\beta' R\omega C_m}{2} \cos \omega t$$

$$+ ER\omega C_m \cos \omega t + \alpha R\omega C_0 \cos \omega t - \alpha' R\omega C_0 \sin \omega t + 2\beta R\omega C_0 \cos 2\omega t$$

$$- 2\beta' R\omega C_0 \sin 2\omega t + \frac{\alpha R\omega C_m}{2} \sin 2\omega t + \frac{\alpha' R\omega C_m}{2} \cos 2\omega t$$

$$- \beta R\omega C_m \sin \omega t - \beta' R\omega C_m \cos \omega t + \alpha \sin \omega t + \alpha' \cos \omega t$$

$$+ \beta \sin 2\omega t + \beta' \cos 2\omega t \tag{18-6}$$

Now if Eq. (18-6) is to equal zero, the coefficients of all sine and cosine terms of a given frequency must be individually equal to zero. Let Eq. (18-6) be rewritten to collect these coefficients.

$$0 = (\sin \omega t)\left[-\frac{\beta R\omega C_m}{2} - \alpha' R\omega C_0 + \alpha \right]$$

$$+ (\cos \omega t)\left[-\frac{\beta' R\omega C_m}{2} + ER\omega C_m + \alpha R\omega C_0 + \alpha' \right]$$

$$+ (\sin 2\omega t)[\alpha R\omega C_m - 2\beta' R\omega C_0 + \beta]$$

$$+ (\cos 2\omega t)[\alpha' R\omega C_m + 2\beta R\omega C_0 + \beta'] \tag{18-7}$$

Now equate each bracket to zero. This gives four equations in four unknowns that can be solved for α, α', β, and β'. The results are

$$\alpha = E \frac{4R^4\omega^4 C_0^3 C_m + R^2\omega^2 C_0 C_m - R^4\omega^4 C_m^3 C_0}{\Delta} \tag{18-8}$$

where

$$\Delta = 2R^4 C_0^2 C_m^2 \omega^4 - R^2 C_m^2 \omega^2 - 5R^2 C_0^2 \omega^2 - 4R^4 C_0^4 \omega^4 - 0.25R^4 C_m^4 \omega^4 - 1 \tag{18-9}$$

$$\alpha' = E \frac{R\omega C_m + 4R^3\omega^3 C_0^2 C_m + 0.5R^3\omega^3 C_m^3}{\Delta} \tag{18-10}$$

$$\beta = -E \frac{3R^3\omega^3 C_m^2 C_0}{\Delta} \tag{18-11}$$

$$\beta' = E \frac{2R^4\omega^4 C_m^2 C_0^2 - R^2\omega^2 C_m^2 - 0.5R^4\omega^4 C_m^4}{\Delta} \tag{18-12}$$

For given numerical circuit parameters, Eqs. (18-8) and (18-10) may be used to find the amplitudes of the fundamental frequency components; Eqs. (18-11) and (18-12) give the amplitudes of the second harmonic.

An example of the increase of second harmonic content in e_c and consequently e_{out} is shown in Fig. 18-4. It can be seen that for low distortion, the change in capacitance must be kept small relative to the value C_0 that prevails when the diaphragm is undisplaced.

For the circuit parameters used in Fig. 18-4, the rms fundamental frequency output voltage is 5.0 at $C_m/C_0 = 0.1$ for a supply voltage

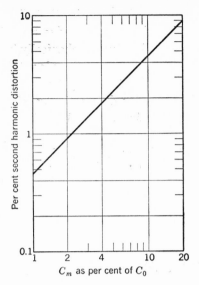

Fig. 18-4. Distortion in capacitance pressure transducer. $C_0 =$ 50 $\mu\mu$f. $R = 20$ megohms, $\omega = 1000$ radians per second.

$E = 100$ volts. The fundamental output varies in direct proportion to C_m and E. To obtain conveniently large output voltages, it is obviously far better to employ a high polarizing voltage E and small diaphragm displacements than vice versa.

By and large, in spite of a certain amount of nonlinearity when used in the circuit of Fig. 18-3, the capacitance transducer is one of the best devices available for pressure measurements. It is extremely rugged, holds its calibration well and is available in a very wide range of pressure ratings. It can be made with special alloys to withstand corrosive liquids or gases. Pressure variations with frequencies of many kilocycles per second can be measured by using thin diaphragms.

18-2. Other pressure transducers

Perhaps to the reader's surprise, most of the common pressure-sensitive transducers have already been covered in earlier chapters, in particular Chapter 13. True, we have not yet taken up the very special transducers and associated circuits employed in the measurement of high vacuum. These are treated in Section 18-3.

Most methods for converting pressure to an electric signal are based on the capacitance transducer just described, the strain gage, the differential transformer, and the piezoelectric effect. In the last three cases, the question is how to adapt the transducer specifically to pressure measurement. The answer involves mechanically ingenuity rather than electronics. Usually one attaches a Bourdon tube, bellows, flexible diaphragm, or similar device to the system where pressure is to be measured. All strain gages, the differential transformer, and the piezoelectric crystal are responsive to small displacements. Consequently any of them may be used to sense the changes in shape or length of a tube or bellows resulting from pressure variations.

The piezoelectric crystal is useful for dynamic, i.e., time-varying, applications only. The other transducers may be used for both static and dynamic pressures with the aid of suitable circuitry. These circuits were described in Chapter 13.

18-3. High-vacuum gages (1)

For the measurement of pressures down to a few millimeters of mercury, we may use the transducers described in Sections 18-1 and 18-2. It is necessary only to provide sufficiently flexible diaphragms, bellows, etc. However, when pressure becomes so low that its measurement is more properly considered a vacuum technique, three special transducers are available. They are known as *thermocouple* vacuum gages, *ionization* vacuum gages, and *Pirani* gages.

The thermocouple and Pirani gages operate on the principle that a wire in a gaseous atmosphere will be cooled by convection. As the gas pressure decreases, the convection cooling becomes less and less effective, and the temperature of the wire increases. In the case of the thermo-

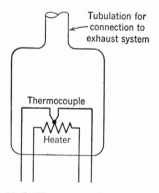

Fig. 18-5. Thermocouple vacuum gage.

couple gage sketched in Fig. 18-5, the pressure measurement is made with a millivoltmeter connected to the thermocouple leads.

Thermocouple gages are not intended for very high (hard) vacuum. About the lowest pressure they can measure is 10^{-4} mm mercury, and many of them will not go this low with any accuracy.

Thermocouple gages are available commercially, usually accompanied by calibration curves. They are fairly easy to make in the laboratory if conventional glass-working equipment is at hand. Resistance wire, thermocouple wire, and glass tubing are the requisites. A "home-made" thermocouple gage must be calibrated; the McLeod gage (Spangenberg, p. 760) is useful for this purpose. When the thermocouple is in use, the heater current must be held constant at the value employed during calibration.

The Pirani gage is even simpler than the thermocouple type. It consists simply of resistance wire in an envelope that can be attached to the vacuum system. For a given heating power, the wire temperature is a function of convection cooling and therefore of gas pressure. The principle is similar to that of the hot-wire anemometers described in Chapter 14. Pirani gages are used in three ways: constant voltage is placed across the heater terminals, and the resistance is measured; constant current is applied, and the resistance is measured; or a feedback system is used for keeping the resistance constant, and the pressure is measured indirectly by the input power. This last scheme is reduced to practice by using the Pirani gage as one leg of a bridge, the bridge being the feedback path in an oscillator. The forward path consists of an amplifier of constant gain. Note this is exactly the same principle as the microwave power meter described in Chapter 8; the Pirani gage simply replaces the bolometer or thermistor.

In cases where the wire resistance is allowed to vary, the Pirani gage is simply connected in one leg of a Wheatstone bridge. The pressure is measured either by observing the deflection of a galvanometer across the bridge, or by balancing the galvanometer to a null with a variable resistor calibrated directly in pressure.

The pressure range accommodated by the Pirani gage is about the same as the thermocouple gage, i.e., it may be used between about 10^{-1} and 10^{-4} mm mercury.

The ionization gage operates on an entirely different principle from the thermocouple and Pirani types. It consists of a triode with a filamentary cathode operated at a relatively low temperature so that the

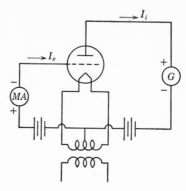

Fig. 18-6. Basic circuit of the ionization gage. I_e = current due to electrons; I_i = positive ion current.

emission is temperature-saturated. Therefore all the emitted electrons are drawn across the tube. The control grid is *positive* and the anode *negative*, as shown in Fig. 18-6. Consequently, the electron current is taken by the grid. Any electrons that do fly through the grid structure are repelled by the negative plate and return to the grid sooner or later. If any gas molecules are present, they will be ionized by collisions with the electrons. The positive ions thus produced are drawn to the negative plate. The plate current is a measure of the abundance of gas molecules and therefore of the gas pressure.

There is a minimum grid voltage below which electrons do not acquire sufficient kinetic energy between collisions to ionize the gas molecules. Once this voltage is exceeded, the plate current increases only slightly with rising grid voltage. The quantity of electrons present also influences the anode current value. The more electrons, the greater the probability that one of them will cause an ionizing collision. Therefore the calibration of an ionization gage is a function of both grid voltage and grid current. The former is controlled by varying the positive supply voltage, and the latter by adjusting the filament current. A typical calibration curve for an ionization gage is shown in Fig. 18-7.

Some gases are more easily ionized than others. Hydrogen and halogens such as freon vapor are examples. If a leak is suspected in a vacuum system, a small jet of hydrogen may be moved along the piping. When the hydrogen is near the leak, it is drawn into the vacuum system and causes a sharp increase in the plate current.

At low pressures, sensitive galvanometers are required. This represents an added expense, and also a hazard since a sudden leak will cause

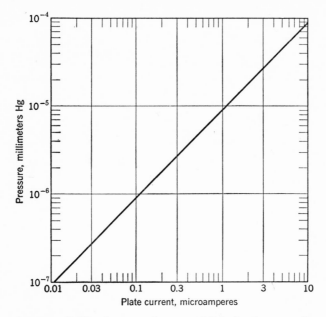

Fig. 18-7. Calibration curve for type 1949 ionization gage. Dry air, grid current = 10 ma, grid voltage = +110, plate voltage = −22.5. (Courtesy, Radio Corporation of America.)

a jump in current and burn out the galvanometer. To avoid the problems associated with a delicate galvanometer, a resistor between 10,000 ohms and 10 megohms is often placed in the plate lead, and the voltage developed across it by positive ion current is measured with a vacuum tube voltmeter.

Ionization gages are the most widely used devices for high-vacuum measurements. They are useful over pressure ranges from 10^{-3} to about 10^{-7} mm mercury. Spangenberg describes a number of refinements in technique for ionization gage measurements, including feedback circuitry to keep the grid current constant.

18-4. Transducers for temperature measurement

A number of different principles are used in transducers for the measurement of temperature. These include the determination of color temperature by infrared-sensitive (S1 characteristic) phototubes, the change of resistance in a wire or semiconductor with temperature, and thermally induced emf's as in the thermocouple.

The thermocouple is discussed in most texts on electrical measurements. It is not primarily an electronic device, and as it is widely known, we shall not treat it in much detail here. However, a brief summary might be in order.

If two dissimilar metals are placed in contact and heated or cooled, an emf is developed between them. This voltage is a linear function of the junction temperature over a wide temperature range. It may be measured by a galvanometer or millivoltmeter connected to the free ends of the thermocouple wires. Such a measurement gives a voltage somewhat less than the *open-circuit value*. This usually does not matter since the galvanometer may be calibrated to read directly in temperature for a given type of thermocouple. Where a true open-circuit voltage is desired, the thermocouple may be connected to any one of a wide variety of potentiometer circuits (*2*). If an amplified emf is required, the thermocouple voltage can be converted to alternating voltage by a chopper in order that direct-coupled amplifiers may be avoided (cf. Sections 7-3 and 7-4).

In practice, it is impossible to have just one temperature-sensitive junction. For example, if a piece of copper wire is spot-welded to a piece of constantan wire, there is indeed a thermocouple. But it is useless until it is connected into a complete circuit. The circuit may involve nothing more than a millivoltmeter with a coil wound of copper wire. Connecting the copper lead from the thermocouple to this coil produces a copper-copper junction, which is thermally insensitive. But when the constantan lead is attached, there is a copper-constantan junction at the *meter terminal* also. This junction is likewise capable of generating a thermal emf. The net emf produced around the closed circuit is a function of the *temperature difference* between the two junctions. To obtain accurate measurements, one junction, known as the *reference* junction, must be held at a fixed temperature. Alternatively, the thermocouple may be used in special temperature-compensating circuits, which adjust for variations in the ambient temperature and give results equivalent to a constant-temperature reference junction.

If current is forced to flow through a junction of two dissimilar metals, there is a heating or cooling effect at the junction, depending on the direction of the current flow. This phenomenon is known as the *Peltier* effect. It is in addition to the ohmic heating caused by I^2R losses. It is of practical importance in thermocouple instruments when a junction is soldered or welded to a heating element. In this case, some of the current flowing through the heater will branch out to flow across the junction, and produce a Peltier rise or drop in temperature depending on the direction of current flow relative to the physical placement of the metals in the junction. This may cause a measurable error in the indication of the voltage in the thermocouple loop. Since reversing the direction of heater current will reverse the Peltier effect, the measured emf may be too high for heater current in one direction and too low if the heater current is reversed. The effect is usually very small, but may have to be considered when thermocouple instruments are used to measure d-c quantities with high precision. Another second-order effect may be evident in instruments having a thermal junction conductively connected to a heater. A voltage is developed across the junction by heater current flowing in the small resistance common to the heater and thermocouple branches of the circuit. This adds to or subtracts from the thermal emf. It is troublesome only if direct current is passed through the heater; with alternating current in the heater, this IR voltage averages zero over a full cycle.

Another widely used principle in temperature-sensitive transducers is the change in resistance of a conducting material with temperature. Most wire has a positive temperature coefficient of resistance; i.e., as the wire temperature rises, the resistance increases. For temperature measurements, a wire with a high temperature coefficient would be selected in most cases. Iron, tungsten, and nickel have fairly high temperature coefficients of resistance. These coefficients, measured at 20°C, are 0.006, 0.0045, and 0.005 ohm per ohm per degree centigrade, respectively (3).

If the coefficient is represented by the symbol α, the resistance of a wire as a function of temperature is

$$R = R_0(1 + \alpha\, \Delta T) \qquad (18\text{-}13)$$

where R is the resistance at a temperature ΔT degrees centigrade *above* the temperature at which an initial resistance R_0 was measured. If the wire is cooled, ΔT is a negative number.

Example: An iron wire has a resistance of 100 ohms at 25°C. At 75°C, $\Delta T = 50$, and $R = 100(1 + 0.006 \times 50) = 130$ ohms.

Temperature coefficients of resistance are relatively low in metals. Certain semiconductor resistors have much larger temperature coefficients, of the order of -0.04. These resistors are made from metal

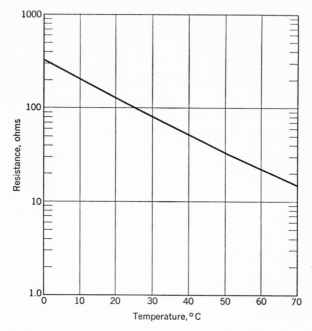

Fig. 18-8. Typical resistance vs. temperature curve for a thermistor.

oxides, such as NiO or ZnO, or various chlorides and sulfides. They are known as *thermistors*.

The negative temperature coefficient means simply that resistance decreases as temperature rises. In some circuits this may be a problem. Suppose that a certain amount of heating power is applied to a thermistor by a constant voltage source. Then the temperature rises, the resistance decreases, and more power is delivered. Whether or not the thermistor will "run away" is determined by the rate at which cooling takes place. If the rate of energy delivery to the thermistor is equal

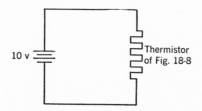

Fig. 18-9. Thermistor with constant applied voltage.

to the rate of energy dissipation, an equilibrium condition prevails.

The question of equilibrium temperature is an interesting one, and we shall explore it further. Suppose a thermistor has the resistance vs temperature characteristic of Fig. 18-8. This thermistor is placed in the circuit of Fig. 18-9. From the values of resistance as a function of tem-

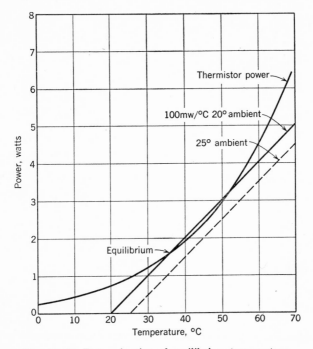

Fig. 18-10. Determination of equilibrium temperature.

perature, we can determine the power that is delivered to the thermistor by the 10-volt supply at any given temperature. This is plotted as the curve marked "Thermistor power" in Fig. 18-10.

Suppose the size and shape of the thermistor are such that it can dissipate 100 milliwatts per degree centigrade above ambient temperature. If the ambient temperature is 20° and the thermistor temperature is 30°, then 1 watt can be dissipated. This can be seen from the curve marked "100 mw/°C 20° ambient" in Fig. 18-10. If the ambient were 25°C, only 0.5 watt would be dissipated at 30°C thermistor temperature, etc. Thus the two straight lines are plots of the power that will be dissipated at a given thermistor temperature for a given ambient temperature.

Now any time the dissipated power equals the power produced in the thermistor, thermal equilibrium prevails. Such a condition is marked in Fig. 18-10, where the thermistor power curve intersects the dissipation curve for 20° ambient. The high point of intersection is *unstable*. If the thermistor cools the slightest bit below 52°, it will continue cooling down to 36°, the point of equilibrium. If it is somehow heated a trifle above 52°, the input power will exceed the dissipation, the temperature will rise still higher, and the circuit will run away.

It is seen in Fig. 18-10 that a slight rise in ambient temperature will result in a case of no intersection between the input and dissipation curves, and a runaway will result. If the ambient temperature should rise to only 25°, the thermistor will destroy itself. The problem could be averted by reducing the supply voltage, which would lower the ther-

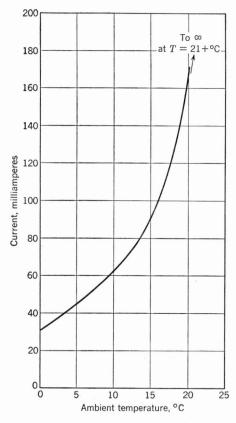

Fig. 18-11. Current as a function of ambient temperature computed for thermistor of Fig. 18-8 in circuit of Fig. 18-9.

mistor power curve. It could also be solved by attaching the thermistor to a heat sink, thereby increasing the slope of the dissipation curves.

If a milliammeter is placed in series with the thermistor of Fig. 18-9, the points of intersection with the dissipation curves in Fig. 18-10 may be used to calibrate the meter indication as a function of temperature. For example, for 20°C ambient temperature, the power at equilibrium is 1.69 watts. This corresponds to a drain of 169 ma from a 10-volt supply. Intersections obtained for other ambient temperatures have been used to compute the current vs temperature relationship of Fig. 18-11.

A good survey of the general properties of thermistors is given in a paper by Becker, Green, and Pearson (4). Among the points they bring out are the following: Ideal thermistors should be

1. Reproducible in manufacture
2. Stable in their properties with use
3. Mechanically rugged
4. Capable of manufacture in various sizes and shapes
5. Available with a wide range of electrical properties

All these requirements are met in commercial practice.

One characteristic of thermistors and other temperature-sensing elements that may be important in some applications is their thermal time constant. The thermal time constant is

$$\tau = H/C \qquad (18\text{-}14)$$

where C is the dissipation constant in watts per degree centigrade, and H is thermal capacitance in joules per degree centigrade. This time constant is the time required for the thermistor to cool to $\Delta T/\epsilon$ degrees above ambient after it has been heated to ΔT above ambient.

The time constant is a function of the size, shape, and environment of the thermistor. It may vary from a fraction of a second to a minute or more. It is about one-tenth as large in still water as in still air. The dissipation constant C depends on both the velocity and the nature of the surrounding liquid or gas. Therefore the thermistor can be used to measure pressure and velocity as well as temperature. The same is true of other temperature-sensitive resistors, as we found in considering the hot-wire anemometer of Chapter 14.

A thermistor should be aged by heating it for a few hours to a week at the time of manufacture. If properly aged, it will hold its calibration to within 0.01°C over several months. A typical thermistor used in a Wheatstone bridge with a galvanometer sensitivity of 2×10^{-10} amp per millimeter can detect a temperature change as small as 0.0005°C. The thermistor current should always be made as small as practical to minimize the effects of its own internal heating.

Typical circuitry for use with thermistors includes the Wheatstone bridge, potentiometers of both the manual and self-balancing type, and bridge oscillators similar to those used with the Pirani gage or the microwave power meter of Chapter 8.

When one wishes to measure temperatures high enough to produce appreciable radiation—say dull red heat or hotter—an infrared-sensitive phototube may be used (5). This technique would be especially adaptable to processes involving large heated surfaces, such as bars of red-hot metal, the inside of coke ovens, etc. As the temperature of the light source rises, the phototube anode current increases. An accurate calibration would best be performed experimentally, probably against an optical pyrometer as the standard.

REFERENCES

1. Karl R. Spangenberg, *Vacuum Tubes* (New York: McGraw-Hill Book Company, Inc., 1948), pp. 766-775.
2. Forest K. Harris, *Electrical Measurements* (New York: John Wiley & Sons, Inc., 1952), chap. 6.
3. Frederick E. Terman, *Radio Engineers Handbook* (New York: McGraw-Hill Book Company, Inc., 1943), p. 27.
4. J. A. Becker, C. B. Green, and G. L. Pearson, "Properties and Uses of Thermistors—Thermally Sensitive Resistors," *Trans. AIEE* (1946), vol. 65, p. 711.
5. W. R. King, "The Photoelectric Pyrometer," *Gen. Elec. Rev.,* November 1936, vol. 39, p. 526.

Chapter 19

RADIOACTIVITY

The field of radioactivity is such a large one, and so specialized in spite of its size, that we shall restrict the contents of this chapter to a discussion of three of the principal transducers employed in radioactivity measurements: the ionization chamber, scintillation counter, and Geiger counter. In addition, it will be well to survey briefly the three best-known particles associated with radioactivity; i.e., the alpha, beta, and gamma particles. The reader interested in the general field of radioactivity can find numerous texts, both broad and specialized, treating most nonmilitary aspects of the subject.

The majority of the information in this chapter on the nature of radioactive particles and energy exchanges is adapted from Glasstone's *Sourcebook on Atomic Energy* (1), by permission of the D. Van Nostrand Company and the United States Atomic Energy Commission.

19-1. The common radioactive particles

There are three types of particles that are of interest in the present chapter: alpha, beta, and gamma particles. Their properties are summarized in Table 19-1.

This table refers to particles emitted by a naturally decaying radioactive material. The various laboratory accelerators are capable of producing much higher masses and penetrating powers.

Note that the gamma particle is not defined in terms of mass and charge. Gamma rays are sometimes considered particles, and it is convenient to think of them as such here. But in reality they are extremely short-wave electromagnetic radiation, roughly between 3 and 3×10^{-2} Å.

TABLE 19-1. SUMMARY OF MOST COMMON PARTICLES

Name	Nature	Mass, grams	Charge in units of 1.6×10^{-19} coulomb	Penetrating power
Alpha	Helium nucleus	6.2×10^{-24}	$+2$	Low: about 0.002 cm of aluminum foil
Beta	Electron (or positron)	9.03×10^{-28}	-1 (or $+1$)	About 100 times the α particle
Gamma	Short-wave x-ray			Very high: several cm of lead at least

19-2. Survey of the common transducers

There are two general categories of transducers for electronic measurement of radioactivity. One group responds to the ionization produced when a particle travels through a gas; the other detects light generated in a phosphor hit by a particle.

There are other ways of detecting atomic radiation. For example, a stack of photographic plates may be exposed to radiation. The path of a particle as it travels through the stack may be determined after the plates are developed. A black dot is left at the point where a particle passed through the emulsion. However, we shall restrict our discussion to electronic techniques.

The detection of particles by ionization of gas is employed in the ionization chamber, proportional counter, and Geiger-Müller tube. Detection by light from a phosphor is the basis of the scintillation counter. We shall explain *briefly* how these transducers operate, and then go around a second time to fill in the details. In particular, a comparison will be made among the ionization types, with the scintillation counter deferred to a later section.

Figure 19-1 shows a gas-filled envelope containing two metal plates connected to a supply voltage in series with a galvanometer. The gas is usually well below atmospheric pressure. If an α, β, or γ particle passes through the gas, it will leave a trail of ionized atoms or molecules. These are attracted to the plates, and a current flows in the external circuit. A galvanometer is shown only for the sake of including an indicating device in the circuit. Frequently a resistor is placed in the

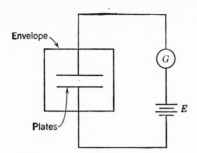

Fig. 19-1. A gas-filled chamber.

spot occupied by the galvanometer. The voltage developed across this resistor may be amplified and used to trigger an electronic counter, or *scaler* as these devices are commonly known in the atomic energy field.

Unless the radiation field is relatively intense, ionizing particles do not enter the chamber often enough to maintain a steady flow of current. Rather, the current flows as small pulses, approximately exponential in shape. The amplitude of the pulses varies with the supply voltage. Indeed, it is the relationship between the voltage and the characteristic nature of the pulse that differentiates between the ionization chamber, proportional counter, and Geiger-Müller tube (referred to in the rest of this chapter simply as a Geiger tube or Geiger counter).

A gaseous discharge develops in one of seven regions, of which six are shown in Fig. 19-2. The seventh is the arc discharge such as we find in

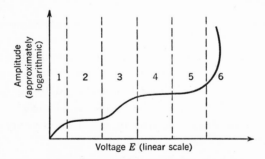

Fig. 19-2. The regions of a gaseous discharge.

ignitron tubes. In Region 1, the applied voltage is so low that many of the electrons and positive ions recombine on the spot into neutral atoms or molecules. Very few of them reach either plate, and the current pulses are exceedingly small. Region 2 exhibits a phenomenon similar to temperature saturation in a filamentary cathode vacuum tube. The applied voltage is high enough to draw all electrons and ions to the plates. The pulses of current are still very small. Radiation detectors operating in Region 2 are known as *ionization chambers.*

In Region 3, the voltage is sufficiently high that electrons or ions acquire enough kinetic energy from the field to ionize some of the molecules they hit. More ions are then produced, and the pulse size is increased. This increase is approximately in *proportion* to the applied voltage. The production of new ions by collision is known as a *Townsend avalanche.* It occurs in Region 3 only in the vicinity of ions produced by the original radioactive particle, and then only when these have acquired additional kinetic energy from the applied field. Transducers operating in Region 3 are known as *proportional counters.*

The fourth region has not been useful. Neither has the sixth, where the voltage is high enough to maintain a glow discharge if even a single ion pair is produced by any agency whatever, such as a cosmic ray. The curve near the top of Region 6 is about to snap back to a high-current low-voltage point at the upper left of the sketch, changing from a glow to an arc.

Region 5 is basically like Region 3, except that the Townsend avalanche is propagated through the entire chamber instead of being confined locally within the gas. The ratio of collision-generated ions to primary ions produced by a radioactive particle may be as high as 10^8. This ratio is known as the *gas amplification factor.* Transducers operating in the fifth region are *Geiger counters.*

The action of a gas tube operating in Region 5 may be likened in some ways to a one-shot multivibrator. A certain minimum triggering pulse will probably cause the multivibrator to deliver an output pulse. But a larger triggering pulse gives more reliable operation. Now in the Geiger counter, reliability of firing is determined by applied supply voltage. The higher this voltage, the better the chances that an α, β, or γ particle will start an avalanche of sufficient intensity to fill the entire tube. The electronic binary counters (Chapter 9) that record output pulses from the Geiger tube are usually designed to operate with relatively large input pulses—about the size a Geiger tube will deliver if its contained gas is fully ionized. If the supply voltage is sufficiently high, even weak ionizing particles will start a full-size Townsend avalanche and register in the binary counters.

For a given density of entering radioactive particles, a curve of counts per minute vs supply voltage will have the appearance of Fig.

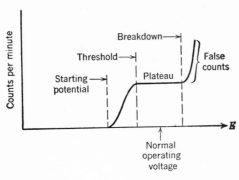

Fig. 19-3. Counting accuracy vs. supply voltage for a Geiger tube.

19-3. At low voltages, none of the incident α, β, and γ particles can start a full-sized avalanche. As the voltage increases, some of the higher-energy incident pulses can start a large avalanche by generating many primary ion pairs by themselves. Finally, when the voltage reaches a value known as the *threshold of the Geiger plateau*, all incident particles initiate a full avalanche that registers in the output counter. Beyond the Geiger plateau, glow and arc discharges set in. The normal operating voltage is about one-third of the way into the plateau: typically around 800 to 1500 volts. Some Geiger tubes of small physical size are available for operation as low as 300 volts.

Table 19-2 summarizes the principal gas-filled transducers for detection of radioactive particles.

TABLE 19-2. COMPARISON OF PRINCIPAL GAS-FILLED DETECTORS

Type	Operating voltage	Gas amplification factor	Filling gas	Used mainly to detect
Ionization chamber	100-500	unity	air, CO_2 N_2, A, CH_4	α
Proportional counter	500-800	10^5 to 10^6	CH_4 with 10% to 25% A	α in the presence of β and γ. Also to separate α and β from each other
Geiger-Müller	800-1500	up to 10^8	A or A with a few % organic vapor or halogen	β, γ.

Now we shall examine the ionization chamber and the Geiger counter in more detail.

19-3. The ionization chamber (2)

The energy of γ rays is not absorbed directly in an ionizing chamber, but indirectly through two processes: the production of *recoil* electrons, and a *photoelectric effect*. A recoil electron is produced by a transfer of energy from a quantum of gamma radiation to an electron. This changes the electron's kinetic energy and usually its direction of motion. A recoil electron might possess enough energy to knock other electrons out of their orbits, thus producing secondary electrons and positive ions until its energy is exhausted. The original γ ray goes its own way in the meantime, producing more recoil (or photo) electrons until its energy is expended.

Photoelectrons are produced in a roundabout manner that may be

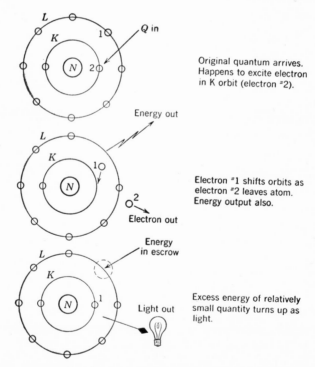

Fig. 19-4. How left-over energy produces a source of light for photoemission.

described in a qualitative way by reference to Fig. 19-4. Suppose that the original quantum has an energy of 50 electron volts. Just to talk in round numbers, say it takes 40 electron volts to knock electron 2 out of its orbit. Perhaps electron 2 acquires a little velocity in the·process, say 2 ev worth. Then as electron 2 departs, it takes 2 ev and leaves 48 behind in the atom. After electron 2 leaves, electron 1 jumps in to fill the gap in the K orbit. In doing so, it moves closer to the nucleus (N), and therefore has less potential energy. The energy it loses by shifting position goes forth as a new quantum that can produce more recoil electrons. Say the binding energy in orbit L is 20 ev. We have already assumed 40 ev for orbit K's binding energy. The difference of 20 ev is the energy of the output quantum produced by the shift in orbits. At this moment, 22 ev of the original 50 have left the atom; 28 are still there.

Eventually a new electron will come along, attracted by the positive charge due to the incomplete L orbit. This electron will fill the gap left by the shift of electron 1 into the K orbit. When this happens, the atom must be prepared to give up an energy equal to the binding energy of the L orbit, i.e., 20 ev. Therefore 20 ev are held in escrow as it were, to be paid on completion of the L orbit. This leaves 8 of the 28 remaining electron volts to be accounted for. These 8 ev are not enough to produce any more recoil electrons. Consequently, they turn up as *light* energy, or more properly, electromagnetic radiation of a short wavelength. It is this energy that can produce photoelectrons, probably at one of the metal plates in the chamber, since metals have relatively low photo-electric work functions (less than 2 ev in some of the rare earths up to about 6 ev in platinum).

It is often convenient to think of a particle traveling with a certain velocity as being equivalent to a quantum of electromagnetic radiation of a certain wavelength. The conversion from one viewpoint to the other is made with the following equation:

$$\lambda = \frac{h}{mv} \tag{19-1}$$

where λ is wavelength in meters, m the mass of the particle in kilograms, and v is the particle velocity in meters per second. This value of λ is known as the *DeBroglie* wavelength. The h is Planck's constant, 6.624×10^{-34} watt sec². If we are dealing with an *electron*, if we prefer the wavelength expressed in Ångstrom units rather than meters, if we include the effects of relativity, and if we choose to deal with an *accelerating voltage* for the electron rather than its velocity in meters, Eq. (19-1) may be modified by appropriate conversion factors to the form of Eq. (19-2).

$$\lambda = \frac{12.26}{\sqrt{V} \sqrt{1 + 0.9788 \times 10^{-6} V}} \qquad (19\text{-}2)$$

In this equation, λ is the wavelength in Å of an electron accelerated through V volts.

Where $V < 20{,}000$, the relativity correction is not required, and

$$\lambda = 12.26/\sqrt{V} \quad \text{in Ångstrom units} \qquad (19\text{-}3)$$

It is also convenient to be able to express V in terms of λ. Where relativity applies,

$$V = \left| \frac{-\lambda^2 + \sqrt{\lambda^4 + 586 \times 10^{-6} \lambda^2}}{1.96 \times 10^{-6} \lambda^2} \right| \qquad (19\text{-}4)$$

Without the relativity correction,

$$V = 150/\lambda^2 \qquad (19\text{-}5)$$

These equations enable us to convert energy back and forth between electron volts and an equivalent wavelength in Ångstrom units.

When a gamma ray enters a substance capable of absorbing energy, such as the gas in an ionization chamber, the amount of energy absorbed may be determined with the aid of Eq. (19-6). Note this equation actually gives the ratio of energy remaining to the original energy, not energy the gamma ray has given up to the absorber.

$$\frac{E_f}{E_0} = \epsilon^{-(\mu/\rho)xd} \qquad (19\text{-}6)$$

where E_f is the energy remaining in the ray after it has penetrated a distance x into the material, ρ is the density the material will have at standard temperature and pressure (STP = 760 mm Hg at 0°C), d is the actual density, and μ is the *linear absorption coefficient*. The ratio μ/ρ is the *mass absorption coefficient*. It is more frequently given in handbooks and other references than μ.

The mass absorption coefficient varies in a rather complicated way with the absorbing medium and the wavelength of the incident energy. Figure 19-5 gives the values of μ/ρ for three common gases.

The engineer faced with the problem of predicting the action of an ionization chamber is concerned with the effects that a given amount of

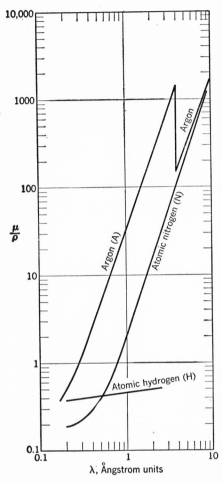

Fig. 19-5. Mass absorption coefficient for several gases. Note discontinuity in curve for argon. (Plotted from data in *Handbook of Chemistry and Physics*, by permission of the Chemical Rubber Publishing Co.)

incident energy can produce. An educated guess may be made by supposing that all the energy absorbed in the chamber is used in ionizing the contained gas. Then the number of ion pairs can be determined, and hence the charge. Equation (19-6) should be used first to find how much of the energy in an incident gamma ray will remain within the chamber; it is fairly safe to assume that all the energy in an alpha or beta particle will be absorbed. If the incident energy *per unit time* is known, it is usually convenient to think of the output of the chamber as *current* rather than charge.

For estimating purposes, we may suppose that only one electron is removed from each atom, and this electron from the outer orbit. The energies in electron volts required to liberate the first outer orbital electron are listed below:

Gas	Energy, ev	Source
He	24.46	Spangenberg*
Ne	21.47	Spangenberg
A	15.68	Spangenberg
Kr	13.96	Spangenberg
Xe	12.08	Spangenberg
Average for air	33.5	Glasstone

* By permission from *Vacuum Tubes* by Karl R. Spangenberg. Copyright, 1948. McGraw-Hill Book Co., Inc.

Typical energies from *natural* radioactive emitters are given by Glasstone as: α particle, 4 to 10 Mev (million electron volts); β particle, 0.1 to 3 Mev; γ rays, 0.1 to 1.0 Mev. These values divided by the energies for first orbital ionization provide an estimate of the number of electrons and positive ions that will be produced in the ionization chamber.

There is a great deal more to the ionization chamber than meets the eye. Victoreen has given a list of possible points of trouble (2). This list is summarized here.

1. The law of absorption (Eq. 19-6) applies only to thin absorbers, not to relatively large volumes.

2. The effects of the chamber walls cannot be neglected. The atoms in the walls may become ionized and inject charged particles into the chamber.

3. Most radiation is not monochromatic, but contains a number of wavelengths with different mass absorption coefficients for each.

4. If the spectral composition of the radiation is not known, and this is often the case, correction factors cannot be applied.

5. As the wavelength is changed, critical phenomena appear. At long wavelengths, photoelectric absorption predominates. Recoil electrons are common at short wavelengths.

6. The mass absorption coefficient is not a continuous curve, but may have sharp discontinuities. An example is shown in the curve for argon in Fig. 19-5. The chamber should be built of material of low

atomic number to prevent such discontinuities from falling within the band of wavelengths most likely to be encountered.

In spite of the complications we have discussed in interpreting the indications of ionization chambers, a particular chamber used under essentially unvarying conditions may be calibrated and give useful information.

The ionization chamber is used primarily for measurement of α radiation, but complications arise when γ radiation is involved. Therefore the effects of γ radiation have been discussed in some detail.

The physical size of an ionization chamber should be as small as practicable for several reasons. Since these chambers are used mostly for α particle detection, small size will not prevent the energy in the particles from being absorbed. An α particle can travel only a few centimeters in air or most gases at pressures near atmospheric. A small chamber will stop the particles and absorb their energy quite satisfactorily. On the other hand, β and γ particles often cross the chamber and exit at the far side without leaving behind enough energy to reveal their passage. Small size has the further advantage that low-voltage supplies can produce sufficient potential gradient for the efficient collection of all ions and electrons. The applied voltage need never be so high as to cause corona discharge in the tube and the attendant spurious readings.

The shape of the chamber is not critical as long as it leads to an essentially constant potential gradient in all parts of the enclosed volume. This insures that ions will be collected regardless of where they are formed. A shape similar to that of Fig. 19-6 is considered satis-

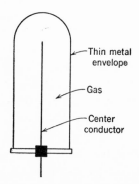

Fig. 19-6. Suggested basic design of an ionization chamber. (After Victoreen.)

factory. The potential gradient is fairly uniform, even in the curved end.

A proposed design for a chamber may be checked for uniformity of field in a flux-plotting tank. Or for simple shapes it is not difficult to find the equipotential contours by solution of the Laplace equation $\nabla^2 V = 0$. The potential gradients are then determined from the distance between equipotential lines.

19-4. Geiger counters (3)

The Geiger counter, as we noted earlier, operates in Region 5 of Fig. 19-2. In this region, a glow discharge is not self-starting. But once started, a glow will try to continue. To prevent this effect, some foreign material such as polyatomic vapor may be sealed into the tube to quench the discharge. Such a tube is known as *self-quenching*. Nonself-quenching tubes must be extinguished by the circuitry with which they operate. For example, after a count is registered, the circuit may apply a negative pulse to the anode for a few microseconds.

The physical construction of a Geiger tube is similar to that of the ionization chamber of Fig. 19-6. The circuit to which the tube is con-

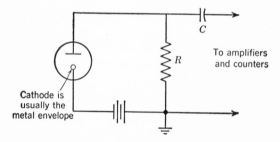

Fig. 19-7. Elementary circuit for Geiger tube operation.

nected is usually an *RC* coupling network with a high-voltage power supply, as illustrated in Fig. 19-7. Usually the positive supply terminal is grounded, with the resistor being at ground potential for direct current, and the tube perhaps 1000 volts off ground.

The rise and fall of a pulse in a Geiger tube proceeds as follows: incident radiation produces a few ions; the electrons from these start avalanches. The avalanches propagate along the anode wire where the field intensity is greatest. The positive ions gradually move toward the metal envelope, where deionization and quenching occur.

There are five steps in the process we have just summarized:
1. The Townsend avalanche
2. The spreading of the discharge
3. Motion of the ion sheath and growth of the output pulse
4. The deionization process
5. Suppression of spurious effects. This includes transfer of ionization from the rare gas filler to the quenching vapor in self-quenching tubes; suppression of secondary emission at the cathode; quenching of metastable states; and photodecomposition of the polyatomic gas.

These steps will now be discussed in more detail.

(a) *The Townsend Avalanche.* The nearer an electron is to the anode when it is liberated as part of an ion pair, the more energy it can take from the field per mean free path of travel. Therefore the better are the chances it will ionize another atom upon collision.

The field strength in the tube is equal to the potential gradient. For a concentric cylindrical electrode structure,

$$E(r) = \frac{dV}{dr} = \frac{V}{r \log_e (b/a)} \qquad r \geq a \qquad (19\text{-}7)$$

where r is the distance from the center of the anode wire, V is the applied potential, a is the anode radius, and b is the cathode radius. For example, let $V = 1000$ volts, $b = 1$ cm, $a = 0.01$ cm, and $r = a$. This gives a field strength of 21.7 kv per cm at the surface of the anode wire. The field intensity drops rapidly as we move away from the anode. At the cathode surface where r is 1 cm, the field is only 217 volts per cm for the same voltage and dimensions. It is not surprising that the Townsend avalanche is developed close to the anode wire.

Much of the avalanche growth is due to photoionization rather than collisions. In fact, the threshold of the Geiger plateau is identified with the release of enough photons per avalanche to guarantee the generation of another avalanche. The quenching gas in self-quenching tubes raises the threshold voltage because part of the energy of a given avalanche is wasted in exciting molecular vibration in this gas.

(b) *Spread of the Discharge and Formation of an Ion Sheath.* Once the threshold has been passed, the efficiency of ionization by photons is very great. However, the effect is localized, just as it is with recoil electrons. Almost every photon produces an ion pair before it journeys very far; few photons survive to reach the vicinity of the cathode. Thus the spread of the discharge by photoemission is also confined to the region of the anode. This has been proved experimentally by placing glass beads along the anode wire. These beads do not pass the predominantly ultraviolet light of which the photons are composed. The discharge is limited to a small amplitude in this experiment because only the region between adjacent beads becomes filled with ions.

The positive ions are large and heavy, and are accelerated much less by the applied field than are the electrons. Therefore the positive ions remain near their points of formation along the anode for a considerable period of time. The electrons are held at the anode by the image force field of these ions. As the ions gradually travel over to the cathode, the electrons are released to flow in the external circuit, and the output pulse develops in R. The pulse actually starts while the ion sheath is first forming, but reaches only a few tenths of its peak by the time the sheath is complete. The time for the pulse to reach its peak is anywhere from a couple microseconds to perhaps as long as a millisecond. This time is a function of R because the IR drop in the resistor due to the pulse reduces the tube voltage and the ions experience less acceleration.

(c) *Dead Time.* After a pulse has formed, another one cannot develop until most of the positive ions have moved well away from the anode wire. The time required for this to happen is called the *dead time.* Dead times as short as 5 μsec are possible, but usually the dead time is an appreciable part of a millisecond.

Even after the dead time, *full-size* pulses are not possible. The ions must reach the cathode before another full amplitude pulse can be produced. Figure 19-8 shows how pulses occurring shortly after the dead time might look. The interval from the end of the dead time to

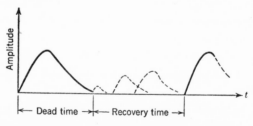

Fig. 19-8. The concepts of dead time and recovery time in terms of possible pulse amplitudes.

the moment when another full-size pulse can be produced is known as the *recovery time*.

(d) *The Quenching Process*. When the positive ion sheath has reached the cathode, the electric field in the tube is fully restored. This opens the way for a new pulse to be produced by *secondary emission* from the cathode. Therefore the chief objective in quenching is to be sure that no excited or ionized molecules or atoms capable of causing secondary emission can ever reach the cathode surface.

The process of quenching in self-quenching tubes operates as follows: an ion collides with a molecule of quencher such as alcohol vapor. It grabs away an electron and neutralizes itself. The alcohol molecule receives the energy of ionization, and the neutralized atom emits recombination energy as radiation. This radiant energy may be absorbed by another molecule of quencher, which dissociates into neutral radicals and gives off energy of a long wavelength. Eventually all the energy radiated as photons is degraded to harmless long wavelengths, incapable of causing photoemission.

The original ionized molecule goes to the cathode where it is neutralized by taking on an electron. It is left in an excited state for a time, and may emit a long-wavelength photon. Or more probably it will dissociate without radiation of energy. An example of the dissociation of ethyl alcohol is given in Eq. (19-8).

$$CH_3CH_2OH \longrightarrow CH_4 + HCHO \qquad (19\text{-}8)$$
$$\text{(ethanol} \qquad \longrightarrow \text{methane + formaldehyde)}$$

Quenching is successfully completed if (1) the excitation energy left with the neutralized molecule is less than the photoelectric threshold of the cathode; or (2) the excitation energy is lost in dissociation before the molecule collides with the wall of the cathode.

Neutralization of a polyatomic ion occurs about 10^{-7} cm from a metal surface whose work function is 4 to 5 ev. After neutralization, the excited molecule must approach to within 10^{-8} cm to produce secondary emission. The molecule should therefore dissociate within the time it takes to travel from 10^{-7} cm to 10^{-8} cm from the cathode. This is about 10^{-12} sec. Alcohol, for example, dissociates in 10^{-13} sec, and so is a suitable quencher.

Some of the quencher molecules are used up every time the Geiger tube generates a pulse. Therefore the self-quenching tube is limited to a finite number of counts. This number is usually of the order of 10^8 to 10^9.

(e) *Circuits Used with the Geiger Counter.* The Geiger tube output pulses are well adapted to feeding directly into binary counters of the type discussed in Chapter 9. Naturally, decade or other number base counting could be used just as well. The Geiger tube is not suited to high repetition rates because of the dead time and recovery time problems. Therefore the electronic counters need not be of an extremely fast type. Certainly there would never be any need for a binary stage capable of operating faster than the dead time of the Geiger tube. Since counter circuits have been described in detail in the earlier chapter, we shall not take them up again here.

With nonself-quenching tubes, provision must be made to drop the supply voltage for a long enough time to allow all the ionized molecules to revert to the neutral state. This might be accomplished by letting part of the supply voltage be the anode-to-cathode potential across one tube in a one-shot multivibrator. When the Geiger tube fires, the one-shot is triggered, the normally off tube in which E_b adds to the Geiger supply voltage will start conducting, and the total voltage drops low enough to prevent glow discharges. The one-shot time interval is adjusted to match the requirements of the Geiger tube.

19-5. Scintillation counters (4)

The principle involved in scintillation counting is that if an α, β, or γ particle strikes a suitable phosphor, a tiny flash (scintillation) of light is produced. With the aid of a photomultiplier tube, this spark of light may be detected, amplified, and leave a record of itself in an electronic scaler or some other device.

A brief discussion of photomultiplier tubes was given in Chapter 17. However, because of the importance of this transducer in radioactivity measurements, we shall go into a bit more detail at this point (5).

As we explained earlier, the photomultiplier tube has a basic arrangement of a photocathode, several dynodes, and an anode. The dynodes are prepared of a material with high secondary emission. A ratio of about four secondary electrons for each primary electron would be typical. Therefore a very small quantity of light, and hence a small cathode current, leads to currents of the order of milliamperes by the time secondary emission multiplication has occurred at a number of dynodes. Multiplication by about 10^6 is typical of tubes with 10 dynodes, and about 10^7 is obtained with 14-dynode tubes.

Photomultiplier tubes designed for scintillation counting are usually constructed with transparent cathodes treated with a photoemissive coating and a thin metallic coating for electric conductivity. There are two general arrangements of dynodes, sketched in Fig. 19-9. The one

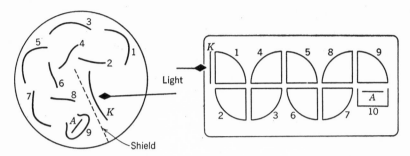

Fig. 19-9. Two common forms of photomultiplier construction.

on the left is used when light is admitted through the side of the envelope. The electrons pass from the cathode (K) through the set of dynodes (1 to 9) and reach the anode (A). The right-hand sketch is typical of the construction of "head-on" tubes. Light is admitted to the cathode through the end of the tube, and electrons travel from the cathode through the dynodes to the anode. This type of construction places the anode physically at a large distance from the cathode, and helps to cut down leakage currents.

Cathodes in scintillation counter photomultiplier tubes are larger than in tubes designed for less exotic applications. Ten or twelve square inches of active cathode surface is not uncommon. Most of the surfaces are of the S9, S11, or S13 type. These are all sensitive in the blue-violet or blue-green portion of the visible spectrum.

Dark current is the limiting factor on sensitivity. This current may be as high as about 0.05 μa at the anode, but usually is almost an order of magnitude less. It corresponds to a light input of around 10^{-9} lumen. The dark current is due in large part to thermally agitated electrons. Therefore the use of refrigerants around the tube will reduce the dark current a great deal. Cooling to $-150°C$ with liquid air decreases the dark current noise by about two orders of magnitude. Coltman reports it is usually unnecessary to refrigerate the tube if efficient phosphors, good light collection methods, and proper circuits are used. Electrons emitted from the *cathode* are almost wholly responsible for the anode dark current, as they receive the full multiplication.

There is no correlation between sensitivity and signal-to-noise ratio in photomultiplier tubes. Some tubes on the market are selected for high sensitivity at the factory, but this is not necessarily an advantage in photomultipliers for scintillation counters. The signal-to-noise ratio may be increased by operating the dynodes at relatively low voltages if one can stand the drop in sensitivity.

The external phosphor which is activated by the radioactive particle should be fairly thick to absorb the energy, and still be transparent to the light. The requirement of transparency renders useless the conventional phosphors of pulverized mineral material such as are employed in cathode-ray tubes. Large, clear, single crystals must be employed in scintillation counter applications. Among the best phosphors for scintillation counters are $CaWO_4$, CaF_2, $LiAlSiO_2$, Al_2O_3, and LiF. Very excellent results are also obtained with KI and NaI activated with small amounts of thallium.

As much light as possible must be collected from a phosphor in order to provide discrimination between signal and noise pulses. This is the

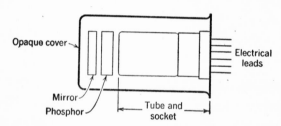

Opaque cover

Electrical leads

Mirror

Phosphor

Tube and socket

Fig. 19-10. Placement of light-gathering elements in a scintillation counter.

reason for the large cathode area in scintillation counter tubes. To provide good light collection, the phosphor is usually backed by a mirror. The arrangement of mirror, phosphor, and tube is sketched in Fig. 19-10. A light-tight shield must be placed over the entire assembly to keep out room light. Frequently a magnetic and/or electrostatic shield is used as well. The same shield could serve all three functions.

The scintillation counter offers several advantages over the Geiger counter and the ionization chamber. It is exceedingly fast in operation, and it is far more sensitive than the other radioactivity transducers. Some scintillation counters are capable of resolving pulses only one or two millimicroseconds apart. Most scintillation counters are not quite this fast, but they all fall within the millimicrosecond range provided phosphors with short decay times are used. Compare this performance to the Geiger counter, with its long dead time and recovery time!

The problem of determining whether a given output pulse from a photomultiplier is a bona fide count or a noise pulse can be solved by the use of coincidence scalers. Two photomultiplier tubes "look" at the same phosphor crystal. When a radioactive particle strikes the crystal, both tubes produce an output pulse. The scaler circuits include gates that permit a count to be registered only when two input lines are pulsed at the same time. Now the chances that both tubes will produce a noise pulse at exactly the same time are rather small. Therefore a noise probably appears on only one of the inputs, and the counter refuses to register a count. Immunity to noise can be increased even more by the use of multiple-coincidence counters that require three or more simultaneous input pulses before registering.

There are certain other factors that help isolate noise from true signal pulses. The noise ordinarily appears at the anode almost in the form of an *impulse;* i.e., mathematically speaking, it is a signal of zero width. True signal pulses usually come in *sets* of several small exponential pulses spaced extremely close together and usually of less individual

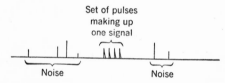

Fig. 19-11. Examples of noise impulses and a set of small exponential pulses constituting one signal.

amplitude than a noise impulse. Figure 19-11 shows some examples of noise and signal pulses.

Where extremely fast resolution is not required, the time constants of the amplifier circuits following the photomultiplier tube may be made long enough to integrate the entire set of signal pulses, thus obtaining one large pulse instead of many small ones. This large pulse will usually be greater than noise pulses. A threshold control may be used with the scaler to accept only pulses larger than the typical noise level. Where extremely fast resolution is necessary, integration is of less value, and noise must be fought with coincidence circuitry and possibly other techniques such as refrigeration of the phototubes.

A circuit such as that of Fig. 19-12 will permit the integration of the

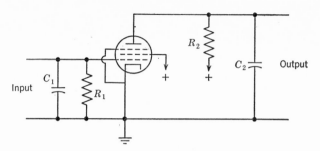

Fig. 19-12. Preamplifier of scintillation counter.

small, closely spaced pulses associated with a single radioactive particle. This means that the *set* of pulses will build up to a larger amplitude at the output than a single noise impulse which may actually contain more charge than any of the *individual* pulses in the signal. The capacitances C_1 and C_2 are often merely the interelectrode and stray capacitances associated with the tubes and wiring.

One practical consideration: there is nothing to gain by using an amplifier with time constants appreciably shorter than the luminous decay time constant of the phosphor.

Suppose we consider an example of the response of the amplifier. Figure 19-13 shows two types of inputs. One is a noise impulse of

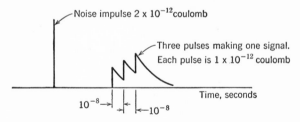

Fig. 19-13. Detail of noise impulse and signal burst.

2×10^{-12} coulomb. The other is a set of three exponentially decaying pulses produced by one trip of a radioactive particle through the phosphor. Each pulse in the set is represented by the expression

$$i = 10^{-4}\epsilon^{-t/\tau} \tag{19-9}$$

The second pulse occurs 10^{-8} sec after the first, and the third is 2×10^{-8} sec after the first. Each pulse represents 10^{-12} coulomb.

The problem of determining the response to each input is most easily solved with the Laplace transform. Figure 19-14 illustrates the equiva-

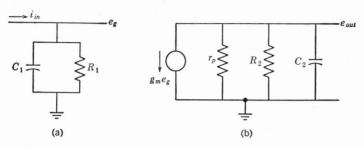

Fig. 19-14. Equivalent circuit for amplifier in Fig. 19-12: (a) grid portion; (b) anode side.

lent circuit of the amplifier in Fig. 19-12. For convenience, it is broken into two sections: the grid and the anode.

We shall suppose that the input is *current*. This is a very realistic assumption, for the input is received from the photomultiplier tube which has an extremely high internal impedance. It is easily shown that the grid voltage $\varepsilon_g(s)$ is

$$\varepsilon_g(s) = \frac{1}{C_1} \frac{\mathcal{J}(s)}{s + 1/C_1 R_1} \tag{19-10}$$

and the output voltage as a function of s is

$$\varepsilon_{out}(s) = -\frac{g_m}{C_1 C_2} \frac{\mathcal{J}(s)}{(s + 1/C_1 R_1)(s + 1/C_2 R_2)} \tag{19-11}$$

Symbols in script type-face indicate quantities in the Laplace transformed state, i.e., in the s domain.

For the noise impulse of 2×10^{-12} coulomb, $\mathcal{J}(s) = 2 \times 10^{-12}$. Let $g_m = 1000$ μmhos, $R_1 = 1000$ ohms, $C_1 = 10$ $\mu\mu$f, $R_2 = 1000$ ohms, and $C_2 = 20$ $\mu\mu$f. Solving Eq. (19-11) for $e_{out}(t)$ gives

$$e_{out} = \frac{\epsilon^{-10^8 t} - \epsilon^{-0.5 \times 10^8 t}}{5} \tag{19-12}$$

The expression for the output due to the *first* of the three exponential pulses is

$$e_{out} = 0.2(\epsilon^{-10^8 t} - \epsilon^{-0.5 \times 10^8 t}) + 10^7 t \epsilon^{-10^8 t} \tag{19-13}$$

The total result for the three pulses occurring at intervals of 10^{-8} sec is most easily found by plotting or tabulating the values from Eq. (19-13) three times, each graph or table displaced by 10^{-8} sec from the previous one. The three graphs or tables are then added. This procedure is justified by the principle of superposition, since we are dealing with a linear system. Figure 19-15 shows the two output signals as functions of time. The voltages are actually negative, but were plotted positive as a matter of convenience. Note the response to the signal is somewhat stronger than the response to the noise impulse. Therefore a threshold adjustment in a subsequent amplifier or electronic counter could dis-

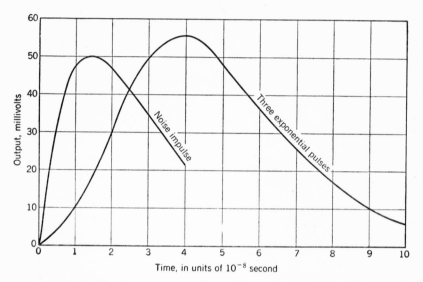

Fig. 19-15. Response of amplifier of Fig. 19-12 to pulses of Fig. 19-13.

tinguish between the noise-produced output and that caused by the radioactive particle.

19-6. Conclusion

It is a little presumptuous to treat the very large and important field of radioactivity instrumentation in one chapter which deals only with the most common transducers. However, the transducers are the principal novelty in instruments for the measurement of radioactivity. The circuits are more or less common to any field of pulse work, be it pulse communications, pulse data processing, or whatever. However, the pulse circuits in radioactivity instruments must often be faster and better than comparable circuits in other applications since millimicrosecond resolving times and pulse widths may be involved.

REFERENCES

1. Samuel Glasstone, *Sourcebook on Atomic Energy* (Princeton: D. Van Nostrand Company, Inc., 1950).
2. John A. Victoreen, "Ionization Chambers," *Proc. I.R.E.*, February 1949, vol. 37, p. 189.
3. Herbert Friedman, "Geiger Counter Tubes," *Proc. I.R.E.*, July 1949, vol. 37, p. 791.
4. J. W. Coltman, "The Scintillation Counter," *Proc. I.R.E.*, June 1949, vol. 37, p. 671.
5. Bernard R. Linden, "Five New Photomultipliers for Scintillation Counting," *Nucleonics*, September 1953, vol. 11, p. 30.

SOURCE INDEX

SUBJECT INDEX